# T E A C H E R

# CoMPANiON

Here Comes the Band

✦

All Through the Town

✦

Out Came the Sun

✦

Morning Bells

✦

Make a Wish

✦

A New Day

GRADE ONE

**Silver Burdett Ginn**

Needham, MA • Morristown, NJ • Atlanta, GA • Dallas, TX • Menlo Park, CA • Deerfield, IL

# Contents

The *Companion* supports all aspects of the reading program and meets the needs of all students. Whether teachers want to give some students additional practice with skills or challenge their most skillful problem solvers, they will find what they need in the *Companion*. Writing, spelling, and language lessons extend activities found in the Teacher Editions and make *New Dimensions in the World of Reading* a fully integrated Language Arts program.

Suggestions for using the *Companion* appear in the Teacher Editions in two places: **Tools of the Trade** references, found throughout the units, and **Reteaching/Meeting Individual Needs**, found at the end of each Teacher Edition for levels 1/1–1/4 and at the middle and end of each unit for levels 1/5–1/6.

© 1993 Silver Burdett Ginn Inc.

ISBN 0-663-55903-0
4 5 6 7 8 9 10 MZ 98 97 96 95 94

# Meeting Individual Needs

These lessons and masters are designed to provide further reinforcement of the skills taught in Grade One.

The **Reteaching** masters include instruction, examples, and graphic aids to assist in children's comprehension.

The **Listening Skills** program contains a teaching plan and accompanying black-line masters. These provide essential instruction and practice in major listening skills. Many exercises may take five to seven sessions to complete. If an exercise is not completed in one session, pertinent directions and text should be reread to children.

**Strategies for Thinking** contains black-line masters and accompanying lesson plans that are intended to provide cognitive exercises in comprehension, elaboration (creative thinking), problem solving, and critical thinking. These activities are especially designed for the skilled reader.

# CONTENTS

# Words with Short a

The letter **a** can stand for the vowel sound you hear in **bag** and **mat**.

bag    mat

**A.** Look at each picture. Then circle the words that have the same vowel sound as in **bag** and **mat**.

1.  fat        cat

4.  big        bag

7.  sad        bat

2.  mad        man

5.  see        bus

8.  dog        rag

3.  fan        off

6.  sat        mat

9.  Pat        cap

**B.** Name each picture. Color the picture that has the same vowel sound as in **bag** and **mat**. Then write **a** next to the picture that has the vowel sound you hear in **bag** and **mat**.

10. _____

11. _____

# Words with Short a

The letter **a** can stand for the vowel sound you hear in **map** and **jam**.

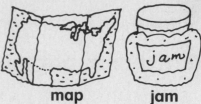

map    jam

**A.** Name each picture. Write **a** to make the word if the picture name has the same vowel sound as in **map** and **jam**.

1. c ___ t

2. d ___ g

3. f ___ n

4. h ___ m

5. p ___ n

6. j ___ m

7. c ___ b

8. b ___ s

9. t ___ g

10. h ___ n

**B.** Draw pictures of four things whose names have the same vowel sound as in **map.** Use another sheet of paper.

# Words with Long a

The letter **a** can stand for the vowel sound you hear in **rake** and **cane.** Look for the **e** marker at the end of a short word. It often points out that the first vowel in the word stands for a long sound.

rake     cane

Read each word. Circle the picture it names.
Then write the word.

**1.** cake

_____
- - - - - - - - - - - - -
_____

**2.** mane

_____
- - - - - - - - - - - - -
_____

**3.** race

_____
- - - - - - - - - - - - -
_____

**4.** pane

_____
- - - - - - - - - - - - -
_____

**5.** gate

_____
- - - - - - - - - - - - -
_____

# Words with Long a

The letter **a** can stand for the vowel sound you hear in **cave** and **rake**. Look for the **e** marker at the end of a short word. It often points out that the first vowel in the word stands for a long sound.

cave   rake

**A.** Name each picture. Circle the picture whose name has the same vowel sound as in **cave** and **rake**.

1.

2.

3.

4.

5.

6.

**B.** Name each picture. Write **a** and **e** if the picture name has the same vowel sound as in **cave** and **rake**. Write **a** if the picture name has the vowel sound you hear in **cat**.

7. g ___ t

8. v ___ s

9. b ___ t

10. c ___ g

11. r ___ t

12. s ___ f

# Sequence

Things happen in a certain order.

These pictures are in order.

Number the pictures in order. Write **1, 2, 3.**

1.

2.

3.

4.

5.

# Sequence

Things happen in a certain order.

These pictures are in order.

Look at the first two pictures. What will happen next?

Circle the picture that shows what will happen next.

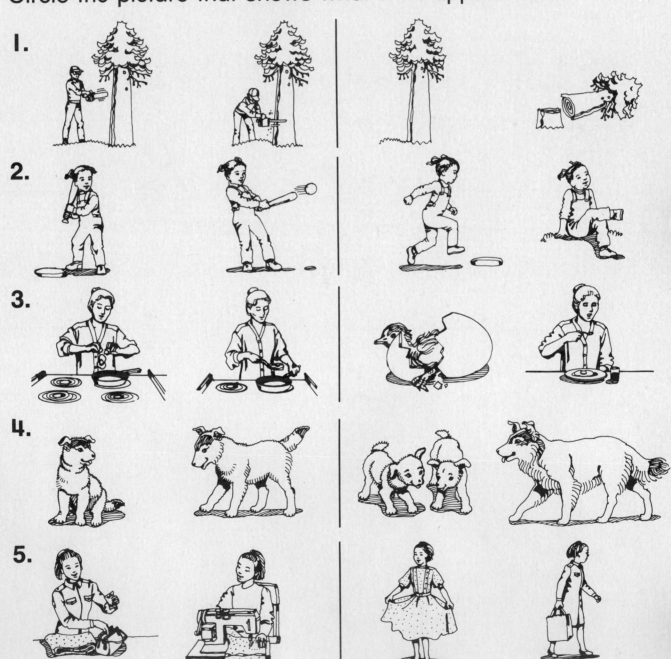

1.

2.

3.

4.

5.

© Silver Burdett Ginn Inc.

# Words with Short e

The letter **e** can stand for the vowel sound you hear in **well** and **jet**.

well          jet

**A.** Underline the words that have the same vowel sound as in **well** and **jet**.

| get | hat | red | web | rid | fed |
|-----|-----|-----|-----|-----|-----|
| hen | bed | win | let | pet | we |
| me | bell | men | come | den | be |

**B.** Name each picture. Write **e** to make a word if the picture name has the same vowel sound as in **well** and **jet**. Write **a** if the picture name has the same vowel sound as in **can** and **cat**.

1.  p __ g

2.  h __ t

3.  t __ n

4.  v __ n

5.  n __ t

6.  m __ n

# Words with Short e

The letter **e** can stand for the vowel sound you hear in **ten** and **bed.**

ten     bed

Write **e** to make a word. Say the word.

Then draw a line to the picture that shows the word.

1. h___n

2. ___gg

3. n___t

4. w___b

5. p___n

6. v___t

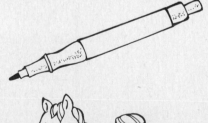

# Words with Long e

The letter **e** at the end of a word can stand
for the sound you hear in **he** and **she.**
Sometimes two letters stand for one sound.
The letters **ee** stand for the vowel sound
you hear in **bee.**

bee

he    she

Read each word. Draw a line to the picture it tells about.

**1.**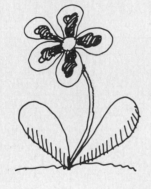

**3.**

tree

Lee

**2.**

**4.**

free

bee

# Words with Long e

The letter **e** at the end of a word can stand for the vowel sound you hear in **she** and **be**. Sometimes two letters stand for one sound. The letters **ee** stand for the vowel sound you hear in **see**.

she      see

Look at each picture. Write its name.

**1.**

Lee     Len

_____

- - - - - - - - - -

_____

**2.**

see     bee

_____

- - - - - - - - - -

_____

**3.**

trim     tree

_____

- - - - - - - - - -

_____

**4.**

we     when

_____

- - - - - - - - - -

_____

# Words with Long e

The letter **e** at the end of a word can stand
for the sound you hear in **he** and **she.**
Sometimes two letters stand for one sound.
The letters **ee** stand for the vowel sound
you hear at the end of **tree.**

he    she    tree

Draw a picture of each word in its box.

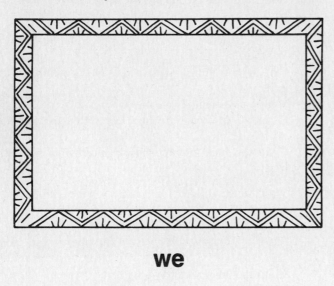

**we**

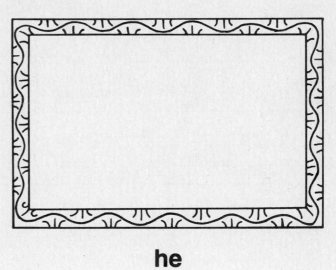

**he**

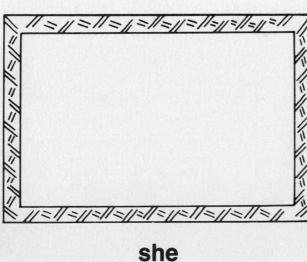

**she**

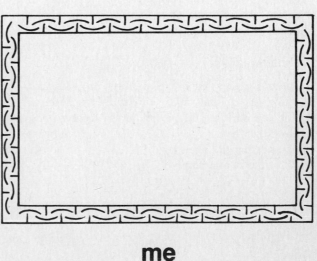

**me**

# Comprehending Relationships:
## Rhyming Words

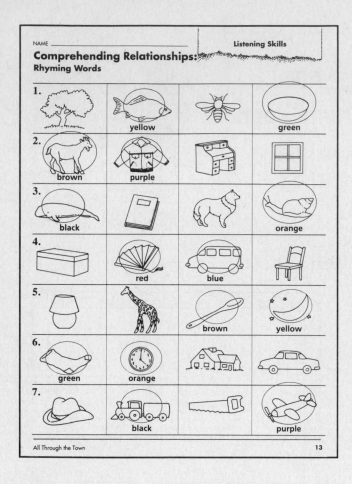

NAME _____     Listening Skills

**Comprehending Relationships:**
**Rhyming Words**

1.
yellow          green

2.
brown    purple

3.
black            orange

4.
red      blue

5.
brown    yellow

6.
green    orange

7.
black            purple

All Through the Town          13

---

**Procedure:**

On the chalkboard, draw a picture of a flower, a cat, and a baseball bat.

*Say to the children:*   Take out your crayons or markers because you will need them for this lesson. Look at the pictures of the flower, the cat, and the bat on the chalkboard. Which two things have names that rhyme with the word *hat?* (cat, bat).

Now look at the first row of pictures on your paper. I am going to say another word. You will look at the pictures in the row and find the two pictures whose names rhyme with the word that I say. You will circle the two pictures with your pencil. Then I will ask you to do something to each of the two pictures.

1.  Find the two things whose names rhyme with the word **wish.**
    With your pencil, circle the two pictures.

Color the first picture whose name rhymes with **wish** yellow.
Color the other picture whose name rhymes with **wish** green.

2.  Find the two things whose names rhyme with the word **float.**
    With your pencil, circle the two pictures.
    Color the first picture whose name rhymes with **float** brown.
    Color the other picture whose name rhymes with **float** purple.

3.  Find the two things whose names rhyme with the word **sail.**
    With your pencil, circle the two pictures.
    Color the first picture whose name rhymes with **sail** black.
    Color the other picture whose name rhymes with **sail** orange.

4.  Find the two things whose names rhyme with the word **pan.**
    With your pencil, circle the two pictures.
    Color the first picture whose name rhymes with **pan** red.
    Color the other picture whose name rhymes with **pan** blue.

5.  Find the two things whose names rhyme with the word **noon.**
    With your pencil, circle the two pictures.
    Color the first picture whose name rhymes with **noon** brown.
    Color the other picture whose name rhymes with **noon** yellow.

6.  Find the two things whose names rhyme with the word **lock.**
    With your pencil, circle the two pictures.
    Color the first picture whose name rhymes with **lock** green.
    Color the other picture whose name rhymes with **lock** orange.

7.  Find the two things whose names rhyme with the word **rain.**
    With your pencil, circle the two pictures.
    Color the first picture whose name rhymes with **rain** black.
    Color the other picture whose name rhymes with **rain** purple.

# Comprehending Relationships:
## Rhyming Words

# Comprehension:
## Following Directions

**Focus:** It is important to read and think carefully in order to follow directions correctly.

**Model:** This activity gives you a set of directions to read and then follow.

**Practice:*** Suppose a direction told you to make an **X** in the middle of your paper. You would find the middle of your paper and make an **X** there.

Now suppose a direction said this: If you are six years old, write 6 at the top of your paper. First, you would have to ask yourself, "Am I six years old?" If the answer is yes, you would write 6 at the top of your paper. If the answer is no, you would not write anything. You would go on to the next direction.

**Apply:** Now work on page 15.

1. First, read all the directions.

2. Then go back and read each direction.

3. Follow each direction as you read it. If you have to ask yourself a question, be sure you know the answer before you follow the direction.

4. Remember that sometimes you will go on to the next direction without writing anything.

**Monitor:** When students have finished, discuss their results.

1. There should be a D in the circle.

2. The dog's name is Bam, so there should be a B in the circle.

3. The cat's name is not Bam, so there should not be a B in the square.

4. The cat's name is not Bam, so the cat's name (Mab) should be in the square.

5. A cat is not a dog, so there should not be a C in the circle.

6. A cat is not a dog, so there should be a C in the square.

**Summary:**

---

* Frequently there are diagrams, charts, or examples in **Practice** which the teacher should place on the chalkboard before the lesson begins.

# Comprehension:
**Following Directions**

It is important to follow directions carefully.

Then what you do will turn out right.

Read all the directions. Do what they say.

1. Write D in the dog's ◯.

2. Is the dog's name Bam? If it is, write B in the ◯.

3. Is the cat's name Bam? If it is, write B in the ▢.

4. If the cat's name is <u>not</u> Bam,

   write the cat's name in the ▢.

5. If a cat is a dog, write C in the ◯.

6. If a cat is <u>not</u> a dog, write C in the ▢.

# Main Idea/Details

Sentences tell about a story.

Underline the sentence that tells the main idea of the story.
Then circle the best answer to each question.

1. The dog was naughty.

   It did not come.

   All it did was run.

What did the dog do?        come        look        run

2. A wheel came off the truck.

   The truck cannot go.

   Bob has to fix the truck.

What came off the truck?        top        web        wheel

What will Bob do?        fix        come        eat

3. Puppies like to play.

   They run all around.

   They jump in the water.

What do puppies jump in?        rain        sand        water

What do puppies like to do?        play        hide        all

# Main Idea/Details

A story is always about something.

All the sentences tell about it.

Read the story. Circle the word that tells what the whole story is about. Then write the word.

**1.** Tim has a big cap.

He has an umbrella.

He has to jump over the water.

rain     sky     sun

_____

Tim is out in the _____ .

**2.** A bicycle is like a bus.

A bus is like a truck.

A truck is like a bicycle.

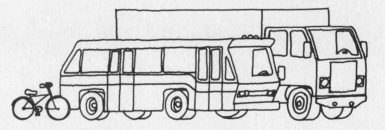

sand     wheels     wind

_____

They all have _____ .

lids     seats     windows

_____

They all have _____ .

# Words with Short i

The letter **i** can stand for the vowel
sound you hear in **mitt.**

mitt

**A.** Say each word to yourself. If the word has the same vowel
sound as in **mitt,** then color the mitt.

1.  big    5.  ran    9.  tin    13.  lit

2.  dog    6.  fit    10.  sad    14.  fix

3.  him    7.  will    11.  fun    15.  red

4.  pal    8.  his    12.  did    16.  sit

**B.** Name each picture. Write **i** to finish the words whose
names have the same vowel sound as in **mitt.**

17.     19.     21.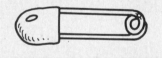

s ___ n    p ___ n    s ___ x

18.     20. 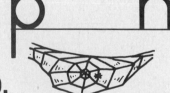    22.

p ___ g    w ___ b    w ___ g

Out Came the Sun

# Short i

The letter **i** can stand for the vowel
sound you hear in **bib** and **sit**.

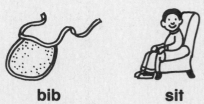

bib     sit

**A.** Name each picture. Write **i** to make the word if the picture
name has the same vowel sound as in **bib** and **sit**.

1. m __ tt

6. f __ x

2. w __ b

7. p __ g

3. r __ p

8. s __ n

4. d __ g

9. f __ n

5. h __ ll

10. l __ d

**B.** Draw a picture on separate paper of five things whose
names have the vowel sound you hear in **ship**.

NAME _____

# Words with Long i

The letter **i** can stand for the vowel sound
you hear in **line** and **ride**.

line

Look for the **e** marker at the end of a word.
It often points out that the first vowel in the
word stands for a long sound.

ride

**A.** Read the words. Circle and color the picture they tell
about. Then underline the words that have the same vowel
sound as in **line** and **ride**.

1. fly with a kite

2. nine pines

3. ride a bike

4. drive a bus

5. slide down

6. five mice

**B.** Draw a **bike** with a **wide white stripe**.

Use another piece of paper.

© Silver Burdett Ginn Inc.

Out Came the Sun

# Words with Long i

The letter **i** can stand for the vowel sound you hear in **dime** and **vine.** Look for the **e** at the end of a short word. It often points out that the first vowel in the word stands for a long sound.

dime

vine

**A.** Name each picture. Circle the picture whose name has the same vowel sound as in **dime** and **vine.**

1.     3.     5.

2.     4.     6.

**B.** Name each picture. Does the word have the long vowel sound you hear in **dime** and **vine?** If it does, write **i** and **e** to make a word. Write **i** if the picture name has the vowel sound you hear in **pin.**

7.  f ___ v ___

8.  f ___ n ___

9.  d ___ m ___

10. 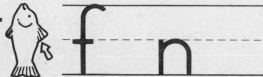 n ___ n ___

# Cause/Effect

One thing can make another thing happen.

Read each sentence. Draw a line to the picture that shows what will happen because of this.

**1.** Pat left her mittens and cap at school.

**2.** They like the puppet play.

**3.** Mike is lost.

**4.** The bell is ringing.

**5.** The wind is blowing.

# Cause/Effect

One thing can make another thing happen.

cause      effect

Read the sentences. Write what caused
the thing to happen.

Example:

School is out. Dave can play.

## School is out.

**1.** The wheel is off.

The truck cannot go.

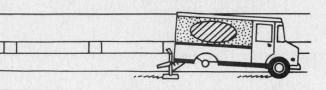

_____

_____

**2.** It is her birthday.

Mom gave her a gift.

_____

_____

**3.** Bill did not get the bus.

He will be late for school.

_____

_____

# Words with Short o

The letter **o** can stand for the vowel
sound you hear in **on** and **cot**.

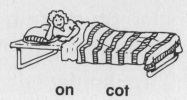

on    cot

**A.** Color each picture whose name has

the same vowel sound as in **on** and **cot**.

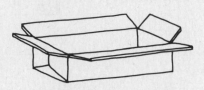  

 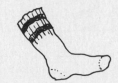 

**B.** Write **o** to make a word that rhymes.

**1.** lot  d _ _ _ _ _ t        **5.** nod  r _ _ _ _ _ d

**2.** top  p _ _ _ _ _ p        **6.** Bob  j _ _ _ _ _ b

**3.** Tom  M _ _ _ _ _ m        **7.** tot  h _ _ _ _ _ t

**4.** ox  b _ _ _ _ _ x        **8.** hop  m _ _ _ _ _ p

Out Came the Sun

# Words with Short o

The letter **o** can stand for the vowel
sound you hear in **top** and **box.**

top          box

**A.** Underline the words that have the same vowel sound as in
**top** and **box.**

| cone | Bob | pup | cot | not | tot |
|------|-----|-----|-----|-----|-----|
| on   | Mom | box | mob | go  | top |
| lap  | so  | lot | pop | hot | so  |

**B.** Name each picture. Write **o** to make a word if the picture
name has the same vowel sound as in **top** and **box.**

1.  g

5.  c    b

2.  f    x

6. 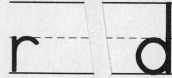 r    d

3.  b    n

7.  p    t

4.  b    x

8. 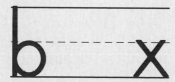 b    g

# Words with Long o

The letter **o** at the end of a word can stand
for the vowel sound you hear in **go** and **no.**

no

**A.** Underline the words that have the same vowel sound as in
**go** and **no.**

| for | ho | too | go | pro | you |
|-----|-----|-----|-----|-----|-----|
| so | no | who | you | on | yo-yo |

**B.** Read each question. Underline the words that have the
vowel sound you hear in **go** and **no.** Then circle **yes** or **no**
to answer each question.

**1.** Can a bear go on a bike?      yes      no

**2.** He said, "Ho, ho, ho!"

Is he happy?                         yes      no

**3.** Does so mean "also"?          yes      no

**4.** Can you say "no"?             yes      no

**C.** Think of a place where you like to **go.**

Draw a picture on another sheet of paper.

Out Came the Sun

# Words with Long o

The letter **o** at the end of a word can stand for the vowel sound you hear in **so** and **go.**

**A.** Circle the correct word to finish each sentence. Then write the word.

so     go

_____

- - - - - - -

**I.** The cat said, "Will you _____ with me?"

no     to

_____

- - - - - - -

**2.** The mouse said, "No, no, _____ !"

so     do

_____

- - - - - - -

**3.** The cat said, "I like you _____ !"

no     ho

_____

- - - - - - -

**4.** The mouse said, "Ho, ho _____ !"

**B.** Think of something else the cat or mouse might say. On another piece of paper, write the word **go, no, ho,** or **so.**

# Sequence

Things happen in a certain order.
These pictures are in order.

Look at the first two pictures in each row. What will happen next? Draw a picture that shows what happens next.

1.

2.

3.

4.

# Sequence

**Procedure:**

*Say to the children:*   When you listen to a story, the order in which things happen is important. If things are out of order, the story will not make sense.

I will tell you about something a person wants to do. Then I will ask you about the order in which the person should do that thing.

Page 31

**1.** Look at the first row of pictures.
Listen carefully.

   Pam wants to shovel the snow.
   What must Pam do first?

Write a number **1** in the box in the picture that tells the right answer. (If children cannot write the numerals, substitute a direction—**circle, X, underline, box**—of your choice.)

What must Pam do next?

Write a number **2** in the box in the picture that tells the right answer.

   What will Pam do last?

Write a number **3** in that box in the picture that tells the right answer.

**2.** Look at the second row of pictures.
Listen carefully.

   Joe is going to school.
   What must Joe do first?

Write a number **1** in the box in the picture that tells the right answer.

   What must Joe do next?

Write a number **2** in that box.

   What will Joe do last?

Write a number **3** in that box.

**3.** Look at the third row of pictures.
Listen carefully.

   Kerry wants to wash her dog.
   What must Kerry do first?

Write **1** in the box in the picture that tells the right answer.

   What must Kerry do second?

Write **2** in that box.

   What will Kerry do third?

Write **3** in that box.

**4.** Look at the fourth row of pictures.
Listen carefully.

   Bill wants to make a sandwich.
   What must Bill do first?

Write **1** in the box in the picture that tells the right answer.

   What must Bill do next?

Write **2** in that box.

   What will Bill do last?

Write **3** in that box.

**Listening Skills**

**Sequence**

1.

2.

3.

4.

32

Out Came the Sun

---

**Page 32**

1. Look at the first row of pictures.
   Listen carefully.

   Paul wants to draw a picture.
   What must he do first?

   Write a number **1** in the box in the picture that tells the right answer.

   What must Paul do second?

   Write a number **2** in that box.

   What will Paul do last?

   Write a number **3** in that box.

2. Look at the second row of pictures.
   Listen carefully.

   Tina wants to fly a kite.
   What must Tina do first?

   Write **1** in the box in the picture that tells the right answer.

   What must Tina do next?

   Write **2** in that box.

   What will Tina do last?

   Write **3** in that box.

3. Look at the third row of pictures.
   Listen carefully.

   Rick wants to grow a plant.
   What must Rick do first?

   Write **1** in the box in the picture that tells the right answer.

   What must Rick do second?

   Write **2** in that box.

   What will happen last?

   Write **3** in that box.

4. Look at the last row of pictures.
   Listen carefully.

   Sue wants to give a present to her friend.
   What must Sue do first?

   Write **1** in the box in the picture that tells the right answer.

   What must Sue do second?

   Write **2** in that box.

   What will happen last?

   Write **3** in that box.

© Silver Burdett Ginn Inc.

Out Came the Sun

# Sequence

# Sequence

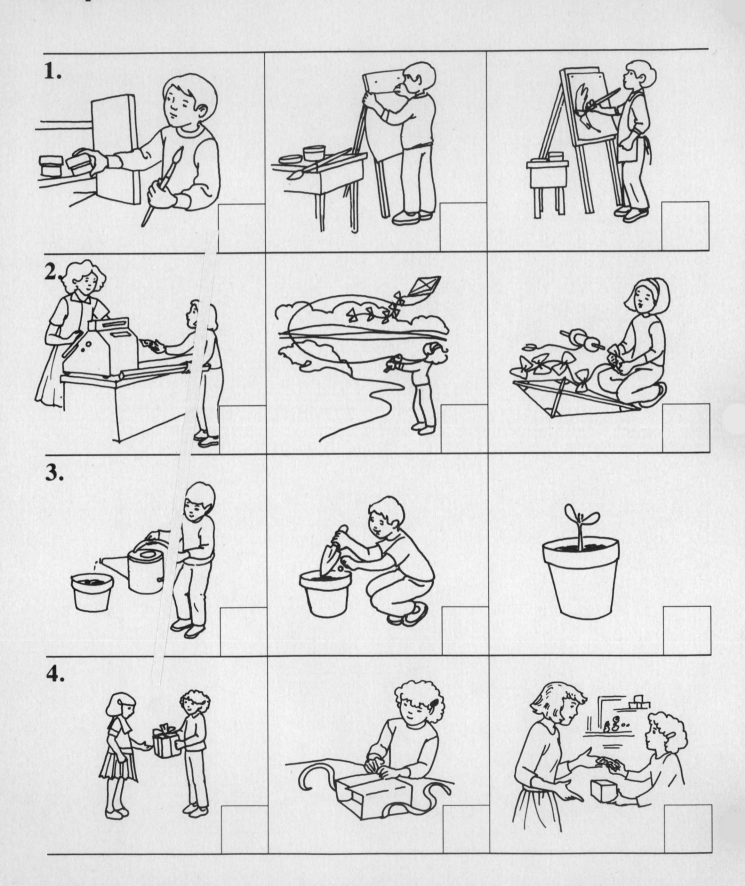

1.

2.

3.

4.

Out Came the Sun

# Critical Thinking:
## Making Statements True

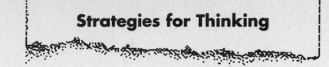
**Focus:** Learning to choose the right words is important. Changing a word can change what a sentence means.

**Model:** This activity gives you some sentences that are not complete. You will pick the best word to make each sentence true.

**Practice:** Suppose you saw this sentence:

_____ dogs are tan.

No   Some

Try the sentence with the first word in the blank—"No dogs are tan." That is not a true statement because dogs can be tan. Try the sentence with the other word—"Some dogs are tan." That is a true statement, so you would write the word *Some* in the blank.

Here are some words that are important because they can make a sentence true or not true.

All          Most          Some          No

**Apply:** Now work on page 34.

1. Read each sentence carefully.

2. Look at the two words below the sentence.

3. Try both words in the sentence.

4. Pick the best word to make the sentence true.

5. Write that word in the blank.

6. Read the sentence again to be sure it is true.

**Monitor:** When students have finished, discuss their choices.

1. It would not be true to say that no people ride bicycles. It is true that some people ride bicycles.

2. It is not true that all wheels are on trucks; some wheels are on cars, buses, and so on. It is true that some wheels are on trucks.

3. It is true that some bicycles are red. It is not true to say that no bicycles are red.

4. It is true that all wheels are round; Wheels would not go well if they were not round.

5. It cannot be true to say that most people ride on the bus. Some people ride in cars, trains, or bicycles. It is true that some people ride on the bus.

**Summary:**

1. Some    2. Some    3. Some

4. All    5. Some

# Critical Thinking:
## Making Statements True

It is important to use the right words to make sentences true.

**A.** Pick the best word to make the sentence true.

**B.** Write that word in the sentence.

1. _____ people ride bicycles.
   Some        No

2. _____ wheels are on trucks.
   All        Some

3. _____ bicycles are red.
   Some        No

4. _____ wheels are round.
   All        Most

5. _____ people ride on the bus.
   Most        Some

# Main Idea/Details

A story is always about something.

All the sentences tell about it.

Read each story title. Color the box beside each sentence that tells about what is in the story.

**1.**          **The Bear and the Cave**

☐ The bear likes honey.

☐ The bear came to a cave.

☐ It went in the cave.

☐ "I will live in this cave," said the bear.

**2.**          **The Ride**

☐ "What will we ride?" said Dad.

☐ "We can ride in the truck," said Bob.

☐ "We can ride on the bus," said Mom.

☐ The sun was out.

**3.**          **The Hat**

☐ I see a hat.

☐ It is a big hat.

☐ I will put on the hat.

☐ I put on a wig.

## Main Idea/Details

A story is always about something.

All the sentences tell about it.

Read the story. Write the word that finishes each sentence.

**Jane and Bingo**

Jane has a dog.

The dog is Bingo.

Jane and Bingo run.

They play in the water.

cat     dog     truck

_____

1. Jane has a _____ .

Bingo     Bitsy     Bob

_____

2. The dog is _____ .

look     ride     run

_____

3. Jane and Bingo _____ .

       Morning Bells

# Words with Short u

The letter **u** can stand for the vowel sound you hear in **bug** and **tub**.

bug        tub

Name each picture. Then write **u** or **o** to make the picture name.

1.    b _ n

2.    m _ p

3.    h _ t

4.    n _ t

5.    b _ s

6.    p _ t

7.    c _ p

8.    s _ n

9.    p _ p

10.   f _ x

11.   h _ g

12.   c _ b

# Words with Short u

The letter **u** can stand for the vowel sound you hear in **bus** and **jug.**

bus          jug

**A.** Say each word to yourself. If the word has the same vowel sound as in **jug,** then color the jug.

1. bud          5. red          9. run          13. rag

2. cub          6. nut          10. had          14. pup

3. but          7. fun          11. did          15. not

4. tap          8. up          12. bug          16. sun

**B.** Read each group of words. Circle the two words in each group that rhyme.

17. but          19. jug          21. mud

    cut              rub              bud

    pot              cub              red

18. gum          20. bun          22. mug

    dim              log              cup

    hum              sun              pup

# Words with Long u

The letter **u** can stand for the vowel sound you hear in **cube** and **flute.** Look for the letter **e** at the end of a short word. It often points out that the first vowel in the word stands for a long sound.

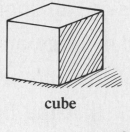

cube

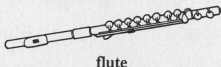

flute

Read the words. Circle and color the picture they tell about. Then underline the words that have the same vowel sound as in **cube** and **flute.**

**1.** a cute cub

**2.** a huge dune

**3.** a tune on a
flute and a lute

**4.** a tube in a tub

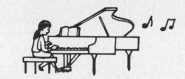

**5.** a day in June

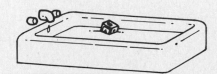

**6.** a ride on a mule

# Words with Long u

The letter **u** can stand for the vowel sound you hear in **huge** and **cute.** Look for the letter **e** at the end of a short word. It often points out that the first vowel in the word stands for a long sound.

huge          cute

Write the word that names each picture.

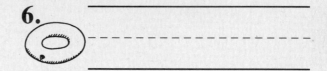

| cube | flute | June | plume | ruler |
|------|-------|------|-------|-------|
| dune | tube | mule | prune | tune |

1. _____

2. _____

3. _____

4. _____

5. _____

6. _____

7. _____

8. _____

9. _____

10. _____

Words with Long u

# Words with Final g, m

The letters **g** and **m** can stand for the sounds you hear at the end of **dog** and **ham.**

ham        dog

Name each picture. Then circle the letter that stands for the ending sound. Write the letter below the picture.

**1.**  m    g

_____

- - - - - - - - -

_____

**4.**  m    g

_____

- - - - - - - - -

_____

**7.**  m    g

_____

- - - - - - - - -

_____

**10.**  m    g

_____

- - - - - - - - -

_____

**2.**  m    g

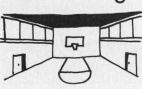

_____

- - - - - - - - -

_____

**5.**  m    g

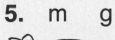

_____

- - - - - - - - -

_____

**8.**  m    g

_____

- - - - - - - - -

_____

**11.**  m    g

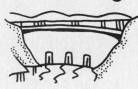

_____

- - - - - - - - -

_____

**3.**  m    g

_____

- - - - - - - - -

_____

**6.**  m    g

_____

- - - - - - - - -

_____

**9.**  m    g

_____

- - - - - - - - -

_____

**12.**  m    g

_____

- - - - - - - - -

_____

# Words with Final g, m

The letters **g** and **m** can stand for the
sounds you hear at the end of **jug** and **ram**.

jug    ram

**A.** Write **m** to make a word. Say the word. Then draw a line
to the picture that shows the word.

1. _ha_    2. _da_    3. _ya_

**B.** Write **g** to make a word. Say the word. Then draw a line to
the picture that shows the word.

4. _ru_    5. _lo_    6. _bu_

# Words with Short a

The letter **a** can stand for the vowel sound you hear in **can** and **cat**.

**can**     **cat**

**A.** Color each picture whose name has the same vowel sound as in **can** and **cat**.

1.

3.

5.

2.

4.

6.

**B.** Name each picture. Write **a** under the pictures whose names have the same vowel sound as in **can** and **cat**.

7.  _____

9.  _____

11.  _____

13. 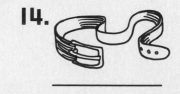 _____

8.  _____

10. _____

12. _____

14. _____

# Words with Short a

The letter **a** can stand for the vowel sound you hear in **rat** and **van**.

rat    van

**A.** Underline the words that have the same vowel sound as in **rat** and **van**.

| Dad | tan | fall | has | and | ate |
|-----|-----|------|-----|-----|-----|
| was | cat | play | pat | can | sand |
| am | what | pal | cave | sad | fat |

**B.** Write **a** to make a word that rhymes. Read your words.

1. can  p___ n

2. Pat  s___ t

3. am  h___ m

4. Dad  m___ d

5. bag  w___ g

6. tan  m___ n

7. cat  r___ t

8. sad  b___ d

© Silver Burdett Ginn Inc.

# Words with Long a

The letter **a** can stand for the vowel sound you hear in **wave** and **cake.** Look for the **e** marker at the end of a short word. It often points out that the first vowel in the word stands for a long sound.

wave    cake

Write the word that names each picture.

| | | | |
|---|---|---|---|
| ape | cage | game | tape |
| base | cane | rake | vase |

1. 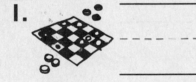 _____

5.  _____

2.  _____

6.  _____

3.  _____

7.  _____

4.  _____

8.  _____

# Words with Long a

The letter **a** can stand for the vowel sound you hear in **page** and **cape.** Look for the **e** marker at the end of a short word. It often points out that the first vowel in the word stands for a long sound.

page    cape

Read each word. Then find two rhyming words from the box and write them.

| | | | |
|---|---|---|---|
| came | date | late | save |
| cave | fame | make | take |

**1.** gate

_____    _____

_____    _____

**2.** wave

_____    _____

_____    _____

**3.** rake

_____    _____

_____    _____

**4.** game

_____    _____

_____    _____

© Silver Burdett Ginn Inc.

# Words with Short e

The letter **e** can stand for the vowel sound you hear in **well**.

**well**

Find the word that has the same vowel sound as in **well**. Circle the word. Then write it.

1. pin　　men　　tan

_____

2. bit　　truck　　net

_____

3. bed　　had　　rod

_____

4. fat　　win　　pen

_____

5. what　　hit　　jet

_____

6. pet　　lid　　fun

_____

# Words with Short e

The letter **e** can stand for the vowel sound
you hear in **bell** and **pen.**

bell    pen

**A.** Color each picture whose name has the same vowel sound
as in **bell** and **pen.**

1.     3.      5.

2.     4.     6.

**B.** Name each picture. Write **e** under the pictures whose
names have the same vowel sound as in **bell** and **pen.**

7.     9.     11.     13.

_____    _____    _____    _____

- - - - - - -    - - - - - - -    - - - - - - -    - - - - - - -

_____    _____    _____    _____

8.     10.    12.    14.

_____    _____    _____    _____

- - - - - - -    - - - - - - -    - - - - - - -    - - - - - - -

_____    _____    _____    _____

# Words with Long e

The letter **e** at the end of a word can stand for the vowel sound you hear in **he** and **she.** Sometimes two letters stand for one sound. The letters **ee** stand for the vowel sound you hear in **jeep.**

he    she

jeep

Read each word. Write a rhyming word.

see    sat

_____

**1.** bee    _____

- - - - - - - - - - - - - - - - -

men    me

_____

**2.** he    _____

- - - - - - - - - - - - - - - - -

fell    free

_____

**3.** tree    _____

- - - - - - - - - - - - - - - - -

she    shag

_____

- - - - - - - - - - - - - - - - -

**4.** we    _____

© Silver Burdett Ginn Inc.

# Words with Long e

The letter **e** at the end of a word can stand for the sound you hear in **me** and **we.** Sometimes two letters stand for one sound. The letters **ee** stand for the vowel sound you hear in **Lee.**

we          Lee

Write the correct word to complete each sentence.

bed          bee

1. _____

   I see a _____.

street          tree

_____

2. The bird is in the _____.

He          They

_____

3. _____ pets his dog.

best          be

_____

4. I will _____ a cat.

# Predicting Outcomes

When you read a story, think ahead and try
to tell what will happen next.

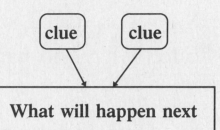

Example:

**Clue 1:** The bicycle tire has a hole.

**Clue 2:** Gail wants to ride her bicycle.

What will happen next? Gail will fix the wheel.

Look at the first two pictures.
Circle the picture that shows what will happen next.

# Predicting Outcomes

When you read a story, think ahead and try
to tell what will happen next.

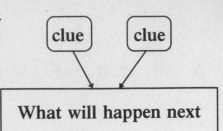

Example:
   **Clue 1:** John put on his hat.
   **Clue 2:** He opened the door.
   What will happen next? He will go outside.

Circle the right word. Write what happens next.
Then draw a picture to show what happens next.

**1.** The wind blows. Jeff runs with the kite.

   back    down    up
   _____

   - - - - - - - - - - - - - - - - - - - -

The kite will go _____ .

**2.** Coral is very tired. She is in bed.

   eat    play    sleep
   _____

   - - - - - - - - - - - - - - - - - - - -

Coral will _____ .

**3.** We can put this together. It is a plane.

   fly    ride    walk
   _____

   - - - - - - - - - - - - - - - - - - - -

Now we will _____ it.

# Words with Short i

The letter **i** can stand for the vowel sound you hear in **Tim** and **fix**.

Tim          fix

**A.** Underline the words that have the same vowel sound as in **Tim** and **fix**.

| | | | | | |
|---|---|---|---|---|---|
| rid | it | kit | in | his | kite |
| den | big | is | ran | lip | tin |
| mix | lap | Jim | win | Bill | fit |

**B.** Look at each picture. Then circle the words that have the same vowel sound as in **Tim** and **fix**.

1.

tot          bib

4.

pot          lid

7.

fix          cup

2.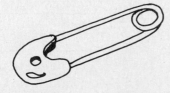

big          pin

5.

cat          kit

8.

wig          bag

3.

pig          dig

6.

top          go

9.

six          pins

# Words with Short i

The letter **i** can stand for the vowel
sound you hear in **pin** and **sit**.

pin      sit

**A.** Find the word that has the same vowel

sound as in **pin** and **sit**. Circle the word. Then write it.

1.

dig      do      find      _____

2.

fall      here      fin      _____

3.

fun      bit      play      _____

4.

win      run      let      _____

5.

man      go      hit      _____

**B.** Draw a picture of a boy named **Jim** doing a **trick** with a

**dish.** Use another sheet of paper.

# Words with Long i

The letter **i** can stand for the vowel sound you hear in **dice** and **pine.** Look for the **e** at the end of a short word. It often points out that the first vowel in the word stands for a long sound.

dice

pine

Read each word. Circle the picture it names. Then write the word.

**1.** bike   _____

**2.** kite   _____

**3.** ride   _____

**4.** nine   _____

**5.** slide  _____

# Words with Long i

The letter **i** can stand for the vowel sound you hear in **five** and **nine.** Look for the **e** at the end of a word. It often points out that the first vowel in the word stands for a long sound.

five

nine

Read each word. Then find two rhyming words. Write them.

| | | | |
|---|---|---|---|
| hide | mine | rice | wide |
| line | nice | ripe | wipe |

1.  mice

_____    _____

_____    _____

2.  vine

_____    _____

_____    _____

3. pipe

_____    _____

_____    _____

4.  bride

_____    _____

_____    _____

# Words with Short o

The letter **o** can stand for the vowel
sound you hear in **hot** and **pot.**

**hot    pot**

Find the word that has the same vowel
sound as in **hot** and **pot.** Circle the word. Then write it.

1.  toy    box    up    _____

2.  dots    ten    big    _____

3.  mop    go    look    _____

4.  get    off    pop    _____

5.  fun    hop    den    _____

6.  fox    bug    went    _____

# Words with Short o

The letter **o** can stand for the vowel
sound you hear in **cot** and **dot**.

cot        dot

**A.** Look at each picture. Then circle the words that have the
same vowel sound as in **cot** and **dot**.

1.

hop    box

4.

fox    cot

7.

hot    pot

2.

lad    cap

5.

rod    cod

8.

big    pop

3.

top    dots

6.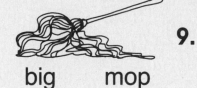

big    mop

9.

bus    stop

**B.** Look at each picture. Then write the correct words to tell
about it.

box      dolls      lot      top

10.

_____      _____

a _____ in a _____

11.

_____      _____

a _____ of _____

# Words with Long o

The letter **o** at the end of a word can stand for the vowel sound you hear in **go, no,** and **so.**

Read each question. Underline the words that have the vowel sound you hear in **go, no,** and **so.** Then write **yes** or **no** to answer the question.

1.  Do they go?

_____

2.  Can you do this?

_____

3.  Is she so happy?

_____

4.  Did he go in water?

_____

5. Will she go?

_____

6.  Will she stay?

_____

# Words with Long o

The letter **o** at the end of a word can stand for the vowel
sound you hear in **no** and **so**.

**A.** Finish the sentence that tells about each picture.

1.

_____      ho

The bus can _____.      go

2.

_____      No

She said, "_____."      So

3.

_____      so

He said, "I told you _____!"      go

4.

_____      no

She will _____.      go

**B.** Answer the question.

5.

_____      Yes

Can you turn left? _____.      No

# Main Idea

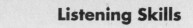

---

NAME _____                    **Listening Skills**

### Main Idea

---

1. ___  Some of the cars had          **X**  There were many
         four doors, and some               different kinds of cars in
         had two doors.                      the parking lot.

---

2. **X**  Polly's room was a           ___  Papers were all over her
         mess.                              bed.

---

3. ___  Then they played on the       **X**  The children played on
         slide.                             three things at the park.

---

4. **X**  It was a wet week.           ___  It rained hard on Sunday
                                            and Monday.

---

5. ___  Lou can shake hands.          **X**  Lou the dog can do tricks.

---

6. **X**  Ted likes green more        ___  Ted has a green bike.
         than any other color.

---

7. **X**  There are four seasons.     ___  Fall means a new school
                                            year.

---

8. ___  *Caps* means almost the       **X**  Some words mean almost
         same thing as *hats*.             the same thing.

---

9. **X**  Sally and Joyce are best    ___  They walk to school and
         friends.                          eat lunch together.

---

62                                                    Morning Bells

---

**Procedure:**

Write the following sentences on the chalkboard:

1.  Jack just read a story about mice.
2.  Jack likes animal stories.

*Say to the children:*   I will read a short story to you.
Listen carefully for what the story is mostly about.

> Jack likes animal stories. He reads stories about
> cats and horses. He reads stories about rabbits. Jack
> just read a story about mice.

Look at the sentences that I have written on the
chalkboard. Which one tells what the story is mostly
about? (Elicit that the second sentence tells what the story
is mostly about; the first sentence tells only about one
kind of animal story that Jack has read. The second
sentence, however, includes all animal stories.)

Now I will read another story. Listen carefully for what
the story is mostly about. Then, on your paper, you will
mark an **X** next to the sentence that tells what the story is
mostly about.

## Story Number 1

Some were new cars, and some were old cars. There
were big cars and little cars. Some of the cars had four
doors, and some had two doors. There were many different
kinds of cars in the parking lot.

## Story Number 2

Polly's room was a mess. Papers were all over her bed.
Toys were all over the floor. Polly's desk was covered with
dust.

## Story Number 3

First, the children played on the merry-go-round. Then
they played on the slide. Next, they played on the swings.
The children played on three things at the park.

## Story Number 4

It was a wet week. It rained hard on Sunday and Monday. It sprinkled on Tuesday, Wednesday, and Thursday.
On Friday and Saturday, it rained hard again.

## Story Number 5

Lou the dog can do tricks. Lou can shake hands. He can
bring the newspaper to the back door. Lou can roll over,
too.

## Story Number 6

Ted has a green bike. His room is painted green, and he
likes green clothes. When he grows up, Ted wants his house
to be painted green. Ted likes green more than any other
color.

## Story Number 7

There are four seasons. Summer is usually warm, and
people go on vacations. Fall means a new school year. In
some places, winter brings snow and cold weather. In
spring, many people plant gardens.

## Story Number 8

*Caps* means almost the same thing as *hats*. *Evening*
means almost the same thing as *night*. *Strange* means almost
the same thing as *odd*. Some words mean almost the same
thing.

## Story Number 9

Sally and Joyce are best friends. They walk to school
together and eat lunch together. After school, Sally and
Joyce walk to the same babysitter's house where they do
their homework together. On Saturdays, Sally and Joyce go
to the park together.

---

# Main Idea

1. ___ Some of the cars had four doors, and some had two doors.　　___ There were many different kinds of cars in the parking lot.

2. ___ Polly's room was a mess.　　___ Papers were all over her bed.

3. ___ Then they played on the slide.　　___ The children played on three things at the park.

4. ___ It was a wet week.　　___ It rained hard on Sunday and Monday.

5. ___ Lou can shake hands.　　___ Lou the dog can do tricks.

6. ___ Ted likes green more than any other color.　　___ Ted has a green bike.

7. ___ There are four seasons.　　___ Fall means a new school year.

8. ___ *Caps* means almost the same thing as *hats*.　　___ Some words mean almost the same thing.

9. ___ Sally and Joyce are best friends.　　___ They walk to school and eat lunch together.

# Elaboration: Creating Inventions

**Focus:**  Using the imagination is important in solving real or imagined problems.

**Model:**  This activity gives you ideas about situations that can be real or imaginary. You will choose one idea and draw an invention that would help people in that situation.

**Practice:**  Suppose you read this idea: All raindrops are as hard as rocks. Draw a new thing that people will need. First, you would imagine a problem that people would have if raindrops were as hard as rocks. You might imagine that people would get hurt when they went out in the rain.

Then you would imagine an invention to solve the problem. You might imagine building roofs over the sidewalks. Then you would draw a picture of your invention.

**Apply:**  Now work on page 64.

1. Read all four ideas.

2. Think about the ideas and choose the one you like best. Circle that idea.

3. Read again the idea that you circled. Think of a problem that people would have.

4. Imagine an invention to solve the problem.

5. Draw a picture of your invention at the bottom of the page.

**Monitor:**  When students have finished, have them display and explain their drawings. Help them to focus on the problems they identified and on how they thought of their solutions.

# Elaboration: Creating Inventions

You can use your imagination to think of new things.

**A.** Read all the ideas.

**B.** Pick the one you like best and circle it.

**C.** Draw the picture.

    **1.** Draw a new thing to help people ride bicycles in the rain.

    **2.** Draw an umbrella you can use when the wind blows hard.

    **3.** Rain does not fall from the sky any more. It comes up from the ground! Draw a new thing that people need.

    **4.** The wind does not blow at all any more. Draw a new thing that people need.

© Silver Burdett Ginn Inc.

# Reality/Fantasy

Some things you read about are **real** and can happen. Other things are not real. They are **make-believe.**

This is real. ⟶

This is make-believe. ⟶

**A.** Look at each picture in a row. Circle the picture that shows something that could really happen.

1.

2.

3.

4.

5.

**B.** On another sheet of paper, draw two pictures. One should show something that could really happen. The other should show something make-believe. Give your pictures to a friend. Have your friend label them **real** and **make-believe.**

# Classification

Some words belong in the same group. These words belong together.

Birds
duck    hen    owl

Circle the word in each row that does <u>not</u> belong with the others. Then write it.

_____

1. one    six    three    run

_____

2. kite    red    puppet    top

_____

3. teeth    nose    bus    chin

_____

4. snow    hippo    lion    elephant

_____

5. lamp    soup    bed    chair

_____

6. breakfast    lunch    dinner    mud

_____

7. walk    run    sit    hop

_____

# Words with ea

Sometimes two letters stand for one sound. The letters **ea** can stand for the vowel sound you hear in **eat** and **read.**

eat         read

**A.** Underline the words that have the same vowel sound as in **eat** and **read.**

|  |  |  |  |  |
|------|-------|------|------|-------|
| bed  | feast | nest | peak | team  |
| meal | them  | heat | well | sneak |
| end  | each  | deal | leaf | red   |

**B.** Look at each picture. Write a word to tell about it.

1. a dream of a _____          beach
                                                                      steam
                                                                      speak

2. teach them to _____          read
                                                                      reach
                                                                      weave

3. a heap of _____          beans
                                                                      leap
                                                                      wheat

4. eat at a _____          beat
                                                                      feast
                                                                      seat

## Predicting Outcomes

When you read a story, think ahead and try to tell what will happen next.

Write the sentence that tells what will happen next.

| Greg will win the race.    Susan will be late for school. |
| --- |

**1.** Susan takes the bus to school.
This morning she got up late.
The bus was gone.

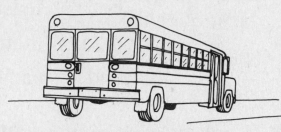

_____

- - - - - - - - - - - - - - - - - -

_____

- - - - - - - - - - - - - - - - - -

_____

**2.** Dave can run very fast.
He can run faster than everyone but Greg.
Dave and Greg will have a race.

_____

- - - - - - - - - - - - - - - - - -

_____

- - - - - - - - - - - - - - - - - -

_____

# Contractions

A **contraction** is two words made into one.

I **+** would = I'd

you **+** will = you'll

Read the two words at the beginning of each row.
Circle the word that is the one made from them.

| | | | | |
|---|---|---|---|---|
| **1.** | he would | he'll | he'd | you'd |
| **2.** | you will | you'd | we'll | you'll |
| **3.** | they would | they'd | they'll | she'd |
| **4.** | she will | she'd | he'd | she'll |
| **5.** | I will | I'd | I'll | he'll |
| **6.** | she would | she'll | she'd | we'd |
| **7.** | he will | he'll | he'd | they'll |
| **8.** | we would | we'll | you'd | we'd |
| **9.** | we will | we'd | we'll | we |
| **10.** | you would | you'd | you'll | she'd |
| **11.** | they will | they'd | they | they'll |
| **12.** | I would | I'll | I'd | I |

# Contractions

A **contraction** is two words made into one.

she **+** would = she'd

he **+** will = he'll

Read the words in the box.
Then write one of the words to finish each sentence.

| I'd   She'll   We'll   You'd |
| --- |

**1.** We will play after school.

_____

- - - - - - - - - - - - - - - - - - - -

_____ fly kites.

**2.** I would like to go home.

_____

- - - - - - - - - - - - - - - - - - - -

_____ like to eat.

**3.** You would like our dog.

_____

- - - - - - - - - - - - - - - - - - - -

_____ play with him.

**4.** Fran will go out.

_____

- - - - - - - - - - - - - - - - - - - -

_____ go to school.

# Context Clues

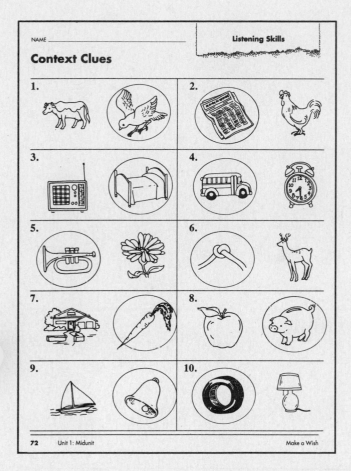

**Context Clues**

1.
2.
3.
4.
5.
6.
7.
8.
9.
10.

72    Unit 1: Midunit                                    Make a Wish

**Procedure:**

*Say to the children:* Sometimes you hear a word that you do not know. If you listen to the other words around that word, you probably will be able to figure out its meaning. (Write the nonsense word **zump** on the chalkboard.) I have written the nonsense word *zump* on the chalkboard. It will take the place of real words in the sentences that I read to you.

Now listen carefully to all of the words in each sentence. You will figure out which picture name **zump** stands for in each sentence. Then you will circle that picture name.

1. The **zump** flew to her nest.

2. Before going to work, Jo reads the **zump.**

3. Al got into his **zump** and went to sleep.

4. The **zump** picked the children up and took them to school.

5. Joan took her **zump** out of its case and played "Happy Birthday."

6. My shoelace has a **zump** in it.

7. The hungry rabbit quickly ate the **zump.**

8. Millie put her coins into the **zump.**

9. Mr. Lee rang the **zump** because recess was over.

10. We were late because our car had a flat **zump.**

# Context Clues

**1.**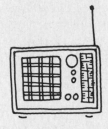

**2.**

**3.**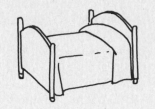

**4.**

**5.**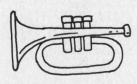

**6.**

**7.**

**8.**

**9.**

**10.**

# Comparison

**Procedure:**

*Say to the children:* People often compare things by telling how the things are alike or how they are different. Let's compare your desk to my desk. How are your desk and my desk alike? (Possible responses: flat tops, used for writing, have a place to store things) How are they different? (Possible responses: size, made of different materials) I am going to read some short stories. In some of the stories, you will have to listen for how certain things are alike. In the other stories, you will have to listen for how certain things are different.

Now I will read the first story. In this story, listen for how two pets are **alike.**

1.     Mert the cat likes to play with yarn. Bert the dog likes to chase balls. Mert *and* Bert like to take naps.

Look at the first row of pictures on your paper. Circle the picture that shows how Mert and Bert are alike.

As I read the next story, listen for how two people are **alike.**

2.     Tim rides his bike to his art class every Saturday, but Jan draws at home. Tim and Jan want to be artists when they grow up. Tim lives in the city, and Jan lives in the country.

Look at the row of pictures next to Number 2. Circle the picture that shows how Tim and Jan are alike.

As I read the next story, listen for how two things are **different.**

3.     Rob got two beach balls for his birthday. Rob thought that he would share the beach balls with his sister. The beach balls are the same size and the same shape, but one of the beach balls is decorated with stars, and the other is decorated with spots.

Look at the row of pictures next to Number 3. Circle the picture of the pair that shows how Rob's beach balls are different.

As I read the next story, listen for how two things are **different.**

4.     Two turtles, Tillie and Tom, enjoy taking walks around the pond. They also like to visit with their neighbors, Fred and Fay Frog. When Fred starts to sing, Tom goes into his shell, but Tillie could listen to Fred for hours.

Look at the row of pictures next to Number 4. Circle the picture that shows how Tillie and Tom are different.

As I read the next story, listen for how two people are **alike.**

5.     Kathy and Lenny go to different schools. Kathy lives in an apartment, and Lenny lives in a trailer. Kathy met Lenny when their baseball teams held a championship game.

Look at the last row of pictures and circle the picture that shows how Kathy and Lenny are alike.

# Comparison

**1.**

**2.**

**3.**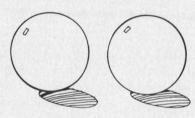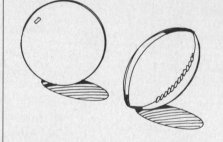

**4.**

**5.**

# Classification

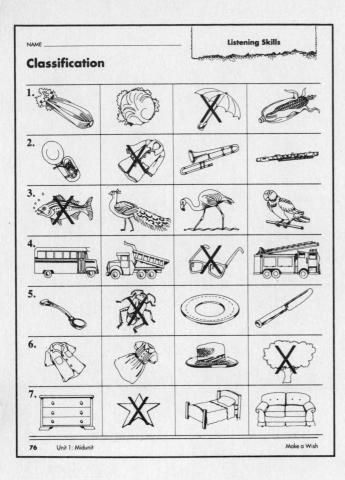

NAME _____

**Classification**

Listening Skills

1.
2.
3.
4.
5.
6.
7.

76    Unit 1: Midunit

Make a Wish

**Procedure:**

On the chalkboard, draw a large rectangle; add a doorway and two windows. Write the words **cat, hen, train,** and **pig** under the rectangle.

*Say to the children:*    The drawing is a house for animals. There are four words written under the house. I will read the words to you. (Read the four words to the children.) Three of the four words name things that are alike in some way. They are *cat, hen,* and *pig.* (Write *cat, hen,* and *pig* "inside" the house.) The words *cat, hen,* and *pig* are alike and belong in the house because they are animals. The word *train* does not belong with the other words because a train is not an animal. What is another word that belongs to the same group as *cat, hen,* and *pig?* (Accept any word that names an animal.) What is another word that does **not** belong to the same group as *cat, hen,* and *pig?* (Accept any word that does not name an animal.)

Write the numerals **6, 7,** and **8** on the chalkboard. Draw a square to the right of the numerals. Then say to the children: I will read three words. You must decide which of the four things on the chalkboard does not belong to the same group of words that I read. (Read the words *one, two,* and *three.* Ask a volunteer to come to the chalkboard and mark an **X** on the thing that does not belong to the group. Elicit that *6, 7,* and *8* belong to the same group as *one, two,* and *three* because they are numbers, but the square is a shape and does not belong to the group "Numbers.") Now look at your paper. I will read three words that are alike in some way. They belong to the same group. After you hear the three words, you will look at the pictures and mark an **X** on the picture that does *not* belong to the group of words that I have read. We'll do the first one together. The three words are *carrot, potato,* and *beet.* Now mark an **X** on the picture that does *not* belong to the group. Which picture should have an **X** on it? (Elicit that the picture of the umbrella should have an **X** on it because an umbrella is not a vegetable; *celery, lettuce,* and *corn* belong to the same group as *carrot, potato,* and *beet* because all six are vegetables.)

Now we will move to number 2. Again, I will read three words that are alike in some way. You will listen carefully to the three words and then you will mark an **X** on the picture that does **not** belong to the group of words that I read.

1.  carrot, potato, beet
2.  piano, guitar, violin
3.  robin, sparrow, crow
4.  cab, van, car
5.  bowl, cup, fork
6.  pajamas, suit, sweater
7.  desk, chair, table

# Classification

1.

2.

3.

4.

5.

6.

7.

# Comprehension: Classification

**Focus:**   It is important to figure out how things are alike in order to put things in the right groups.

**Model:**   This activity shows you figures that are different in some ways but that are all alike in one way. You must find another figure that belongs with them.

**Practice:**   Suppose you were shown these two faces:

You can see that they have different noses and different mouths. They are the same in these ways: both are round and both have round eyes.

Now suppose you were shown these two faces:

You want to figure out which one of these faces goes with the other two. Remember how the other faces are alike—they are round and they have round eyes. Both of these faces are round, so either one could go with the others. But look at the eyes. Only one of these faces has round eyes. That is the one that goes with the others.

**Apply:**   Now work on page 78.

1. Look at the first three figures in the row.

2. Decide how the three are alike.

3. Look at the other two figures. Figure out which one is like the first three.

4. Write on the line the name of the one that is like the others.

**Monitor:**   When students have finished, discuss their choices.

1. The first three figures have hair. Tim has hair, so Tim is like them.

2. The first three have shoes. Mike has shoes, so Mike is like the others.

3. The first three have their left arms (the arms on your right) raised. Jane has her left arm raised, so Jane is like them.

4. The first three are leaning to their left. (your right) Nat is leaning the same way, so Nat is like them.

5. The first three have their right legs up. Bitsy has her right leg up, so Bitsy is like them.

**Summary:**

1. Tim
2. Mike
3. Jane
4. Nat
5. Bitsy

# Comprehension: Classification

It is important to know how things are alike.

Then you can put the things that are alike together.

## Do The Hokeypokey

**A.** Find the one that goes with the others.

**B.** Write the name.

1.

Tim    Tom

_____

- - - - - - - - - - - - - - - - - - - - -

_____

2.

May    Mike

_____

- - - - - - - - - - - - - - - - - - - - -

_____

3.

Jane    Fran

_____

- - - - - - - - - - - - - - - - - - - - -

_____

4.

Nat    Pat

_____

- - - - - - - - - - - - - - - - - - - - -

_____

5.

Becky    Bitsy

_____

- - - - - - - - - - - - - - - - - - - - -

_____

# Problem-Solving:
## Reasoning from Clues

**Focus:** Knowing how to combine information from several different clues to reach a solution is an important reasoning skill.

**Model:** This activity gives you a problem and some clues. You can solve the problem by putting the clues together.

**Practice:** Suppose you are trying to answer the question "Where is Jerry?" Jane and Joe are standing near a cave. Jane gives you this clue: I saw Jerry go into the cave. Joe gives you this clue: I did not see Jerry come out of the cave. You can put the two clues together to figure out where Jerry is—Jerry is in the cave.

**Apply:** Now work on page 80.

1. Read the problem on the sign.

2. Then read all the clues and look carefully at the picture. Look at where each bear is standing and what each bear said.

3. Draw a line to show where B.B. went. The clues will help you figure it out.

4. Make an **X** on the place where you think B.B. is.

**Monitor:** When students have finished, discuss their answers.

1. Betty saw B.B. go up the mountain, so he must have started at the bottom of the mountain.

2. Ben saw B.B. play in the water, so B.B. must have been near the stream.

3. Bitsy saw B.B. at the top of the mountain, near the fir trees.

4. Bob did not see B.B. come down the mountain, so B.B. must still be on the mountain.

5. Draw a line from Betty to Ben (across the bridge) to Bitsy, and into the fir trees where Bitsy is pointing. B.B. did not pass Bob, and we can't see B.B. coming down the mountain, so he must still be in the fir trees. The **X** should be on the fir trees.

**Summary:**

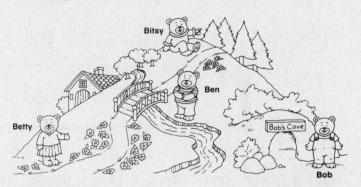

© Silver Burdett Ginn Inc.

# Problem-Solving:
**Reasoning from Clues**

It is important to think about how clues fit together.

That will help you figure out things for yourself.

B.B. Bear is lost! Help us find him.

**A.** Read the clues and look at the picture.

**B.** Draw a line to show where B.B. went.

**C.** Make an **X** where you think B.B. is.

**Clues:**  **1. Betty:** I saw B.B. go up the mountain.

**2. Ben:** I saw B.B. play in the water.

**3. Bitsy:** I saw B.B. over there.

**4. Bob:** I did not see B.B. at all.

© Silver Burdett Ginn Inc.

NAME _____

# Words with -er, -est

The ending **-er** can compare two things.
The ending **-est** can compare three things.

long

longer

longest

Look at the pictures.

Add **-er** or **-est** to each to compare all three things.

1.

old  old  old

2.

$$\begin{array}{r} 1041 \\ -987 \\ \hline \end{array}$$

$32 + 97 - 13 \times 9 =$   $396 \times 27 \div 112 =$

hard  hard  hard

3.

small  small  small

4.

strong  stronger  strong

# Contractions

A **contraction** is two words made into one.

we **+** would = we'd
they **+** will = they'll

Write the contraction for each set of words.

| | | | | |
|---|---|---|---|---|
| he'd | I'd | she'd | they'd | you'd |
| he'll | I'll | she'll | we'll | you'll |

**1.** she + would

_____

- - - - - - - - - - - - - - - - - - - -

_____

**2.** you + will

_____

- - - - - - - - - - - - - - - - - - - -

_____

**3.** I + would

_____

- - - - - - - - - - - - - - - - - - - -

_____

**4.** we + will

_____

- - - - - - - - - - - - - - - - - - - -

_____

**5.** I + will

_____

- - - - - - - - - - - - - - - - - - - -

_____

**6.** they + would

_____

- - - - - - - - - - - - - - - - - - - -

_____

**7.** he + will

_____

- - - - - - - - - - - - - - - - - - - -

_____

**8.** you + would

_____

- - - - - - - - - - - - - - - - - - - -

_____

© Silver Burdett Ginn Inc.

NAME _____

# Main Idea/Details

A **main idea** tells about the whole story. All the sentences tell about the main idea. These sentences are **details.**

Round things are all around you. → Main Idea
The sun is round. ——————→ Detail
Wheels are round. ——————→ Detail

Read each main idea. Color the circle before each detail that tells about the main idea.

1. Balloons are nice.
   - ⃝ Balloons are pretty colors.
   - ⃝ Balloons are fun to blow up.
   - ⃝ Balloons are stretchy.

2. Maud is a good dog.
   - ⃝ Maud can do tricks.
   - ⃝ Maud digs holes.
   - ⃝ Maud carries the paper.
   - ⃝ Maud eats a lot.

3. The park is fun.
   - ⃝ The park is far away.
   - ⃝ The park has swings.
   - ⃝ The park has a little pool.

# Classification

Some words belong in the same group.

These words belong together.

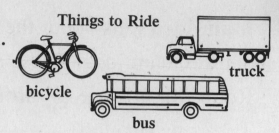

Things to Ride

bicycle    truck    bus

Circle the word in each row that does not belong with the others. Then write it.

1. red          green        six        yellow      _____

2. elephant     kitchen      giraffe    monkey      _____

3. feet         arms         nose       snow        _____

4. bell         den          nest       house       _____

5. game         puppet       orange     kite        _____

6. five         warm         three      one         _____

© Silver Burdett Ginn Inc.

# Alphabetical Order

The letters of the alphabet come in a certain order. This is called **ABC order.**

A B C D E F G H I J K L M N O P Q R S T U V W X Y Z

a b c d e f g h i j k l m n o p q r s t u v w x y z

Draw a line from one letter to another. Follow ABC order.

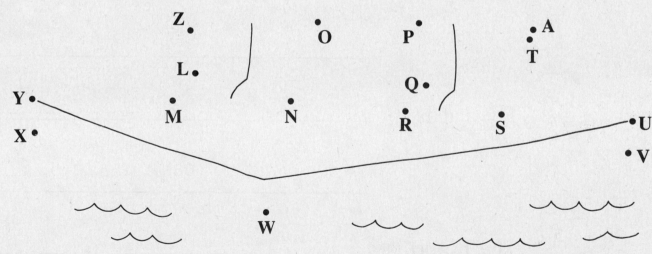

bear    dog    pig

_____

- - - - - - - - - - - - - - - - - - - -

What picture did you make? _____

# Action Words with -ing

An action word with **-ing** at the end shows that the action is still going on.

Look at each picture. Write the action word. Add **-ing** to the action word to show that the action is still happening.

bark

**1.** The dog is _____ .

fly

**2.** The bird is _____ .

cry

**3.** The cat is _____ .

eat

**4.** The hippo is _____ .

cluck

**5.** The hen is _____ .

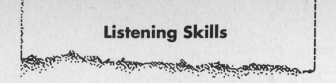

# Comprehending Fiction

**Procedure:**

*Say to the children:*    I am going to read the story "Willy the Walrus" to you. After I have read the story, I will ask you some questions about it.

### Willy the Walrus

Willy the Walrus was good at swimming, but he was not very good at telling what time it was. Each day, his mom told him not to stay out too long. Each day, Willy came home late. After a while, Willy's mom was upset.

"If you do not start coming home on time," said his mom, "I will not let you go out at all. I worry when you are late."

"I do not want to stay out late," said Willy. "It's just that I do not have a way of telling time."

Mom said, "If you want to go out, you are just going to have to find a way of telling time."

That afternoon, Willy turned on the TV set. When the TV came on, he saw a man holding up a watch.

"Good afternoon, friends," said the man. "Today I am selling a wonderful watch. It's made just for creatures of the sea. This watch works under water. You can wear it when you swim! Hurry and get one today!"

"I'll send away for that watch," said Willy. "A watch that works under water is really good. I can tell time when I'm swimming."

The very next day, Willy's watch came. He took it out of the box and put it on. It was a beautiful watch. There was just one thing wrong with it. It was very loud. It went TICK-TICK, TICK-TICK, TICK-TICK.

"If you want to wear that watch, you must go outside," said Willy's mom. "It's much too loud to wear inside."

"I was just on my way out," said Willy. "I'm going to swim in the sea with my friends, the seals. Now I have a wonderful watch. I'll know when it's time to come home."

When Willy reached the sea, his friends, the seals, were not in the water. The seals were sitting on some rocks.

"Look at my new watch," said Willy. "It's loud, but it works under water. I can wear it when I swim."

"We do not care if you can wear it when you swim," said one seal. "All we care about is that you do not wear it around us. We have a lot of thinking to do. We can't think if you are wearing that loud watch!"

"What is it you have to think about?" asked Willy. "Maybe I can help you."

"There is a big fish out in the water," said one of the seals. "He hides behind rocks. Then when we are not looking, he swims out to chase us. He makes us worry so much, we can't have any fun. We have to find a way to tell when he is around."

Willy sat down to think. All the while, his watch was going TICK-TICK, TICK-TICK, TICK-TICK. "I have it!" said Willy. "I'll give this watch to the big fish and get a quiet underwater watch for myself."

The next day, Willy got his quiet watch. He took the loud watch to the sea and gave it to the big fish. The big fish was very happy; he put the watch on his tail. Now when Willy and his friends hear the loud TICK-TICK, TICK-TICK, TICK-TICK, they jump out of the water because they know that the big fish is nearby.

**Comprehending Fiction**

1. <u>a walrus</u>     a duck     a cow

2. sing     <u>swim</u>     run

3. make friends     think     <u>get home on time</u>

4. happy     <u>upset</u>     sleepy

5. in a book     from his mom     <u>from TV</u>

6. quiet     funny     <u>loud</u>

7. inside     <u>outside</u>     in school

8. dogs     fish     <u>seals</u>

9. <u>on some rocks</u>     on chairs     on the grass

10. talked to them     <u>chased them</u>     gave them fish

11. <u>behind rocks</u>     behind trees     behind snails

12. loud     pretty     <u>quiet</u>

13. the seals     Willy's mom     <u>Willy</u>

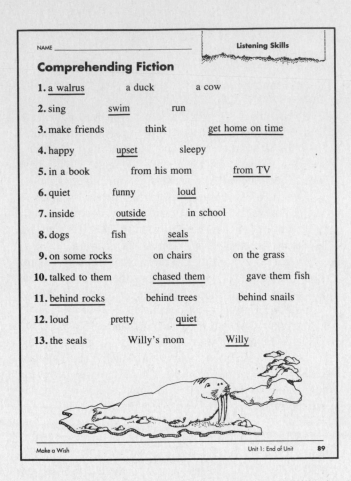

**Comprehending Fiction**

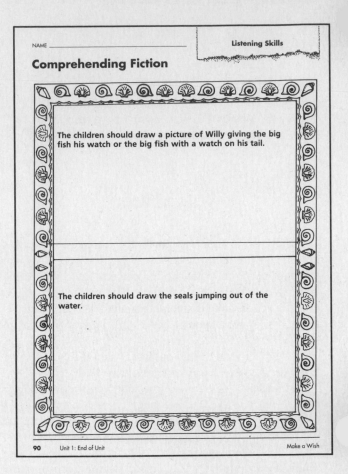

The children should draw a picture of Willy giving the big fish his watch or the big fish with a watch on his tail.

The children should draw the seals jumping out of the water.

Now I will ask some questions about the story "Willy the Walrus." Underline the correct answer on your paper.

1. What kind of animal is Willy?

2. What did Willy do well?

3. What didn't Willy do well?

4. How did Willy's mother feel about Willy's problem?

5. Where did Willy hear about the first watch?

6. How did Willy's first watch sound?

7. Where did Willy's mother tell him to wear his watch?

8. Who are Willy's friends?

9. When Willy reached the sea, where were his friends sitting?

10. What did the big fish do to the seals?

11. Where did the big fish hide?

12. How did Willy's second watch sound?

13. Who solved the seals' problem with the big fish?

(Reread the story "Willy the Walrus.") *Say to the children:* There are two boxes on your paper. In the first box, draw a picture of what happened to the loud watch. In the second box, draw a picture of what the seals do now when the big fish is nearby.

# Comprehending Fiction

1. a walrus       a duck       a cow

2. sing       swim       run

3. make friends       think       get home on time

4. happy       upset       sleepy

5. in a book       from his mom       from TV

6. quiet       funny       loud

7. inside       outside       in school

8. dogs       fish       seals

9. on some rocks       on chairs       on the grass

10. talked to them       chased them       gave them fish

11. behind rocks       behind trees       behind snails

12. loud       pretty       quiet

13. the seals       Willy's mom       Willy

# Comprehending Fiction

# Elaboration: Imagining

**Focus:**   Imagining is an important kind of thinking.

**Model:**   This activity asks you to imagine what some different animals might do.

**Practice:**   Suppose you read this question: What pet would an alligator have? You know that alligators do not have pets, so you must use your imagination to think of what kind of pet an alligator would have if alligators did have pets.

Since alligators like to be in water, you might think that an alligator would like a pet elephant. The alligator could train the elephant to squirt water with its trunk so the alligator could stay wet when it is on dry land.

You could write your answer: elephant, or you could draw a picture of an elephant.

**Apply:**   Now work on page 92.

1. Read the question.

2. Imagine the best answer you can. Think of reasons why your answer is good.

3. You can write your answer, or draw your answer, or do both.

**Monitor:**   When students have finished, discuss their ideas.

Ask children to share what they wrote or drew. In discussing their work, focus on the reasons they had for their answers, and the process of imagining.

# Elaboration: Imagining

Using your imagination is an important way of thinking.

**A.** Think of the best answer you can.

**B.** Write or draw your answer.

**1.** What gift will a  give his brother?

_____

- - - - - - - - - - - - - - - - - - - -

_____

**2.** What game does a  play with her sister?

_____

- - - - - - - - - - - - - - - - - - - -

_____

**3.** What toy will Mother give  ?

_____

- - - - - - - - - - - - - - - - - - - -

_____

**4.** What surprise will Father give  ?

_____

- - - - - - - - - - - - - - - - - - - -

_____

# Problem-Solving:
## Logical Thinking

**Focus:** It is important to think about facts you know in order to figure out other facts.

**Model:** This activity gives you a set of facts and then asks a question. You can answer the question by using the facts.

**Practice:** Suppose you read these facts:

Max has only one brother.
Nat is Max's brother.

Now you have to answer this question:

Who is Nat's brother?

To answer the question, think about the facts. You know from the first fact that Max has one brother. You know from the second fact that Max's brother is named Nat. Now you know that Max and Nat are brothers, so you know the answer to the question Who is Nat's brother? The answer is Max.

**Apply:** Now work on page 94.

1. Read the facts and the question.

2. Think about each fact and the information it gives you.

3. When you have figured out the answer, write it in the space.

**Monitor:** When students have finished, discuss their answers.

1. The first fact tells you that Bob has a sister. The next fact tells you that his sister's name is Ann. Now you know that Bob and Ann are brother and sister. The question asks what Ann's brother is named. You know that Bob and Ann are brother and sister, so you know that Ann's brother is named Bob.

2. The first fact tells you that Becky's mother has a red car. The next fact says that Becky's father has a blue car. The next fact says that Fran is Becky's sister. If Fran and Becky are sisters, they have the same father. Fran's father is the same person as Becky's father, so his car is blue.

3. The first fact tells you that Jane has a brother. Her brother is either John or Tim. The next fact tells you that John's sister is not Jane. If John's sister is not Jane, then John is not Jane's brother. That means that Tim must be Jane's brother and Jane is Tim's sister. The answer to the question Who is Tim's sister? is Jane.

**Summary:**

1. Bob        2. blue        3. Jane

# Problem-Solving:
**Logical Thinking**

It is helpful to think about facts and how they fit together.

**A.** Read the facts.

**B.** Read each question.

**C.** Write your answer to the question.

1. Bob has a sister.

   Her name is Ann.

   What is Ann's brother named?

   _____

   - - - - - - - - - - - - - - - - - - -

   _____

2. Becky's mother has a red car.

   Becky's father has a blue car.

   Fran is Becky's sister.

   What color is Fran's father's car?

   _____

   - - - - - - - - - - - - - - - - - - -

   _____

3. Jane's brother is John or Tim.

   John's sister is not Jane.

   Who is Tim's sister?

   John   Jane   Tim   Pat

   _____

   - - - - - - - - - - - - - - - - - - -

   _____

© Silver Burdett Ginn Inc.

NAME _____

# Cause/Effect

One thing can make another thing happen. An **effect** is what happens. A **cause** is what makes it happen.

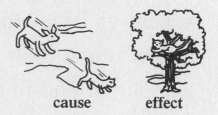

cause    effect

**A.** Read the sentences. Underline the sentence that tells what made something happen.

    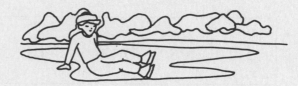

**1.** Pat slipped on the ice. She fell down.

**2.** Billy left the door open. The cat ran away.

**B.** Read the sentences. Circle the part that tells what happened because of something else.

**3.** The dog played in the mud. Max gave it a bath.

**4.** It was Peter's birthday. He got a nice surprise.

# Words with -es

When **-es** is added to a naming word, it means **more than one thing.** Add **-es** to words that end in **s, ch, tch, sh, x,** or **z.**

peach + es     peaches

**A.** Write four words from the box that mean **more than one thing.**

| benches    boxes    bus    grass    lunches    watches |

1. _____        3. _____

2. _____        4. _____

**B.** Write a word you wrote in one of the sentences.

5. We ate our _____ in the yard.

6. Joe used two _____ to time the race.

7. I keep my shoes in _____ .

© Silver Burdett Ginn Inc.

# Action Words with -ing

An action word with **-ing** at the end shows
that the action is still going on.

The people are
waiting.

Write the correct word to finish each sentence.

asking     asks

_____

- - - - - - - - - - - - - - - - - - - - - - - - - - - - - - - - - - -

**1.** Peter is _____ where to go.

tell     telling

_____

- - - - - - - - - - - - - - - - - - - - - - - - - - - - - - - - - - -

**2.** She is _____ him.

go     going

_____

- - - - - - - - - - - - - - - - - - - - - - - - - - - - - - - - - - -

**3.** Peter is _____ to the bus.

helping     helps

_____

- - - - - - - - - - - - - - - - - - - - - - - - - - - - - - - - - - -

**4.** They are _____ him.

thank     thanking

_____

- - - - - - - - - - - - - - - - - - - - - - - - - - - - - - - - - - -

**5.** He is _____ them.

# Sequence

Things in a story happen in a certain order. $\boxed{1} \rightarrow \boxed{2} \rightarrow \boxed{3}$

These sentences are in order.

It was raining.

The sun came out.

We saw a rainbow!

Number the sentences in order. Write **1, 2, 3.**

1. _____

_____ The ducks come to her.

_____ Peggy calls the ducks.

_____ She feeds the ducks.

2. _____

_____ The bear sleeps until it is warm again.

_____ It finds a good cave.

_____ The bear sees the snow fall.

# Words with ey, y

city

monkey

When the letter **y** is at the end of a word, it can stand for the vowel sound you hear at the end of **city.** Sometimes two letters stand for one sound. When the letters **ey** are at the end of a word, they can stand for the vowel sound you hear at the end of **monkey. City** and **monkey** have the same vowel sound at the end.

**A.** Read the words. Underline the words in which **y** and **ey** stand for the vowel sound at the end of **city** and **monkey.**

happy    way    turkey    today    story    key    try
funny    tiny    why    alley    stay    money    honey

**B.** Write six of the words you underlined. Write words with **y** under **city** and words with **ey** under **monkey.**

city

monkey

1._____    4._____

2._____    5._____

3._____    6._____

# Predicting Outcomes

When you read a story, think ahead and try
to tell what will happen next.

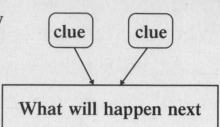

Example:

**Clue 1:** Terry looked down at the
water.

**Clue 2:** She closed her eyes.

What will happen next? She will jump into the water.

Read each story. Write the word that tells what
will happen next.

**1.** I like to feed the ducks.
I give them bits of sandwich.
My sandwiches are all gone.

food    ducks

_____

I will get some more _____.

**2.** Alex came home from school.
He wanted something to eat.
He saw some peaches.

eat    cook

_____

Alex will _____ one.

© Silver Burdett Ginn Inc.

# Words with ai, ay

Sometimes two letters stand for one sound.
The letters **ai** and **ay** can stand for the vowel
sound you hear in **rain** and **ray**. The words
**rain** and **ray** have the same vowel sound.

rain

ray

Circle the word that names each picture. Then write it.

**1.**     hail     hay

**6.**     claim     clay

**2.**     trait     tray

**7.**     pail     pay

**3.**     sail     say

**8.**     sprain     spray

**4.**     plain     play

**9.**     braid     bray

**5.**     mail     may

**10.**     train     tray

# Alphabetical Order

The letters of the alphabet come in a certain order. This is called **ABC order.**

A B C D E F G H I J K L M N O P Q R S T U V W X Y Z

a b c d e f g h i j k l m n o p q r s t u v w x y z

Write the letters in ABC order.

**1.** q   r   p   o   t   s

**2.** b   e   d   c   g   f

**3.** y   u   z   v   x   w

**4.** k   m   h   j   i   l

**5.** i   f   j   g   e   h

# Problem-Solving: Logic Matrix

**Focus:** Examining clues in an orderly way is an important method of solving problems.

**Model:** This activity gives you a problem and some clues. It also gives you a special kind of chart, or matrix. You can solve the problem by writing information from the clues in the boxes on the chart.

**Practice:** Suppose you want to solve this problem: Hi and Ho are a dog and a cat. Which animal has which name?

Here is the chart, or matrix, that you would use to solve this problem:

|  | dog | cat |
|---|---|---|
| Hi |  |  |
| Ho |  |  |

The top row across is Hi's row. If Hi is the dog, it will say Yes in the first box in Hi's row, under the word dog. If Hi is not the dog, it will say No in that box. If Hi is the cat, it will say Yes in the other box in Hi's row, the one under the word cat. If Hi is not the cat, it will say No in that box.

Now suppose you have this clue: Hi can bark. You can tell from that clue that Hi is the dog. You would write Yes in the box under the word dog in Hi's row.

Then you can write No in the next box because Hi is the name of only one of the animals. If you know that one animal is named Hi, you know that the other animal or animals in that row cannot be named Hi.

You can also write No in the box under the word dog in Ho's row. If Hi is the dog, then Ho cannot be a dog. That leaves just one empty box in Ho's row. The other box says No, so this box must say Yes.

Here is how the chart will look when you are finished writing the information from the clues:

|  | dog | cat |
|---|---|---|
| Hi | Yes | No |
| Ho | No | Yes |

The chart tells you that Hi is the dog and Ho is the cat.

**Apply:** Now work on page 104.

1. Read the problem and the clues.

2. Read the first clue again. Write **Yes** or **No** in every box you can.

3. Read the second clue again and write **Yes** or **No** in every box you can.

4. Remember that each name belongs to one of the animals. If two boxes in a row say No, the other box must say Yes.

**Monitor:** When students have finished, discuss the solution.

1. The first clue tells you that Happy can fly. Rabbits and turtles cannot fly, so you know that Happy is the bird. The word *Yes* goes in the box in Happy's row under the word *bird*.

2. Since Happy is the bird, Huffy and Hokey are not birds. You can write **No** in the boxes for Huffy and Hokey under the word *bird*.

3. You also know that Happy is not a rabbit or a turtle; write **No** in those boxes in Happy's row.

4. The next clue tells you that Huffy is not a rabbit; write **No** in the box under rabbit in Huffy's row.

5. Now you know that Huffy is not a bird or a rabbit, so Huffy must be the turtle. Write **Yes** in the box under turtle in Huffy's row.

6. Since Huffy is the turtle, Hokey cannot be the turtle. Write **No** under turtle in Hokey's row.

7. Since Hokey is not a bird or a turtle, Hokey must be the rabbit. Write **Yes** under rabbit in Hokey's row.

**Summary:**

|  | bird | rabbit | turtle |
|---|---|---|---|
| Happy | Yes | No | No |
| Huffy | No | No | Yes |
| Hokey | No | Yes | No |

Happy is the bird; Huffy is the turtle; Hokey is the rabbit.

# Problem-Solving: Logic Matrix

Writing clues on a chart can help you solve a problem.

**A.** Read the problem and the clues.
**B.** Write **Yes** or **No** in each box.

**Problem:** Happy, Huffy, and Hokey are animals. One is a bird. One is a rabbit. One is a turtle. Find out which animal has which name.

**Clues:** 1. Happy can fly.
2. Huffy is not a rabbit.

|  | 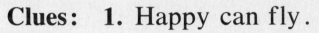 | | |
|---|---|---|---|
| Happy | | | |
| Huffy | | | |
| Hokey | | | |

# Elaboration: Imagining

**Focus:** Imagining is an important way to think of new ideas.

**Model:** This activity asks you to imagine different ideas and draw pictures to show what you imagine.

**Practice:** Suppose you read this: Pretend you are a mouse. Draw a picture of your house. You would have to imagine what it would be like to be a mouse. You would imagine where you would live. Maybe you would imagine that you live in a little hole in the wall of a house. You might have a nest made from something you found in the house.

Maybe you would imagine that you are a field mouse. You might imagine your home in a hole under the ground with a nest of grass and weeds.

Then you would draw a picture of what you imagined.

**Apply:** Now work on page 106.

1. Read the sentences for number 1. Take some time to imagine. Swim around for a while. Find your favorite place. Take time to imagine it. Try to see it clearly in your mind.

2. Then draw your picture.

3. Do the numbers 2 and 3 the same way.

**Monitor:** When students have finished, discuss their ideas. Have them show and explain their pictures. Focus on the imagining process that helped them get a picture in their minds before they drew on their papers.

# Elaboration: Imagining

One important way to think is to use your imagination.

Draw a picture in each space.

**1.** Pretend you are a fish.
Draw a picture of your favorite place to hide.

**2.** Pretend you are an ice cube.
Draw a picture of something you like to do.

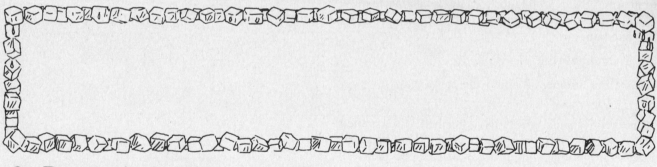

**3.** Pretend you are a moffus. Draw a picture of yourself. (There is no such thing as a moffus! Imagine it!)

# Drawing Conclusions

Sometimes you need to figure out things that are not told in a story. This is called drawing a **conclusion**.

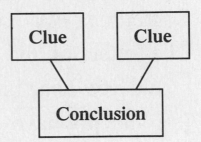

| Clue | Clue |
| --- | --- |

| Conclusion |
| --- |

Read the story. Use clues and what you already know. Circle the best answer to complete each sentence. Then write it.

Betsy sat under a tree. She put on her new skates. She stood up and walked onto the ice. She began to move her feet. She fell down! Betsy stood up again. She moved one foot. She put out her arms. She fell down again! Betsy got right back up. She tried to skate again.

does not know     knows

_____

- - - - - - - - - - - - - - - - - - - - - - - - - -

1. Betsy _____ how to skate.

inside     outside

_____

- - - - - - - - - - - - - - - - - - - - - - - - - -

2. Betsy is _____ .

go home     learn

_____

- - - - - - - - - - - - - - - - - - - - - - - - - -

3. Betsy wants to _____ .

© Silver Burdett Ginn Inc.

# Words with ai, ay

Sometimes two letters stand for one sound.
The letters **ai** and **ay** can stand for the vowel
sound you hear in **jail** and **jay.** The words
**jail** and **jay** have the same vowel sound.

jail

jay

**A.** Read each sentence. Underline letters that stand for the
vowel sound you hear in **jail** and **jay.** Then draw a picture
for one sentence.

1. Gail has a pail of gray paint.

2. It is a fine day for a sail
on the bay.

**B.** Look at the picture. Write a sentence to tell about it.
The words in the box will help you.

| paint | snail | The | tray | will | the |
|-------|-------|-----|------|------|-----|

_____

- - - - - - - - - - - - - - - - - - - - - - - - - - - - - - - - - -

_____

- - - - - - - - - - - - - - - - - - - - - - - - - - - - - - - - - -

_____ .

© Silver Burdett Ginn Inc.

# Words with ey, y

The letters **y** and **ey** as in **puppy** and **donkey** have the same sound.

puppy    donkey

Read each clue. Write the word that fits it.

**1.** a space between buildings

    alley       every       only

**2.** make something exactly alike

    chimney    country    copy

**3.** the place between two hills

    very       valley     volley

**4.** why you laugh at something

    family     funny     furry

**5.** your mother, father, and you

    family     many     happy

**6.** something to read or tell

    sorry     story     sunny

**7.** how a rabbit feels

    silly     furry     turkey

# Comprehending Nonfiction

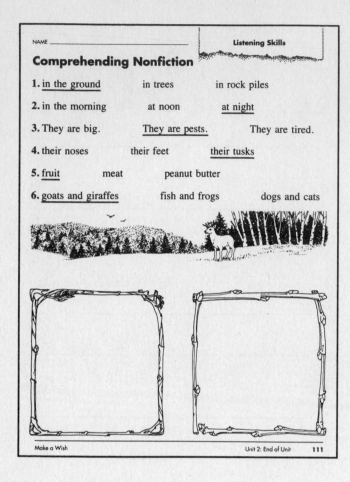

NAME _____  Listening Skills

**Comprehending Nonfiction**

1. <u>in the ground</u>      in trees      in rock piles

2. in the morning      at noon      <u>at night</u>

3. They are big.      <u>They are pests.</u>      They are tired.

4. their noses      their feet      <u>their tusks</u>

5. <u>fruit</u>      meat      peanut butter

6. <u>goats and giraffes</u>      fish and frogs      dogs and cats

Make a Wish      Unit 2: End of Unit      **111**

## Procedure:

*Say to the children:*   I am going to read the article "Four Kinds of Wild Animals" to you. After I have read the article, I will ask you some questions about it.

### Four Kinds of Wild Animals

Wild rabbits live all over the world. They usually are gray or brown. Some rabbits that live where it snows in the winter have fur that changes from brown to white. The white fur helps this kind of rabbit hide from its enemies. Wild rabbits live in the ground. They dig holes for their homes. Often, many rabbits will dig their homes next to one another. Rabbits like to eat plants.

A raccoon looks as if it is wearing a mask. It is about the size of a cat and has a long, bushy tail. Most raccoons sleep during the day and look for food at night. Some people think raccoons are pests because the animals get into people's garbage or eat corn from their fields.

Did you know that there are wild pigs? Most wild pigs live in wooded areas. They have short tusks that they use for digging up roots. Besides eating roots, wild pigs eat small animals, grasses, and leaves. Wild pigs can be very dangerous. Their tusks not only are used for digging but also for defending themselves. If a wild pig is disturbed, the animal's tusks become dangerous weapons.

Forests are homes for many deer. These wild animals eat leaves or grass. One kind of deer eats fruit that falls from trees in the forest. The deer has two relatives that you might have seen on a farm and a zoo. The relatives are the goat and the giraffe.

Now I will ask you some questions about the article "Four Kinds of Wild Animals." Underline the correct answer on your paper.

1. Where do wild rabbits make their homes?
2. When do raccoons look for food?
3. What do some people think about raccoons?
4. What do wild pigs use for digging up roots?
5. What does one kind of deer eat?
6. What are two relatives of the deer?

Listen to the part that tells what the raccoon looks like. (Reread paragraph 2.)

Now draw the raccoon and what it eats in box 1.

Listen to the part that tells about wild rabbits. (Reread paragraph 1.)

Now draw wild rabbits and where they live in box 2.

# Comprehending Nonfiction

**1.** in the ground        in trees        in rock piles

**2.** in the morning        at noon        at night

**3.** They are big.        They are pests.        They are tired.

**4.** their noses        their feet        their tusks

**5.** fruit        meat        peanut butter

**6.** goats and giraffes        fish and frogs        dogs and cats

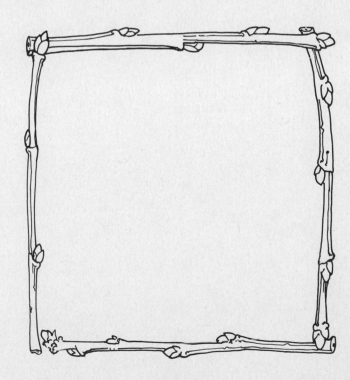

# Drawing Conclusions

**Procedure:**

On the chalkboard, draw a flower, a sailboat, a pencil, and a fish.

*Say to the children:*    To make a decision about something, you often have to think about what you already know. I have drawn a flower, a sailboat, a pencil, and a fish on the chalkboard. Now listen as I read the following complete sentence and incomplete sentence.

> Bill wants to write a letter to his grandmother.
> Bill has paper, but he will need a _____ .

Which thing on the chalkboard will Bill need? (Elicit that Bill will need a pencil.) You know that Bill will need a pencil because you already know that to write a letter, you must have something to write with; you also know that you do not need a flower, a sailboat, or a fish to write a letter.

Now I will read another complete sentence and another incomplete sentence. Listen carefully as I read them. Then look at the four pictures in the row on your paper and circle the picture of the thing that would best complete the incomplete sentence.

NAME _____

**Listening Skills**

**Drawing Conclusions**

114    Unit 2: End of Unit    Make a Wish

1.  Ms. Jones has a lot of leaves in her yard.
    She will need a _____ .

2.  Little Oink the pig slept through breakfast and lunch.
    When he woke up, he wanted _____ .

3.  The Smiths have many large things to move into their new house.
    They will have to move their things in a _____ .

4.  The children saw the deep snow.
    They put on their winter clothes and grabbed their

    _____ .

5.  Ms. Williams walks to work.
    Today, it is raining, so Ms. Williams took her

    _____ .

6.  The storm caused Tim's lights to go out.
    To see in the dark, Tim needed a _____ .

7.  Mr. Donner wanted to know if he had gained any weight.
    Mr. Donner got on a _____ .

© Silver Burdett Ginn  Inc.

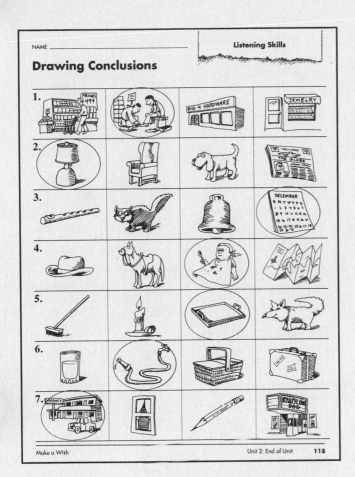

**Drawing Conclusions**

1. The twins need new shoes.
   They will go to a _____ .

2. Even during the day, Jane's office is dark.
   She will have to get another _____ .

3. George wants to know if his birthday is on a Friday
   or Saturday.
   George looked for a _____ .

4. The baby is a messy eater.
   His father should buy the baby a _____ .

5. Paul is going to bring six glasses of juice from his
   kitchen to his living room.
   To do this in one trip, Paul should use a _____ .

6. Janet wanted to water her big garden because it
   hadn't rained for weeks.
   Janet needed a _____ .

7. Bernard had been driving for hours.
   He saw a sign, and drove toward the _____ .

# Drawing Conclusions

1.

2.

3.

4.

5.

6.

7.

# Drawing Conclusions

**1.**

| PRUNES 49¢ | | BIG 4 HARDWARE | JEWELRY |

**2.**

| | | | THE GLOBE |

**3.**

| | | | DECEMBER S M T W T F S 1 2 3 4 5 6 7 8 9 10 11 12 13 14 15 16 17 18 19 20 21 22 23 24 25 26 27 28 29 30 31 |

**4.**

**5.**

**6.**

**7.**

| VACANCY | | | RALPH THE DOG |

# Problem-Solving:
## Figural Sequences

**Focus:** By thinking about the order in which things are shown, you can often figure out what will come next.

**Model:** This activity gives you a set of pictures and asks you to draw the picture that comes next in each set.

**Practice:** Suppose you saw this set of pictures:

You have to draw the picture that comes next.

Look at the pictures in the set. The first one is a circle, the next is a circle with a line through the middle. The next picture is a plain circle, and the next is another circle with a line through it. The next picture is a plain circle again.

You can see this pattern in the set: circle/ circle with line/circle/circle with line. Since the last picture is a circle, you know that the next one will be a circle with a line. You would draw a circle with a line.

**Apply:** Now work on page 117.

1. Look at the pictures in each row.

2. Try to see how each picture is the same as or different from the others.

3. Figure out the pattern.

4. Draw the next picture in the set.

**Monitor:** When children have finished, discuss their results.

1. The pattern is little circle at the top/two little circles at the bottom/circles at all three points. The next figure in the set has circles at all three points.

2. The pattern is stripe in one corner/two stripes in the same corner. The next picture will have two stripes in the same corner as the last picture in the row.

3. The pattern is no tail/tail/tail. The next cat in the set should have a tail.

4. The pattern is circle in one corner/circles in two corners/circles in three corners. The next picture should have circles in all four corners.

5. The pattern is little shape up high/ little shape in big shape/little shape down low. The next picture should be a little circle on the line.

6. The pattern is big fir tree and little fir tree/little shade tree and big shade tree/little fir tree and big fir tree. The next picture should be a big shade tree and a little shade tree.

**Summary:**

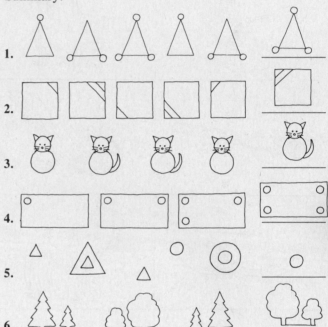

# Problem-Solving:
## Figural Sequences

Looking at the order of things can help you know what comes next.

Pretend you are an artist.
Draw the picture that comes next in each line.

1.      _____

2.      _____

3.     _____

4.    _____

5.   _____

6.    _____

# Critical Thinking:
## Making Judgments

**Focus:** It is good to be able to judge how important different things are.

**Model:** This activity gives you some choices in a box. You look at a picture and pretend to be the animal or thing in the picture. Then you choose the thing from the box that is most important to you.

**Practice:** Suppose you have these two things in the box:

> fur
> water

You are supposed to pretend you are a fish. Now you have to choose the thing from the box that is most important to you. You know that fur is important to many different kinds of animals, but it is not important to a fish. Water is very important to a fish, so you would write **water** next to the picture of the fish.

**Apply:** Now work on page 119.

**1.** Look at all the words in the box.

**2.** Look at each picture and pretend to be the thing that the picture shows.

**3.** Try to figure out which thing in the box would be most important to you.

**4.** When you have picked the thing from the box, cross off that word in the box.

**5.** Write the word next to the picture.

**6.** If you cannot decide what is most important, skip that picture and go on to the next one. You can come back to the one you skipped later. You may be able to figure it out when more of the words in the box have been crossed out.

**Monitor:** When students have finished, discuss their answers. The answers that follow are reasonable; accept other answers as well if students can justify them.

**1.** Horses eat hay, so hay is probably most important to the horse.

**2.** Kites need wind in order to fly, so wind is probably most important to the kite.

**3.** Most books have words in them, so words are probably most important to the book.

**4.** A bus needs wheels in order to run, so wheels are probably most important to the bus.

**5.** A bee drinks nectar from flowers, so flowers are probably most important to a bee.

**6.** A tree needs rain in order to grow, so rain is probably most important to the tree.

**Summary:**

| | | | |
|---|---|---|---|
| **1.** | hay | **4.** | wheels |
| **2.** | wind | **5.** | flowers |
| **3.** | words | **6.** | rain |

# Critical Thinking:
**Making Judgments**

It is good to know what things are most important and why.

**A.** Pretend you are the animal or thing in the picture.
**B.** Pick the most important thing from the box.
**C.** Write it.

| flowers hay rain wheels wind words |
| --- |

1. _____

2. _____

3. _____

4. _____

5. _____

6. _____

# Comprehension:
## Story Coherence and Sequence

**Focus:** Understanding how the parts of a story go together and the order they go in is an important skill.

**Model:** This activity gives you six sentences to read. Three of the sentences belong in one story, and the other three sentences belong in another story. The sentences are all mixed up.

**Practice:** Suppose you had to show what stories these sentences belong in:

> Two wings popped out on the horse's back.
> A mouse helped an elephant.
> A horse wished it had wings.
> Then the mouse and the elephant were friends.

First you would read all the sentences. You would find out that two of the sentences tell about a horse and wings. The other two sentences tell about a mouse and an elephant. You would know then that the sentences about the horse and its wings are both part of one of the stories. You would underline the first sentence and the third sentence to show that they are parts of the same story.

You would also know that the second sentence and the fourth sentence are parts of another story, about a mouse and an elephant. You would circle those sentences.

Now you would read the two sentences you underlined and decide what order they should be in. It wouldn't make sense for the wings to pop out and then for the horse to wish that it had wings. It makes sense for the horse first to wish for wings, so you would write **1** by that sentence. You would write **2** by the other sentence. Then you would read the sentences you circled and put them in order.

**Apply:** Now work on page 121.

1. Read all the sentences carefully.

2. Underline the first sentence. Figure out which two other sentences go in the same story as this sentence. Underline them, too.

3. Make sure the other three sentences also go together in a story. Circle those sentences.

4. Read the underlined sentences again. Write **1** by the sentence that tells what happened first. Write **2** by the sentence that tells what happened next. Write **3** by the sentence that tells what happened last.

5. In the same way, read the circled sentences and write **1, 2,** and **3** to show the right order.

**Monitor:** Discuss children's answers.

1. The first sentence tells about some rabbits. It is underlined.

2. The next sentence does not tell about rabbits. It tells about a bear and is part of a different story. It is circled.

3. The next sentence also tells about the bear, so it is also circled.

4. The next sentence tells about more than one animal (*they*) hopping home. This might be about the rabbits, but you cannot tell for sure yet.

5. The next sentence is about some rabbits, as the first sentence is. This sentence is underlined.

6. This sentence tells about a ladder. You cannot tell from the sentence who it is about. Looking back at the other sentences, you see one that tells about the bear coming up a ladder. Now you know that this last sentence is about the bear. This sentence is circled.

7. Now three sentences are circled and two are underlined. The other sentence must be part of the underlined story because it tells about hopping.

8. The underlined sentence that tells what happened first in that story is about the three rabbits setting out to see the world. That is Number 1. Number 2 tells that they heard a loud noise. Number 3 tells that they hopped home as fast as they could go.

9. In the circled story, sentence Number 1 tells how the bear fell in the hole. Number 2 tells about his friends making a ladder. Number 3 tells that the bear came up the ladder.

**Summary:**

2 — The rabbits heard a loud noise.

1 — (A bear went walking and fell in a hole.)

3 — (The bear came up the ladder.)

3 — They hopped back home as fast as they could go.

1 — Three rabbits set out to see the world.

2 — (His friend made a ladder out of branches.)

© Silver Burdett Ginn Inc.

# Comprehension:
## Story Coherence and Sequence

It is important to know how the parts of a story go together.

Two stories are all mixed up!

**A.** Underline the sentences that go in one story.
**B.** Circle the sentences that go in the other story.
**C.** Put each story in order. Write 1, 2, 3 for each story.

_____ The rabbits heard a loud noise.

_____ A bear went walking and fell in a hole.

_____ The bear came up the ladder.

_____ They hopped back home as fast as
_____ they could go.

_____ Three rabbits set out to see the world.

_____ His friends made a ladder out of branches.

# Characterization

A **character** is a person or animal in a story. You can know what characters are like by what they say and do.

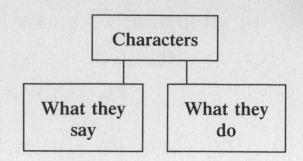

Example:

Dave lost his dog. Dave is crying because he is sad.

Look at each person. Write the word that tells how each person feels.

cold    happy    hungry    sorry    tired    warm

**1.**

_____

- - - - - - - - - - - - - - - - - - - -

_____

**2.**

_____

- - - - - - - - - - - - - - - - - - - -

_____

**3.**

_____

- - - - - - - - - - - - - - - - - - - -

_____

**4.**

_____

- - - - - - - - - - - - - - - - - - - -

_____

**5.**

_____

- - - - - - - - - - - - - - - - - - - -

_____

**6.**

_____

- - - - - - - - - - - - - - - - - - - -

_____

# Compound Words

Two small words can be put together to make
a longer word. The longer word is called a
**compound word.** The new word has some of
the meaning of both small words.

dog + house = doghouse

Put the two small words together. Write the new long word.

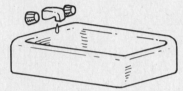

**1.** bath + tub = _____

**2.** rain + fall = _____

**3.** bird + bath = _____

**4.** sea + shell = _____

**5.** black + bird = _____

# Making Inferences

Use story clues and what you already know to figure
out things that the story doesn't tell you.

| Story Clues |
| :---: |
| What I Know |
| Inference |

Read each story. Then draw a line
under the best answer to each question.

**1.** The girls climbed higher and higher. There was no more grass under
their feet. Now there was only rock. They looked up. They would have
to climb even higher to get to the top. What were the girls climbing?

   a ladder          a mountain          some stairs

**2.** Terry looked out the window at the nice spring day. He wanted to
play baseball after he finished his work. Then his teacher asked him to
write on the board. Where was Terry?

   at a game          at school          in his bedroom

**3.** Susan looked at all of the displays. She saw food and animals and
clothes. She heard some loud music. Where was Susan?

   at a game          at a fair          on a mountain

**4.** William looked up. The trees were very tall. There were a lot of
them, too. He could hardly see the sky. Where was William?

   in a forest          in his school          on a big lake

**5.** The only sound Kit heard was of birds singing. There were no people.
There were only the water and trees and sky. Where was Kit?

   in a building          in a city          in the country

© Silver Burdett Ginn Inc.

# Contractions

A **contraction** is a short way of writing
two words.

| |
|---|
| I + am = I'm |
| they + are = they're |
| you + have = you've |

**A.** Look at the two words at the beginning of each row.
   Circle the word that is the contraction of the two words.

**1.** I have      I've      we've      they've

**2.** you are      we're      you've      you're

**3.** we have      I've      we're      we've

**4.** they have      they're      they've      you've

**5.** I am      I've      I'm      we're

**6.** they are      they've      you're      they're

**7.** we are      we're      they're      we've

**8.** you have      you're      we've      you've

**B.** Write the two words that make the contraction.

**9.** they've _____

**10.** I'm _____

© Silver Burdett Ginn Inc.

# Words with Long u

The letter **u** can stand for the vowel sound you hear in **tube** and **mule.** Look for the letter **e** at the end of a short word. It often points out that the first vowel in the word stands for a long sound.

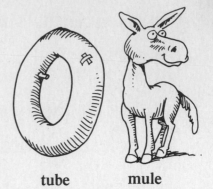

tube    mule

**A.** Underline the words that have the same vowel sound as in **tube** and **mule.**

| | | | | | |
|---|---|---|---|---|---|
| rule | but | up | dune | cube | use |
| prune | June | bus | huge | pull | tune |
| put | run | rude | flute | us | fuse |

**B.** Look at each picture. Circle the picture whose name has the vowel sound you hear in **tube** and **mule.** Then write the word that names the picture.

**1.**

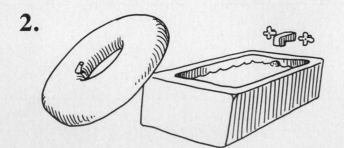

cub    cube

_____

- - - - - - - - - - - - - - - - - -

_____

**2.**

tub    tube

_____

- - - - - - - - - - - - - - - - - -

_____

A New Day

# Words with y

When the letter **y** is at the end of a word, it can stand for the vowel sound you hear in **sky.**

sky

**A.** Read the words. Underline the words in which **y** stands for the vowel sound you hear in **sky.**

| dry | happy | by | shy | try | many |
|-----|-------|-----|-----|-------|------|
| funny | my | cry | fly | bunny | why |
| spy | fry | city | sky | sly | any |

**B.** Write nine of the words you underlined.

_____  _____  _____

1._____  4._____  7._____

2._____  5._____  8._____

3._____  6._____  9._____

# Words with -igh

Sometimes many letters stand for one sound. The
letters *igh* stand for the vowel sound you hear in
**night.**

igh → night

Read the story. Draw a line under the words that have the vowel sound
you hear in **night.**

   Nick saw a strange sight one night. Some very bright lights were high
in the sky. "It might be a strange ship," he said. He was frightened and
ran home. Soon his dad came home. "Did you see any bright lights
tonight?" he asked. "My airplane flight went right over our house."
Nick sighed to himself. "Dad was my scary thing tonight."

Read the sentences. Draw a circle around the word with the vowel sound
you hear in *night* that finishes each sentence.

fight

**1.** Nick saw a strange _____ .                    sight

bright

**2.** There were very _____ lights.                light

frightened

**3.** He was _____ .                               lightning

lights

**4.** His dad asked if Nick had seen _____ .       might

fight

**5.** The airplane _____ had gone over the house.  flight

# Synonyms

**Synonyms** are words that mean almost the same thing.

glad    happy

These words have almost the same meaning.

Circle the two words in each row that have almost the same meaning.

1. far        close       near        back

2. little     hard        big         small

3. fix        stop        begin       end

4. jump       leap        walk        run

5. pull       eat         watch       look

6. nap        play        sleep       ride

7. left       came        went        heard

8. ill        hurry       soft        rush

9. see        help        look        try

10. hurry     fast        quick       slow

11. wanted    talked      listened    heard

12. woods     sand        beach       forest

13. come      enjoy       like        happy

14. sound     turn        loud        noise

# Words with oa

Sometimes two letters stand for one sound.
The letters **oa** can stand for the vowel sound
in **boat** and **soap.**

boat    soap

**A.** Read the words. Underline the words that have the same
vowel sound as in **boat** and **soap.**

| | | | | | |
|---|---|---|---|---|---|
| road | groan | out | but | oat | toad |
| cow | roam | goal | coat | cook | loaf |
| rain | coal | say | foam | loan | toast |

**B.** Look at each picture. Make some funny sentences by writing
two words to tell about the picture.

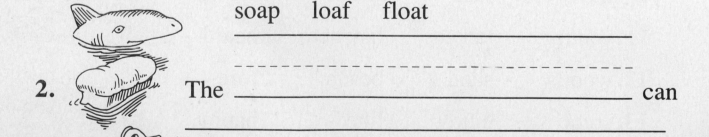

boat    goat    toast

1. The _____ will row the

_____

_____ .

soap    loaf    float

2. The _____ can

_____

_____ .

# Words with oa

Sometimes two letters stand for one sound.
The letters **oa** can stand for the vowel sound
you hear in **home** and **loaf.** The words **home**
and **loaf** have the same vowel sound.

home        loaf

Read each word. Circle and color the picture it names.
Then write the word.

**1.** oak

**2.** coast

**3.** road

**4.** toad

**5.** coal

# Making Inferences

**Procedure:**

Write the following sentences on the chalkboard:

1. Gail is feeding the cows and the pigs.
2. Next, Gail will clean the barn.

Beneath the second sentence, write the words **boat, lake,** and **farm.**

*Say to the children:* I will read the two sentences on the chalkboard to you. (Read the sentences.) Now look at the three words beneath the second sentence. Which word tells where Gail is? (farm) Even though the sentences do not say "Gail is on a farm," you know from the words *cows, pigs,* and *barn* that Gail is on a farm and not on a boat or a lake.

Now I will read another pair of sentences and a question. Listen carefully and then look at your paper. Mark an **X** on the picture that answers the question.

1. Jim heard the pilot say, "We are passing over Elm City."
   Jim said, "Elm City looks small from up here."
   Where is Jim?

2. Maggie opened a drawer and put the book next to a box of paper clips.
   Then she closed the drawer.
   Where is the book?

3. Ms. Potter pulled out all of the weeds.
   Then she picked some tomatoes and some corn.
   Where is Ms. Potter?

4. Shirley watched him swim back and forth.
   She knew that he would be a good pet for her tiny bedroom.
   What is Shirley looking at?

5. George had never seen such tall trees.
   In one of the trees, he saw two squirrels.
   Where is George?

# Making Inferences

**1.**

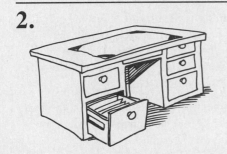    

**2.**

**3.**

**4.**

  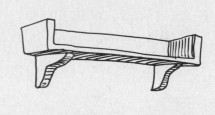  

**5.**

© Silver Burdett Ginn Inc.

# Making Inferences

NAME _____

Listening Skills

**Making Inferences**

1.
2.
3.
4.
5.

A New Day                                    Unit 1: Midunit    **135**

**Procedure:**

On the chalkboard, draw a fish and a ball.

*Say to the children:*    Many times, you can answer a question about information even though the information does not tell you the answer word-for-word. Listen to this pair of sentences:

> Sara put her line into the water.
> She waited for a pull on the line.

Now look at the drawings of the fish and the ball on the chalkboard. Which thing is Sara trying to catch? (Elicit that Sara is trying to catch a fish.) Even though the sentences do not say that Sara is trying to catch a fish, you know from the words "line" and "water" that Sara is trying to catch a fish and not a ball.

Now I will read another pair of sentences and a question. Listen carefully and then look at your paper. Mark an **X** on the picture that answers the question.

1.  Jim looked for shells.
    Then he made a sand castle.
    Where is Jim?

2.  Mr. James could smell the bread.
    Soon, he could take it out and let it cool.
    Where is the bread?

3.  The driver pulled up to the curb.
    Another person got out and emptied the cans into the open back end.
    What is the driver driving?

4.  With her finger, Peg traced the highways and roads to Sally's new home.
    Now she easily could find her way.
    What is Peg looking at?

5.  Elephants did tricks, and clowns rode tiny bicycles.
    The crowd clapped and cheered.
    Where is the crowd?

# Making Inferences

1.

2.

3.

4.

5.

# Following Directions

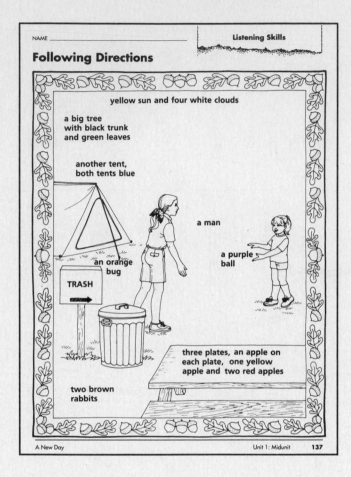

NAME _____

**Following Directions**

yellow sun and four white clouds

a big tree
with black trunk
and green leaves

another tent,
both tents blue

a man

a purple
ball

an orange
bug

TRASH

three plates, an apple on
each plate, one yellow
apple and two red apples

two brown
rabbits

A New Day · Unit 1: Midunit · **137**

## Procedure:

*Say to the children:* Take out your crayons or markers because you will need them for parts of this lesson. Now look at the picture of the campground on your paper. I am going to give you some directions to complete the picture. Listen carefully to each direction. Use your pencil unless I tell you to color something on the paper.

1. Draw the sun and four clouds in the sky.
   Color the sun yellow, but leave the four clouds white.

2. Draw another tent **next to** the tent in your picture.
   Color both tents blue.

3. **Behind** the tents, draw a big tree with leaves.
   Color the trunk of the tree black and the leaves green.

4. Draw a man **between** the woman and the girl.

5. Draw a ball in the girl's hand.
   Color the ball purple.

6. Draw three plates on the picnic table.

7. Draw an apple on each plate.
   Color any one of the apples yellow and then color the other two apples red.

8. Draw two rabbits **in front of** the trash can.
   Color both rabbits brown.

9. On the sign that points to the trash can, write the word **TRASH** in capital letters. I will spell the word for you: T-R-A-S-H.

10. On the top edge of the sign, draw a bug.
    Color the bug orange.

# Following Directions

# Comprehension:
## Following Directions

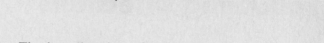
**Focus:** The ability to follow directions correctly is an important skill.

**Model:** This activity gives you a set of directions to read and follow.

**Practice:** Suppose a direction said this: If an apple is not an orange, write **I**. You know that an apple is not an orange, so you would write **I** on your paper.

Then suppose the next direction said this: If you wrote I, write **H** before the I. You did write I, so now you would write **H** before it. Here is what you would have if you followed directions correctly:

HI

**Apply:** Now work on page 139.

**1.** First, read all the directions.

**2.** Then go back and follow each direction in the right order.

**3.** Pay careful attention to what each direction says. You may have to write or draw something, or you may not have to do anything.

**Monitor:** When students have finished, discuss their results.

**1.** The first direction tells you to write an **E** in the middle of the box.

**2.** The next direction says to do something if day is night. You know that day is not night, so you should not do what the direction says; you should not draw a flower in the top left corner.

**3.** This direction says to write **ND** after the E if red is not blue. You know that red is not blue, so you should write **ND** after E.

**4.** This direction says to draw a sun in the top right corner.

**5.** This direction says to write **OK** before the E if you drew a flower in Step 2. However, you did not draw a flower in Step 2, so you should not write OK.

**6.** This direction says to write something *if* you did not draw a flower. You did not draw a flower, so you should write **RI** before the E.

**7.** This direction tells you to draw two happy faces if you wrote RI before the E. You did write RI, so you should draw the happy faces in the bottom left corner.

**8.** The last direction tells you to write **S** at the end of the word and **F** at the beginning.

**Summary:** If you followed directions correctly, you should have written the word FRIENDS, with a sun in the upper right corner and two happy faces in the lower left corner.

# Comprehension:
## Following Directions

It is important to follow directions carefully to get the results you want.

Do what the directions tell you. Work in the box.

1. Write **e** right in the middle of the box.

2. If day is night, draw a flower in the top left corner.

3. If red is not blue, write **nd** after the **e**.

4. Draw a sun in the top right corner.

5. If you drew a flower in Step 2, write **ok** before the **e**.

6. If you did not draw a flower, write **ri** before the **e**.

7. If you wrote **ri** before the **e**, draw two happy faces in the bottom left corner.

8. Write **s** at the end of the word and **f** at the beginning.

# Comprehension: Visualizing

**Focus:**   Creating pictures in your mind as you read is an important way to understand what you read.

**Model:**   This activity gives you two short stories to read. You must form pictures in your mind as you read and then draw the pictures.

**Practice:**   Suppose you read this:

A small brown dog ran with a huge orange cat.

You would see a picture in your mind of a dog that is small and brown running with a cat that is orange and very big. Maybe the cat in your picture is even bigger than the dog.

The cat and dog in your picture might be running down a city street or across a grassy field. You will see the picture your own way, but it should match what you read in the story.

**Apply:**   Now work on page 141.

1.   Read the story for Number 1. As you read, try to see a picture in your mind.

2.   Draw your picture in the box below the story.

3.   Now do the same for Number 2.

**Monitor:**   When children have finished, discuss their pictures.

1.   Each person's picture may look different, but every picture should show these things from the story: a large gray elephant, a red ball under a bush, the elephant either trying to reach the ball or looking sad because the ball is out of reach.

2.   Each picture should show these things from the story: Three little pigs either in a puddle or next to it. They should all be wearing sneakers that are wet and muddy. The smallest pig is looking in the direction from which Mother Pig is coming toward them.

## Comprehension: Visualizing

It is good to make pictures in your mind when you read.

**A.** Read each story and make a picture
in your mind.

**B.** Draw your picture.

1. A large gray elephant played with a red ball.
The ball rolled under a bush. Poor Elephant
wants the ball.

2. Three little pigs fell in a puddle. Their new sneakers
are all wet and muddy. The smallest pig sees
Mother Pig coming.

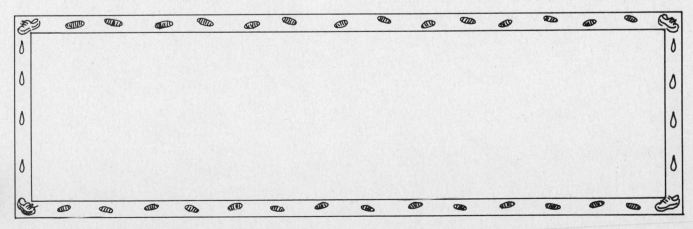

# Elaboration: Creative Thinking

**Focus:** You can use your imagination to think of other uses for everyday things.

**Model:** This activity shows you pictures of some things you see every day. You have to imagine what an animal would do if it found one of these things.

**Practice:** Suppose you read this: A bird finds a pencil. What will he do with it? You must draw a picture to answer the question.

You know that birds do not write, so the bird will probably not use the pencil the same way a person would. You may imagine that the bird would put the pencil across two branches of a tree to make a bridge. You could draw a picture of the bird sitting on the pencil that it has placed across the branches.

You might imagine that the bird would use the pencil as a flagpole. Maybe the flag could be a leaf. You could draw a picture of the bird standing next to its new flagpole.

**Apply:** Now work on page 143.

1. Read each sentence and each question.

2. Use your imagination to think of a good answer to the question.

3. Think of how you can show your answer in a picture.

4. Draw the picture.

**Monitor:** When children have finished, discuss their ideas, having them display and explain their pictures. Help them focus on the thinking processes they used, such as imagining that they were the animal, imagining how the object would look to that animal, and so on.

© Silver Burdett Ginn Inc.

# Elaboration: Creative Thinking

Using your imagination is an important kind of thinking.

Draw a picture to answer each question.

**1.** A pig finds a 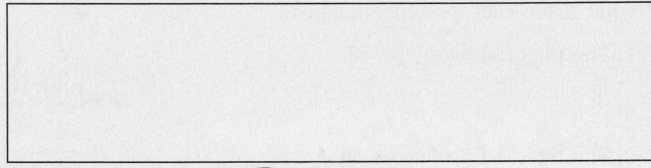 in her pen.
What will she do with it?

**2.** A duck finds a  in the pond.
What will he do with it?

**3.** A mouse finds a in the field.
What will she do with it?

# Cause/Effect

One thing can make another thing happen. An **effect** is what happens. A **cause** is what makes it happen.

cause        effect

Read each sentence. Draw a line to the picture that shows what made each sentence happen.

**1.** The pigs ran away.

**2.** The tree had no leaves on it.

**3.** The turtle won the race.

**4.** The hat was flat.

**5.** The straw house fell down.

**6.** The ducklings came out of the eggs.

# Cause/Effect

One thing can make another thing happen.
An **effect** is what happens. A **cause** is what
makes it happen.

cause        effect

Read the sentences. Write what caused something to happen.

1. The farmer does not want rabbits in the garden because
   they eat the beans.        they work very hard.

   _____

   - - - - - - - - - - - - - - - - - - - - - - - - - - - - - - - - - -

   _____

2. Emily eats lots of spinach because
   she does not like it.      it is good for her.

   _____

   - - - - - - - - - - - - - - - - - - - - - - - - - - - - - - - - - -

   _____

3. John was late for school because
   he got up on time.      he missed the bus.

   _____

   - - - - - - - - - - - - - - - - - - - - - - - - - - - - - - - - - -

   _____

4. The work was done fast because
   everyone helped.        Grandfather came to visit.

   _____

   - - - - - - - - - - - - - - - - - - - - - - - - - - - - - - - - - -

   _____

# Synonyms

**Synonyms** are words that mean almost the same thing.

Read each numbered word. Write a word from the list that has almost the same meaning.

race    dash

| | | | | | |
|---|---|---|---|---|---|
| call | end | left | mom | sick | start |
| cook | glad | many | nap | small | think |

**1.** begin _____

**2.** ill _____

**3.** happy _____

**4.** believe _____

**5.** mother _____

**6.** little _____

**7.** lots _____

**8.** stop _____

**9.** went _____

**10.** sleep _____

**11.** bake _____

**12.** yell _____

# Synonyms

**Synonyms** are words that mean almost the same thing.

These words have almost the same meaning.

nap     sleep

Read the first word in each row. Find the word that has almost the same meaning. Underline the word. Then write it.

_____

1. **boat**    bus      truck      ship      _____

2. **yellow**    red      gold      green      _____

3. **call**    yell      wait      sit      _____

4. **beetle**    bird      bug      plant      _____

5. **father**    dad      mom      brother      _____

6. **looked**    found      saw      heard      _____

# Words with r-Controlled Vowels

When the letter **r** follows a vowel, it changes the sound that the vowel letter usually stands for.

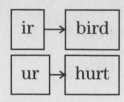

Read the sentences. Draw a circle around the word that best finishes each sentence Then write the word.

_____

1. A bear has thick _____ .

                                fur    girl    sir

_____

2. She _____ a sound far away.

              burned    heard    learn

_____

3. A _____ is a small animal.

           gerbil    nurse    turn

_____

4. He began to _____ the soup.

               first    hurt    stir

_____

5. We sat on the floor in a _____ .

                certainly    circle    surprise

_____

6. We _____ on the TV.

         heard    surprised    turned

© Silver Burdett Ginn Inc.

# Compound Words

Two small words can be put together to
make a longer word. The longer word is
called a **compound word.** The new word
has some of the meaning of both small words.

rain + coat = raincoat

Choose a word from List 1. Draw a line to a word in List 2
that goes with it. Put the two words together to make a
compound word. Write the word. The first one is done.

| 1 | 2 |
|------|-------|
| farm | book |
| day | boat |
| cook | house |
| sail | time |
| bread | water |
| rain | box |

1. farmhouse

2. _____

3. _____

4. _____

5. _____

6. _____

# Comparison

When we **compare** things, we think about how they
are alike and how they are different.

Think about the two things. Then answer the questions.
Draw a line under each answer.

Alike and Different

    kite—airplane

**1.** How are they alike?

  **a.** They both fly.

  **b.** They have wheels.

  **c.** They both have wings.

  **d.** They go up.

  **e.** They can be used for fun.

  **f.** They are both used by adults only.

  **g.** They are the same shape.

  **h.** They are both flown by someone.

  **i.** They can be seen in the sky.

**2.** How are they different?

  **a.** One has wings. One does not have wings.

  **b.** One needs wind to fly. One needs an engine to fly.

  **c.** One is used only by children. One is used only by adults.

  **d.** One has many colors. One has only one color.

  **e.** One has seats. One does not have seats.

  **f.** One is very big. One is small.

  **g.** One is very quiet. One makes a lot of noise.

  **h.** One is held to the ground. One is not.

# Words with ch, tch

Sometimes two or three letters stand for the same sound. The consonants **ch** can stand for the beginning sound in **chain** and the ending sound in **arch.** The consonants **tch** stand for the ending sound in **ditch.**

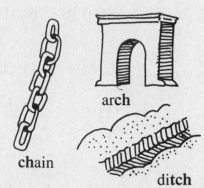

arch

chain

ditch

Look at each picture. Write two words to tell about it.

branch    chair    cheer    chop    perch
catch     champ    chest    ditch   pitch

1. _____    _____

   a _____ in a _____

2. _____    _____

   _____ the _____

3. _____    _____

   _____ for the _____

4. _____    _____

   _____ up the _____

5. _____    _____

   _____ on the _____

# Antonyms

Some words mean the opposite.

↑        ↓
Up     Down

Circle the words in each row that have opposite meanings.

**1.** over        across        under        between

**2.** saw        found        closed        lost

**3.** back        left        right        side

**4.** old        warm        tall        new

**5.** glad        sad        good        tired

**6.** run        stop        sleep        start

**7.** looked        opened        pulled        pushed

**8.** give        win        take        hide

**9.** come        go        could        line

**10.** we        me        yes        no

# Synonyms and Antonyms

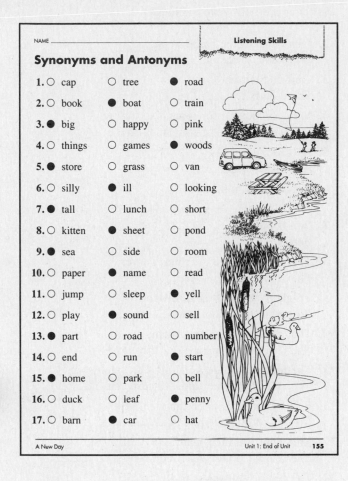

NAME _____  Listening Skills

**Synonyms and Antonyms**

1. ○ cap    ○ tree    ● road
2. ○ book    ● boat    ○ train
3. ● big    ○ happy    ○ pink
4. ○ things    ○ games    ● woods
5. ● store    ○ grass    ○ van
6. ○ silly    ● ill    ○ looking
7. ● tall    ○ lunch    ○ short
8. ○ kitten    ● sheet    ○ pond
9. ● sea    ○ side    ○ room
10. ○ paper    ● name    ○ read
11. ○ jump    ○ sleep    ● yell
12. ○ play    ● sound    ○ sell
13. ● part    ○ road    ○ number
14. ○ end    ○ run    ● start
15. ● home    ○ park    ○ bell
16. ○ duck    ○ leaf    ● penny
17. ○ barn    ● car    ○ hat

A New Day      Unit 1: End of Unit    **155**

Write the words **big, red, little,** and **coat** on the chalkboard.

*Say to the children:*  Some words mean about the same thing. Listen to the following sentence:

   That bug is tiny.

Which word on the chalkboard means about the same thing as *tiny?* (little) Now I will write four more words. (Write *jumps, tells, trucks,* and *works* on the chalkboard.) Listen to the following sentence:

   The frog hops.

I will read part of the sentence again. You must complete it by choosing a word from the chalkboard that means about the same thing as *hops.* (Say: "The frog *blank.*") Which word means about the same thing as *hops?* (jumps) Now I will read both sentences. The frog hops. The frog jumps.

I will read another sentence. Then I will read it again, but you must fill in the circle next to the word on your paper that means about the same thing as the last word in the first sentence that I have read. Let's do the first one together.

1. The dog walked down the street.
   The dog walked down the _____ .

You will fill in which circle? (the circle next to the word *road*) Now we will move to Number 2.

2. Jo rode in the ship.
   Jo rode in the _____ .

3. That house is large.
   That house is _____ .

4. The bird lives in the forest.
   The bird lives in the _____ .

5. Jill bought a tool shop.
   Jill bought a tool _____ .

6. Martin was sick.
   Martin was _____ .

7. The office building is high.
   The office building is _____ .

8. She read the words on the page.
   She read the words on the _____ .

9. The whale lives in the ocean.
   The whale lives in the _____ .

10. We couldn't remember the book's title.
    We couldn't remember the book's _____ .

11. Our teacher said that we shouldn't shout.
    Our teacher said that we shouldn't _____ .

12. Rico heard a loud noise.
    Rico heard a loud _____ .

13. Barb was looking for the missing piece.
    Barb was looking for the missing _____ .

14. The race was about to begin.
    The race was about to _____ .

15. Ms. Johnson found a new house.
    Ms. Johnson found a new _____ .

16. Craig reached into his pocket and pulled out one cent.
    Craig reached into his pocket and pulled out one _____ .

17. Betty will sell her blue auto.
    Betty will sell her blue _____ .

Listening Skills

## Synonyms and Antonyms

1. ○ home ● wet ○ flat
2. ● late ○ sad ○ like
3. ● fat ○ good ○ mine
4. ○ eat ○ fly ● sell
5. ○ little ● neat ○ here
6. ○ fun ○ apple ● hot
7. ● asleep ○ nice ○ playing
8. ○ could ● no ○ begin
9. ○ down ● left ○ hard
10. ● friend ○ animal ○ bird
11. ○ out ○ around ● up
12. ○ in ● on ○ far
13. ○ today ○ here ● last
14. ○ big ● weak ○ happy
15. ● light ○ green ○ large
16. ○ morning ○ noon ● night
17. ○ marked ● lost ○ saw

156    Unit 1: End of Unit    A New Day

---

Write the words **run, day, small,** and **old** on the chalkboard.

*Say to the children:*   Some words have opposite meanings. Listen to the following sentence.

      That truck is new.

Which word on the chalkboard means the opposite of *new?* (old) Now I will write four more words. (Write the words **fast, clean, short,** and **it** on the chalkboard.) Listen to the following sentence.

      The string is long.

I will read part of the sentence again. You must complete it by choosing a word from the chalkboard that means the opposite of *long.* (Say: "The string is *blank.*") Which word on the chalkboard means the opposite of *long?* (short) Now I will read both sentences. The string is long. The string is short.

I will read another sentence. Then I will read it again, but you must fill in the circle next to the word on your paper that means the opposite of the last word in the first sentence that I have read. Let's do the first one together.

  1. The coat is dry.
     The coat is _____ .

You will fill in which circle? (the circle next to the word *wet*) Now we will move to Number 2.

  2. Jack came to the game early.
     Jack came to the game _____ .

  3. That dog is thin.
     That dog is _____ .

  4. Maria is looking for something to buy.
     Maria is looking for something to _____ .

  5. Al's room is messy.
     Al's room is _____ .

  6. Our soup is cold.
     Our soup is _____ .

  7. Ben is awake.
     Ben is _____ .

  8. The answer to the question is "yes."
     The answer to the question is _____ .

  9. To get to the school, turn right.
     To get to the school, turn _____ .

  10. That cat is the mouse's enemy.
      That cat is the mouse's _____ .

  11. The museum guide said, "Please step down."
      The museum guide said, "Please step _____ ."

  12. Ron forgot to turn the fan off.
      Ron forgot to turn the fan _____ .

  13. The twins did their math homework first.
      The twins did their math homework _____ .

  14. The zoo's lion was very strong.
      The zoo's lion was very _____ .

  15. Martha's desk chair is heavy.
      Martha's desk chair is _____ .

  16. Mr. Evans reads the newspaper during the day.
      Mr. Evans reads the newspaper during the _____ .

  17. Steve asked, "Is this the pencil you found?"
      Steve asked, "Is this the pencil you _____ ?"

# Synonyms and Antonyms

1. ○ cap          ○ tree          ○ road

2. ○ book         ○ boat          ○ train

3. ○ big          ○ happy         ○ pink

4. ○ things       ○ games         ○ woods

5. ○ store        ○ grass         ○ van

6. ○ silly        ○ ill           ○ looking

7. ○ tall         ○ lunch         ○ short

8. ○ kitten       ○ sheet         ○ pond

9. ○ sea          ○ side          ○ room

10. ○ paper       ○ name          ○ read

11. ○ jump        ○ sleep         ○ yell

12. ○ play        ○ sound         ○ sell

13. ○ part        ○ road          ○ number

14. ○ end         ○ run           ○ start

15. ○ home        ○ park          ○ bell

16. ○ duck        ○ leaf          ○ penny

17. ○ barn        ○ car           ○ hat

# Synonyms and Antonyms

1. ○ home       ○ wet       ○ flat

2. ○ late       ○ sad       ○ like

3. ○ fat        ○ good      ○ mine

4. ○ eat        ○ fly       ○ sell

5. ○ little     ○ neat      ○ here

6. ○ fun        ○ apple     ○ hot

7. ○ asleep     ○ nice      ○ playing

8. ○ could      ○ no        ○ begin

9. ○ down       ○ left      ○ hard

10. ○ friend    ○ animal    ○ bird

11. ○ out       ○ around    ○ up

12. ○ in        ○ on        ○ far

13. ○ today     ○ here      ○ last

14. ○ big       ○ weak      ○ happy

15. ○ light     ○ green     ○ large

16. ○ morning   ○ noon      ○ night

17. ○ marked    ○ lost      ○ saw

# Cause and Effect

---

NAME _____

**Cause and Effect**

Listening Skills

1. ___ It was hot.          **X** It was raining.

2. ___ Mr. Hall didn't water     **X** Mr. Hall put too much
       it.                        water on it.

3. ___ Pigs ate the corn.        **X** Mice ate the corn.

4. **X** Ken opened the          ___ Ken was singing.
       window.

5. ___ She didn't want to go     **X** She forgot two books.
       with Mary.

6. **X** The horse had to brush   ___ The cow was too early.
       himself.

7. **X** He missed two days of    ___ He didn't like math.
       school.

8. ___ She looked outside.        **X** Her puppy was missing.

9. **X** It was too noisy.        ___ It had too many old
                                      buildings.

10. ___ He liked parties.         **X** It was his sister's
                                      birthday.

A New Day                          Unit 1: End of Unit    **159**

---

**Procedure:**

*Say to the children:*  When you listen to a story, you often will hear how one thing in the story causes another thing to happen. I will read a short story. Listen for how one thing in the story causes another thing to happen.

> Fox carefully took two eggs from his refrigerator. He set them on a little table. As Fox turned around to close the refrigerator door, his tail brushed the eggs off the table, and they broke.

Why did the eggs break? (Fox's tail brushed them off the table.) Fox's tail movement *caused* the eggs to fall off the table and break.

I will read another short story. Then I will ask a question. After I have asked the question, you will read the two sentences on your paper and mark an **X** next to the sentence that correctly answers the question.

**Number 1**

The first graders were playing on the playground. It started to rain. The first graders ran toward the school. Why did the first graders run toward the school?

**Number 2**

Mr. Hall got a beautiful plant for his office. After two weeks, all of the leaves had turned black. Mr. Hall was sad; he had given the plant too much water. Why did all of the plant's leaves turn black?

**Number 3**

Two pigs wanted to have a party. They decorated their pigpen and went to the cupboard where they kept their corn. When they opened the cupboard, they saw that mice had eaten all of the corn. ''We can't serve corn at the party this time,'' said one of the pigs. Why couldn't the pigs serve corn at the party?

**Number 4**

Ken was watching a robin from his window. Ken wanted to hear the robin sing. Ken opened the window, but the sound scared the robin away. What scared the robin away?

**Number 5**

Mary and Denise were walking to the library. Suddenly, Denise ran back toward her house. ''Where are you going?'' shouted Mary. ''I forgot two books,'' yelled Denise. Why was Denise running toward her house?

**Number 6**

A horse and a cow were going to a fair. The cow got to the horse's house on time and rang the doorbell. The horse answered the door and said, ''I can't go to the fair looking like this. You'll have to wait until I have brushed myself.'' Why did the cow have to wait for the horse?

**Number 7**

Paul had one page in his reading workbook to finish and two pages in his math book to complete. He also had a science worksheet to finish. Paul had missed school for two days, so he had to catch up with his work. Why did Paul have schoolwork to finish?

### Number 8

Maria was late for the play. Her puppy was missing, and Maria was looking for him. Maria looked under her bed and behind the sofa. She went outside and looked behind the trees and bushes. Finally, Maria saw her puppy in her neighbor's yard. Why was Maria late for the play?

### Number 9

Victor did not like the city because it was too noisy. He was tired of the horns and sirens. Even though he had lived in the city for many years, Victor decided to move to the country. "I will find a job and I will plant a garden," he said. So Victor packed his belongings, hired some movers, and left the city for a more quiet life. Why did Victor leave the city?

### Number 10

Bill was planning a party. He made a list of all the things that he would need. Bill wrote down "food," "balloons," and "prizes." He also wrote down "gift" because it was his sister's birthday, and he was planning the party for her. Why was Bill planning a party?

# Cause and Effect

---

1. ___ It was hot.          ___ It was raining.

2. ___ Mr. Hall didn't water it.          ___ Mr. Hall put too much water on it.

3. ___ Pigs ate the corn.          ___ Mice ate the corn.

4. ___ Ken opened the window.          ___ Ken was singing.

5. ___ She didn't want to go with Mary.          ___ She forgot two books.

6. ___ The horse had to brush himself.          ___ The cow was too early.

7. ___ He missed two days of school.          ___ He didn't like math.

8. ___ She looked outside.          ___ Her puppy was missing.

9. ___ It was too noisy.          ___ It had too many old buildings.

10. ___ He liked parties.          ___ It was his sister's birthday.

# Comprehension: Analogies

**Focus:** It is important to be able to see how parts of two different things can be alike.

**Model:** This activity shows you parts of two different things. You have to think about how each part of one is like a part of the other. Then you have to match the parts that are alike.

**Practice:** Suppose you read this: A girl pretends to be a car. You have to decide what parts are alike. Here are the parts of the girl: eyes, legs. Here are the parts of the car: wheels, headlights.

Think about a girl's eyes and a car's headlights. The girl uses her eyes to know where to go. A car uses its headlights to know where to go. Eyes and headlights are alike in that way, so you would draw a line from eyes to headlights.

A girl uses her legs to move from place to place. A car uses its wheels to move from place to place. Legs and wheels are alike in that way, so you would draw a line from legs to wheels.

Now suppose you had sentences with blanks in them. The sentences say this:

A girl's _____ are like a car's _____.
A girl's _____ are like a car's _____.

You would write eyes and headlights in one sentence. You would write legs and wheels in the other sentence. The completed sentences would say this:

A girl's eyes are like a car's headlights.
A girl's legs are like a car's wheels.

**Apply:** Now work on page 161.

**1.** Look at the pictures of the boy and the bird.

**2.** Look at the small pictures. Match each thing on the left with the thing on the right that is like it. Draw lines to show the things that match.

**3.** Write the names of the things that match from numbers 1–4 in sentences 5–8 so that the sentences are true.

**Monitor:** When children have finished, discuss their answers.

**1.** The boy's arm is at his side. He can move it and flap it up and down. The boy's arm is like the bird's wing, so you should have a line from the boy's arm to the bird's wing.

**2.** The boy opens his mouth to eat and to speak. The bird opens its mouth to eat and to chirp or sing. The boy's mouth is like the bird's beak, so the line should go from the mouth to the beak.

**3.** The boy rests and sleeps in his bed. The bird rests and sleeps in its nest. A line should go from the bed to the nest.

**4.** The apple is food for the boy. The worm is food for the bird. The apple and the worm are alike in that way, so the line should go from the apple to the worm.

**5.** The line from number 1, the boy's arm, goes to the bird's wing to show that they are alike. The words *arm* and *wing* make sense in the sentence.

**6.** The line from number 2, the boy's mouth, goes to the bird's beak to show that they are alike. The words *mouth* and *beak* make sense in the sentence.

**7.** The line from number 3, the boy's bed, goes to the bird's nest to show that they are alike. The words *bed* and *nest* make sense in the sentence.

**8.** The line from number 4, the apple, goes to the worm to show that they are alike. The words *apple* and *worm* make sense in the sentence.

**Summary:**

1. arm—c. wing
2. mouth—d. beak
3. bed—a. nest
4. apple—b. worm
5. A boy's *arm* is like a bird's *wing*.
6. A boy's *mouth* is like a bird's *beak*.
7. A boy's *bed* is like a bird's *nest*.
8. A boy's *apple* is like a bird's *worm*.

# Comprehension: Analogies

It is important to see ways that different things are alike.

A. Draw lines to show which things are alike.

A boy pretends to be a bird.

1. 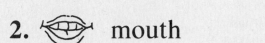 arm

2.  mouth

3. 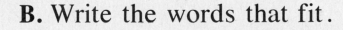 bed

4. 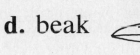 apple

a. nest

b. worm

c. wing

d. beak

B. Write the words that fit.

5. A boy's _____ is like a bird's _____ .

6. A boy's _____ is like a bird's _____ .

7. A boy's _____ is like a bird's _____ .

8. A boy's _____ is like a bird's _____ .

# Critical Thinking: Word Choices

**Focus:** It is important to think about the meanings of words so that others can understand exactly what you want to say.

**Model:** This activity gives you some sets of three words each. You are to write the word that best explains what you think a friend should do.

**Practice:** Suppose you saw these three words under a writing line:

     swim        draw        play

You would think about each word and whether it tells something that you think a friend should do. The first word is *swim*. If you really love to swim and do it all the time, it might be important to you to have a friend that swims. This would not be the word that most people would choose, however.

The next word is *draw*. It might be nice to have a friend who can draw, but that is probably not an important thing that you think friends should do.

The last word is *play*. When you are with your friends, it is probably important to you to play. You might decide that play tells best what you think friends should do. You would write the word **play.**

**Apply:** Now work on page 163.

1. Read each set of three words.

2. Think about each word. Decide which one tells best what you think friends should do.

3. Write that word.

4. At the bottom of the page, there are lines for you to write your own words. Think of four more words that tell what you think friends should do. Write those words.

**Monitor:** When children have finished, discuss their choices. The following are reasonable choices; the children, however, may have good reasons for choosing other words. Encourage them to discuss the reasons for their choices.

1. Many people think it is important for friends to help each other.

2. It is fun to be with people who smile and make you feel happy.

3. Many people think it is important for friends to share.

4. A friend is a person who will listen to you.

Have children share the words they wrote at the bottom of the page, focusing on how and why they thought of these words.

**Summary:** (Possible answers)

1. help         3. share
2. smile       4. listen

© Silver Burdett Ginn Inc.

# Critical Thinking: Word Choices

It is important to choose the right words to tell what you think and feel.

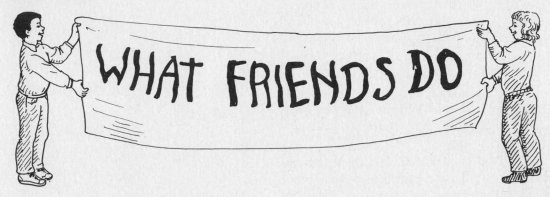

**A.** Choose the word in each set that tells what **you** think friends should do.

**B.** Write the word.

1. _____
   sing   run   help

2. _____
   push   smile   win

3. _____
   trick   share   ask

4. _____
   listen   shout   work

**C.** Write more words that tell what friends do.

_____

_____

_____

# Critical Thinking:
## Evaluating Arguments

**Focus:** It is important to recognize arguments for and against a point of view.

**Model:** This activity lists sentences that two people might say. The two people disagree about something. You must decide which sentences each person would say.

**Practice:** Suppose you know that someone likes dogs and someone else likes cats. You read this sentence: Dogs make a lot of noise. You must decide which person said it.

You think about the sentence. Most people probably do not think it is good for pets to make a lot of noise. The person who likes dogs would probably not say that they are noisy. The person who likes cats might say this, though, to show why cats are better than dogs.

**Apply:** Now work on page 165.

1. Read what Lee and Pat say in the pictures.

2. Read each sentence on the rest of the page and decide whether Lee said it or Pat said it.

3. Write **Lee** or **Pat** to show who said each sentence.

**Monitor:** When children have finished, discuss their answers.

1. The first sentence says something good about a horse. Pat likes horses, so Pat would say this.

2. Sentence 2 sounds as if it is saying something bad about cows. It might be all right for an animal to be slow, but this person says that cows are too slow. Pat wants to show that horses are better than cows, so Pat probably said this.

3. Sentence 3 says that horses do not give us milk. Giving us milk is a good thing that cows do. The person who said this was probably trying to show that horses are not as good as cows. Lee likes cows, so Lee probably said this.

4. Sentence 4 tells something good about horses, so Pat must have said it.

5. Sentence 5 says that cows do not run away. It is not good for animals to run away, so this sentence is saying something good about cows. Lee must have said it.

**Summary:**

| | | |
|---|---|---|
| 1. Pat | 2. Pat | 3. Lee |
| 4. Pat | 5. Lee | |

# Critical Thinking:
**Evaluating Arguments**

It is important to see the good and bad points
of something.

Lee

Pat

Write the name of the one who will say each thing.

_____

1. _____ "You can ride a horse."

2. _____ "Cows are too slow."

3. _____ "Horses do not give us milk."

4. _____ "A horse can pull a wagon."

5. _____ "Cows do not run away."

# Reality/Fantasy

Some things you read about are **real** and can happen. Other things are not real. They are **make-believe.**

This is real. ⟶

This is make-believe. ⟶

Read each pair of sentences. Circle the sentence that tells about something that could not really happen.

1. The bear made a wish on his birthday.

   Susan made a wish on her birthday.

2. A bird flew over the house.

   Bob flew over the house.

3. Greg is green.

   Grass is green.

4. The ant is bigger than the elephant.

   The elephant is bigger than the ant.

5. Jane had a ride on a bicycle.

   Jane had a ride on a butterfly.

6. The wind blew the house down.

   The wolf blew the house down.

© Silver Burdett Ginn Inc.

# Words with oa

Sometimes two letters stand for one sound.
The letters **oa** can stand for the vowel sound
you hear in **mole** and **toad.** The words **mole**
and **toad** have the same vowel sound.

mole

toad

Write the two words the sentence tells about.

| cloak | goat | moan | toad |
|-------|-------|-------|-------|
| coat | groan | roast | toast |

**1.** People do this when they feel bad.

_____    _____

- - - - - - - - - - - - -    - - - - - - - - - - - - -

_____    _____

**2.** These are things to keep you warm.

_____    _____

- - - - - - - - - - - - -    - - - - - - - - - - - - -

_____    _____

**3.** These are animals.

_____    _____

- - - - - - - - - - - - -    - - - - - - - - - - - - -

_____    _____

**4.** People do these things to food.

_____    _____

- - - - - - - - - - - - -    - - - - - - - - - - - - -

_____    _____

# Words with ou, ow

Sometimes two letters stand for one sound. The letters *ou* and *ow* may stand for the vowel sound you hear in *shoulder* and *flow*.

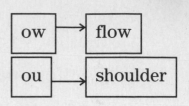

Write the words in the box to match the riddles.

| bowl   dough   crowed   row   shoulder   snow |
|---|

**1.** What did a rooster do each day?

_____

_____

**2.** What is white and cold and falls from the sky?

_____

_____

**3.** What is the part of the body where the arms are fastened?

_____

_____

**4.** What do you mix to bake bread?

_____

_____

**5.** What is a small deep dish for soup?

_____

_____

**6.** How do you move a boat in the water?

_____

© Silver Burdett Ginn Inc.

# Predicting Outcomes

When you read a story, think ahead and try
to tell what will happen next.

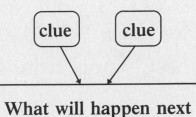

Example:

**Clue 1:** Greg does not like the water.

**Clue 2:** His friends want to go for a swim.

What will happen next? Greg will stay at home.

Read each story. Write what will happen next.

1. The lion has little cubs. First, they play.
   After that, they eat.

      Now they will run away.     Now they will sleep.

   _____

   - - - - - - - - - - - - - - - - - - - - - - - - -

   _____

   - - - - - - - - - - - - - - - - - - - - - - - - -

2. The rabbit and the turtle have a race.
   The rabbit is faster than the turtle.
   The rabbit takes a nap.
   The turtle keeps on going.

         The rabbit wins.     The turtle wins.

   _____

   - - - - - - - - - - - - - - - - - - - - - - - - -

   _____

# Classification

Some words belong in the same group.
These words belong together.

| Things with Wheels | | |
|---|---|---|
| bicycle | bus | truck |

Read each list of words. Write the word that tells about the whole list.

| Animals | Colors | Days | Food | Plants | Times |
|---|---|---|---|---|---|

**1.** afternoon
morning
night

_____

- - - - - - - - - - - - - - -

_____

**2.** flower
grass
tree

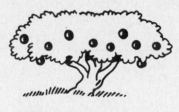

_____

- - - - - - - - - - - - - - -

_____

**3.** Saturday
Monday
Thursday

_____

- - - - - - - - - - - - - - -

_____

**4.** green
orange
purple

_____

- - - - - - - - - - - - - - -

_____

**5.** goat
mole
pig

_____

- - - - - - - - - - - - - - -

_____

**6.** pancakes
soup
popcorn

_____

- - - - - - - - - - - - - - -

_____

# Contractions

A **contraction** is a short way of writing
two words.

| |
|---|
| I + am = I'm |
| you + are = you're |
| we + have = we've |

Write the correct contraction for each set
of words.

_____  I'm

_ _ _ _ _ _ _ _ _ _ _ _ _ _ _ _ _

**1.** I  +  have  _____  I've

_____  you're

_ _ _ _ _ _ _ _ _ _ _ _ _ _ _ _ _

**2.** you  +  are  _____  you've

_____  they've

_ _ _ _ _ _ _ _ _ _ _ _ _ _ _ _ _

**3.** they  +  have  _____  they'll

_____  we'd

_ _ _ _ _ _ _ _ _ _ _ _ _ _ _ _ _

**4.** we  +  are  _____  we're

_____  I'm

_ _ _ _ _ _ _ _ _ _ _ _ _ _ _ _ _

**5.** I  +  am  _____  I'll

_____  you've

_ _ _ _ _ _ _ _ _ _ _ _ _ _ _ _ _

**6.** you  +  have  _____  you're

# Words with r-Controlled Vowels

When the letter **r** follows a vowel, it changes the
sound that the vowel letter usually stands for.

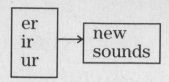

Read the sentences. Write the words from the box
that finish the sentences.

| fur | nurse | perfect | purr | swerved | thirsty |
|-----|-------|---------|------|---------|---------|

_____

1. Cathy was _____ so she got a drink.

_____

2. The kitten will _____ when you pet her.

_____

3. The _____ helped the sick boy.

_____

4. Kim had a _____ score in spelling.

_____

5. The car _____ on the icy road.

_____

6. The dog's _____ is long.

# Words with ch, tch

Sometimes two or three letters stand for the same sound. The consonants **ch** can stand for the beginning sound in **chick** and the ending sound in **March.** The consonants **tch** stand for the ending sound in **match.**

chick   March

match

Write the word that names each picture.

arch      chalk      cheese      inch      porch
branch      check      ditch      patch      watch

1.  _____

6. _____

2. _____

7. 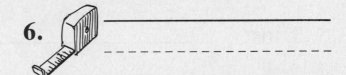 _____

3.  _____

8. _____

4. _____

9. _____

5. _____

10. _____

# Antonyms

Some words mean the opposite.

Start _____ End

Write the opposite of each word.

go    left    little    off    won    yes

1. big _____

2. no _____

3. lost _____

4. on _____

5. right _____

6. come _____

day    gave    in    naughty    opened    start

7. stop _____

8. good _____

9. out _____

10. closed _____

11. night _____

12. took _____

# Antonyms

Some words mean the opposite.

Over
_____
Under

Circle the opposite of each underlined word. Then write it.

liked    looked    lost

_____

- - - - - - - - - - - - - - - - - - - - - - -

**1.** Greg <u>found</u> his mitten. _____

give    go    grow

_____

- - - - - - - - - - - - - - - - - - - - - - -

**2.** Gail will <u>stay</u>. _____

opened    out    over

_____

- - - - - - - - - - - - - - - - - - - - - - -

**3.** Bill <u>closed</u> the door. _____

place    pulled    put

_____

- - - - - - - - - - - - - - - - - - - - - - -

**4.** Anna <u>pushed</u> the box. _____

# Comprehending Fiction

**Procedure:**

*Say to the children:* I am going to read the story "Pat's Goldfish" to you. After I have read the story, I will ask you some questions about it.

### Pat's Goldfish

Pat wanted a goldfish. Her dad went with her to the fish shop.

"We want a goldfish," said Pat to the shopkeeper.

"I can't help you," he said. "This bowl was full of goldfish, but I have sold them all."

Then Dad asked Pat if she wanted a red fish.

"No," said Pat sadly. "I just want a goldfish."

Pat and Dad went back home.

"Did you get your goldfish?" asked Pat's mom.

"No," said Pat. "The shop was all sold out of goldfish."

"Jim's fishbowl is full of fish," said Mom. "Maybe you can borrow a goldfish from him."

"I do not want to borrow a goldfish from my brother," said Pat. "I want a goldfish that is all mine."

"Don't be sad," said Mom. "Sooner or later you'll have your goldfish."

The next day, Pat and Jim went with Mom and Dad to Playland. When they were inside Playland, they sat down on a bench.

"You may go on the rides," said Mom. "Dad and I will wait for you here on this bench. Don't be too long."

Pat and Jim went on all the rides. Soon they were tired.

"It's time to go," said Jim. "Mom and Dad will be upset if we stay too long."

On the way back to the bench, they stopped to listen to a man. "Quick! Quick, while there is still time," was his yell. "Play the fish game. All you have to do is push the ball. Make it roll into one of the empty fishbowls. If you can do it, you'll win a goldfish in a bowl!"

"Did you hear that?" asked Pat. "Maybe we can win a goldfish!"

"Let me play," said Pat to Jim. "I want to win a goldfish."

"You can't play well," said Jim. "I'll push the ball."

The man gave the ball to Jim. Then he pushed the ball and let it roll. It landed on top of a bowl. It jumped up and down and then fell. It did not go into any of the empty fishbowls.

"You had your try," laughed Pat. "Let me have mine."

The man gave the ball to Pat. She gave the ball a spin and let it roll. It rolled to one of the empty fishbowls and in it fell! Pat jumped up and down. "I did it! I did it!" she said.

"You did well," said Jim. "Next time, you can try first."

The man gave Pat a goldfish in a fishbowl to take home.

Pat felt proud. "This is my lucky day," she said.

### Comprehending Fiction

NAME _____

**Listening Skills**

1. the park | the zoo | <u>the fish shop</u>

2. five | <u>none</u> | many

3. brown | black | <u>red</u>

4. <u>home</u> | to Playland | to school

5. Jim | <u>Pat's mom</u> | Pat's dad

6. three | seven | <u>many</u>

7. <u>to Playland</u> | to stores | to work

8. on a ride | <u>on a bench</u> | on the grass

9. <u>all</u> | none | seven

10. <u>Jim</u> | Mom | Pat

11. throw it | <u>push it</u> | bounce it

12. water | paper | <u>nothing</u>

13. in a bowl | beside a bowl | <u>on top of a bowl</u>

14. <u>"You did well."</u> | "Cheater!" | "I'm next."

15. Dad | Jim | <u>Pat</u>

178    Unit 2: Midunit                          A New Day

Now I will ask some questions about the story "Pat's Goldfish." Underline the correct answer on your paper.

1. Where did Pat and her dad look for a goldfish?

2. How many goldfish were left there?

3. Pat's dad asked her if she would like a different fish. What color was that fish?

4. Where did Pat and her dad go next?

5. Who suggested that Pat borrow one of her brother's goldfish?

6. How many fish did Pat's brother have?

7. Where did Pat, Jim, and their mom and dad go?

8. Where did Pat's mom and dad sit at Playland?

9. How many rides did Pat and Jim go on?

10. Who played the fish game first?

11. In the fish game, what did the player have to do with the ball?

12. What was inside the fishbowls that were used in the fish game?

13. Where did Jim's ball land?

14. What did Jim say when Pat won the fish game?

15. The next time Pat and Jim go to Playland, who will play the fish game first?

### Comprehending Fiction

NAME _____

**Listening Skills**

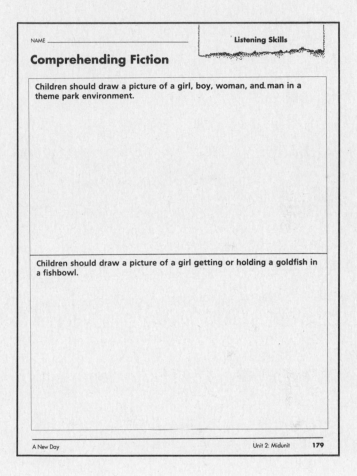

Children should draw a picture of a girl, boy, woman, and man in a theme park environment.

Children should draw a picture of a girl getting or holding a goldfish in a fishbowl.

A New Day                          Unit 2: Midunit    **179**

(Reread the story "Pat's Goldfish.") *Say to the children:* There are two boxes on your paper. In the first box, draw a picture of Pat, Jim, and their mom and dad at Playland. In the second box, draw a picture of what happened after Pat won the goldfish game.

# Comprehending Fiction

1. the park      the zoo      the fish shop

2. five      none      many

3. brown      black      red

4. home      to Playland      to school

5. Jim      Pat's mom      Pat's dad

6. three      seven      many

7. to Playland      to stores      to work

8. on a ride      on a bench      on the grass

9. all      none      seven

10. Jim      Mom      Pat

11. throw it      push it      bounce it

12. water      paper      nothing

13. in a bowl      beside a bowl      on top of a bowl

14. "You did well."      "Cheater!"      "I'm next."

15. Dad      Jim      Pat

# Comprehending Fiction

© Silver Burdett Ginn Inc.

# Elaboration: Hypothesizing

**Focus:**  Using one's imagination to deal with new situations is an important thinking skill.

**Model:**  This activity asks you to imagine two brand-new situations and what you would do if you were in those situations.

**Practice:**  Suppose you read this: You and a friend go exploring and find a bush that grows shoes instead of berries. You would spend some time imagining that situation. Imagine what you and your friend would say and do. You might want to imagine several different possibilities.

For example, you might decide that you and your friend would pick all the shoes off the bush. You might fill up a big box with shoes and bring it home. Then you could give the shoes to people who need them.

Another person might decide to take seeds from the shoe bush and use them to plant shoe bushes all over the world.

You might write on your paper the best idea that you come up with.

**Apply:**  Now work on page 181.

**1.**  Read sentence number 1. Spend some time thinking about different things that you and your friend might do.

**2.**  Pick your best idea and write it on the lines. If you want to write more, you can use another sheet of paper.

**3.**  When you have finished number 1, do the same thing with sentence number 2.

**Monitor:**  When children have finished, have them share and discuss their ideas. Help them focus on how they used both their knowledge of the world and their imaginations to think of ways to deal with something new.

# Elaboration: Hypothesizing

Your imagination can help you think about what to do when a brand new thing happens.

Pretend that you go exploring with a friend.
**A.** Read about the things you find.
**B.** Write what you and your friend would do.

**1.** You find a cave filled with rocks as soft as cotton.

**2.** You find a leaf that lights up when you touch it.

# Problem-Solving:
## Spatial Reasoning

**Focus:** Understanding how a figure looks when it is turned or placed in a different position is an important skill.

**Model:** This activity shows you a block of a certain shape and size. You have to pick out the block that is the same shape and size from a row of blocks. The block in the row is in a different position.

**Practice:** Suppose you see this block:

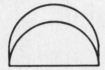

Then you see this row of blocks:

You would look at the first block to see what shape it is, how tall it is, how thick it is. You can see that this block has a side that is shaped like half a circle.

Now you would look at the blocks in the row. The first block is long and thin. None of its sides look like half circles. The second block looks like a half circle lying on its side. You can see that this is the same block as the first one; it is just in a different position. You would circle this second block.

**Apply:** Now work on page 183.

**1.** Look at the first block for number 1. Think about how big it is, what shape it is, how tall or long it is, how thick it is.

**2.** Now look at the three blocks in the row for number 1. Try to picture in your mind how the first block would look if it were turned or placed in different positions. Decide which block in the row is the same as the first block but in a different position.

**3.** Circle the block that is the same as the first one.

**Monitor:** Discuss answers.

**1.** Your block is longer than it is wide. It is thin. Each side has four corners. The middle block in the row is the same size and shape, but it is standing up on its side instead of lying down.

**2.** Your block is square on one side. It is not very thick. It is standing up on one of its thin sides. The first block in the row is the same size and shape, but it is lying down.

**3.** Your block is short and thick and round. The middle block in the row is the same size and shape, but it is lying on its side instead of standing on end.

**4.** Your block is small. It is longer than it is wide. It has a square side, too. It is lying on its side. The last block in the row is the same size and shape, but it is standing on end.

**5.** Your block is standing up. It has one side that is a triangle. The first block in the row is the same size and shape, but it is lying down rather than standing up. (The second block in the row is also a triangle, but it is bigger than your block.)

**6.** Your block is a cube. The last block in the row is also a cube, but it has been turned a little bit.

## Summary

| Your Block | Your Friend's Block |
|---|---|
| **1.** | |
| **2.** | |
| **3.** | |
| **4.** | |
| **5.** | |
| **6.** | |

# Problem-Solving:
## Spatial Reasoning

It is important to understand how objects look when they are turned different ways.

You and your friend have some blocks. You both take the same kind of block each time, but you turn them different ways.

**A.** Look at your block.

**B.** Find your friend's block. Circle it.

**Your Block**          **Your Friend's Block**

1.

2.

3.

4.

5.

6.

# Classification

Some words belong in the same group.
These words belong together.

Ways Things Look

bright    fat    small

Write each word under the picture it names.
Then you will have a group of words about a farm.

| | | | |
|---|---|---|---|
| barn | goat | corn | horse |
| ducks | pig | farmer | vegetables |

**1.**
_____
- - - - - - - - - - - - - - - -
_____

**5.**
_____
- - - - - - - - - - - - - - - -
_____

**2.**
_____
- - - - - - - - - - - - - - - -
_____

**6.**
_____
- - - - - - - - - - - - - - - -
_____

**3.**
_____
- - - - - - - - - - - - - - - -
_____

**7.**
_____
- - - - - - - - - - - - - - - -
_____

**4.**
_____
- - - - - - - - - - - - - - - -
_____

**8.**
_____
- - - - - - - - - - - - - - - -
_____

# Spelling Changes

When an ending that begins with a vowel
letter is added to a word that ends in **e,**
the final **e** is dropped.

| place + ed = placed |
| skate + ing = skating |

Add **ing** or **ed** to each word. Write the new word.
Remember to drop the final **e.**

1. bake _____

2. love _____

3. smile _____

4. share _____

5. move _____

6. hike _____

7. dance _____

# Spelling Changes

When an action word has one vowel letter and one final consonant letter, double the final consonant before adding *-ed* or *-ing*.

| Word | + | -ed -ing | = | New Word |

Example: stop, stop*ped,* stop*ping*

Draw a line under the right word to finish each sentence.

**1.** The dancers _____ dancing when the bell rang.

      stopped       stopping     stepped

**2.** The dance teacher was _____ a new dance.

      running       planned     planning

**3.** The dancers were _____ on the floor.

      stopping      sitting     stopped

**4.** They _____ when they heard the new plan.

      clapped      clapping     slipped

**5.** Lisa _____ out of the room.

      dropped      slipped     slipping

**6.** She was going to take a _____ lesson.

      swimming      stopping     slipping

**7.** She _____ her mother who was waiting for her.

      hugged      hugging     stopped

# Words with Long u

The letter **u** can stand for the vowel sound you hear in **cube** and **tube.** Look for the letter **e** at the end of a short word. It often points out that the first vowel in the word stands for a long sound.

cube    tube

Write the correct word to finish each sentence.

_____

mule

1. I will ride on a _____.    muse

_____

tube

2. June will play a _____.    tune

_____

3. There are _____ buildings    huge

in the city.    use

_____

rude

4. A school _____ is "Do not run."    rule

_____

duke

5. We slid down the sand _____.    dune

_____

plume

6. A _____ is good to eat.    prune

# Main Idea/Details

A **main idea** tells about the whole story. All the sentences tell about the main idea. These sentences are **details.**

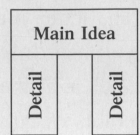

| Main Idea | |
|:---:|:---:|
| Detail | Detail |

Read each story. Then draw a line under the sentence that tells what the story is mostly about.

1. People use water in many ways. We sail boats on water. We cook food in water. We swim in water.

   Cooking is done in water.

   People use water in many ways.

   There are many kinds of boats.

2. People cannot live under the water. People need air to live. People cannot get air from water.

   People and fish need air.

   People cannot live under the water.

   People can catch fish.

3. Many things are under the ground. Some animals live under the ground. Plants grow under the ground.

   You can find gold under the ground.

   Plants and animals are under the ground.

   Many things are under the ground.

# Words with au, aw

Sometimes two letters stand for one sound.
The letters *au* and *aw* stand for the sound
you hear in *pause* and *jaw*.

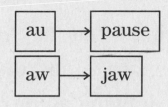

**A.** Read the words in the box. Then read the story. Write the words
from the box to finish the story.

| auto | awful | drawing | fawn | lawn | Paul | straw |

_____

The boys found a _____ that had been hit

by an _____ . They made a bed of

_____ for it on the _____ .

"I am _____ a picture of it,"

said _____ . "I want to remember the

_____ thing that happened to it."

# Drawing Conclusions

Sometimes you may need to figure out things that are not told in a story. This is called drawing a **conclusion.**

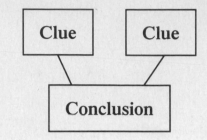

Example:

Clue 1: Becky had <u>one</u> white flower and <u>two</u> yellow ones.
Clue 2: Max had <u>two</u> purple flowers and <u>two</u> red ones.
Conclusion: Max had <u>more flowers</u> than Becky.

Read the stories. Use clues and what you already know to circle the answers to the questions. Then write them.

1. Fran wanted to go for a swim. Her mother said she could go if it was a nice day. If the day was not nice, Fran could go to a show. It rained all day. What did Fran do?

    swim    go to a show

    _____

    - - - - - - - - - - - - - - - - - - - - - - - - -

    _____

2. Farmer Woods and Farmer Brown had five cows each. Then Farmer Woods bought another cow. Farmer Brown gave two of her cows away. Who had more cows?

    Farmer Woods    Farmer Brown

    _____

    - - - - - - - - - - - - - - - - - - - - - - - - -

    _____

# Drawing Conclusions

Sometimes you need to figure out things that are not told in a story. This is called drawing a **conclusion.**

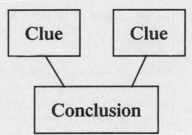

Read the conclusion and the clues that led to it.
Write one more clue that goes with each conclusion.

1. Conclusion: It was time for dinner.
   Clues: Mom and Dad put the food on the table.
   They called Max.

_____

- - - - - - - - - - - - - - - - - - - - - - - - - - - - -

_____

_____

- - - - - - - - - - - - - - - - - - - - - - - - - - - - -

_____

Max went out to play.    Max came to the kitchen.

2. Conclusion: Pat loves dots.
   Clues: Pat has a scarf with dots on it.
   She has a ribbon with green dots.

_____

- - - - - - - - - - - - - - - - - - - - - - - - - - - - -

_____

_____

- - - - - - - - - - - - - - - - - - - - - - - - - - - - -

_____

Pat has new yellow mittens.    Pat has a hat with red dots.

# Elaboration: Creative Writing

**Focus:** Creating a story from a few words selected at random is a good exercise in imagination.

**Model:** This activity contains a word chart. You circle a word in each row on the chart. Then you use those words to write a sentence that starts your story. You can write or draw the rest of the story.

**Practice:** Suppose you were given this chart:

| 1. | rain | snow |
|----|------|------|
| 2. | fell | ended |

First you would circle a word in Row 1. You might circle **rain.** Then you would circle a word in Row 2. You might circle **ended.**

Now you would add any other words you want to make a sentence using the words you circled. For example, your sentence might be At last the rain ended. You would write that sentence on the lines under the chart.

Then, on another sheet of paper, you would write more sentences or draw pictures to tell the rest of your story.

**Apply:** Now work on page 193.

**1.** Read the words on the chart. Do you notice that all the words in Row 1 are words that describe? All the words in Row 2 name animals. Think about how the words in the other rows are the same.

**2.** Now choose one word from each row. Circle that word.

**3.** Write a sentence using the words you circled. You may add as many other words as you need. Remember that the sentence you write is going to be the first sentence of your story. You may want to try out several different sentences on scrap paper. Then write your best sentence on the lines.

**4.** On another sheet of paper, write down ideas about what will happen next in the story and how the story will end. You may want to draw pictures instead, or you may combine words and pictures.

**5.** When your story is finished, tell it to someone.

**Monitor:** When students have finished, discuss their results. You may want to discuss briefly the classifications for Rows 3 and 4 of the chart—action words, and words that name people or things.

Have students share the words they chose and the sentences they created from those words. If possible, have them tell their stories. You may want to arrange a time and place for them to do so.

## Elaboration: Creative Writing

Your imagination can help you build a story from just a few words.

### Be a Storyteller

**A.** Circle one word in each row going down.

Use the words <u>a</u>, <u>an</u>, and <u>the</u>, too.

| 1. | huge | tiny | brave | silly |
|---|---|---|---|---|
| 2. | ant | elephant | lion | goat |
| 3. | made | saw | found | threw |
| 4. | friend | ball | castle | hat |

**B.** Write a sentence that uses the words you circled.

_____

- - - - - - - - - - - - - - - - - - - - - - - - - -

_____

- - - - - - - - - - - - - - - - - - - - - - - - - -

_____

- - - - - - - - - - - - - - - - - - - - - - - - - -

_____

**C.** Decide what will happen next. How will the story end?

**D.** On separate paper, write ideas for your story or draw pictures that show what happens.

# Problem-Solving:
## Inductive Reasoning

**Focus:** The ability to combine clues and reach a conclusion based on those clues is an important thinking skill.

**Model:** This activity gives you sets of words. The words are in boxes that are connected. You have to put all the words in the connected boxes together to figure out what the storyteller is telling about.

**Practice:** Suppose you saw this set of boxes:

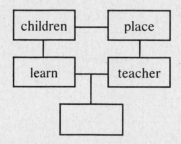

The word in the first box tells you that the storyteller is telling about something that has to do with children. You would look at the other boxes for more clues—place, learn, teacher.

A place for children might be a playground, but that would not fit the other two clues. A place where children learn with a teacher is school. School is the word that all the clues lead to when you put them together, so you would write **school** in the bottom box.

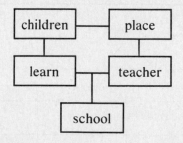

**Apply:** Now work on page 195.

**1.** Read the five words in the first set of connected boxes.

**2.** Put the clues together in your mind. Let the clues lead you to the word that tells what the storyteller's story is about.

**3.** Write the word in the bottom box.

**4.** Do the others the same way.

**Monitor:** When students have finished, discuss their answers.

**1.** The five clues together lead to the word *frog*—a small, green animal that hops, lives near a pond, and has bumpy skin.

**2.** The five clues together lead to the word *carrot*—a long, thin, orange vegetable that is sometimes cut into sticks.

**3.** The five clues together lead to a word such as *plane*, *airplane*, or *jet*—a silver thing with wings that makes a loud noise and flies in the sky.

**4.** The five clues together lead to the word *lion*—the "king of the jungle" that is wild, strong, has a mane, and roars.

You may want to ask for examples of other word clues that the storyteller could use for each of the four items.

**Summary:**

**1.** frog      **3.** plane

**2.** carrot      **4.** lion

# Problem-Solving:
## Inductive Reasoning

Putting clues together to figure something out is an important thinking skill.

**A.** Think about the storyteller's clues.

**B.** Write the word.

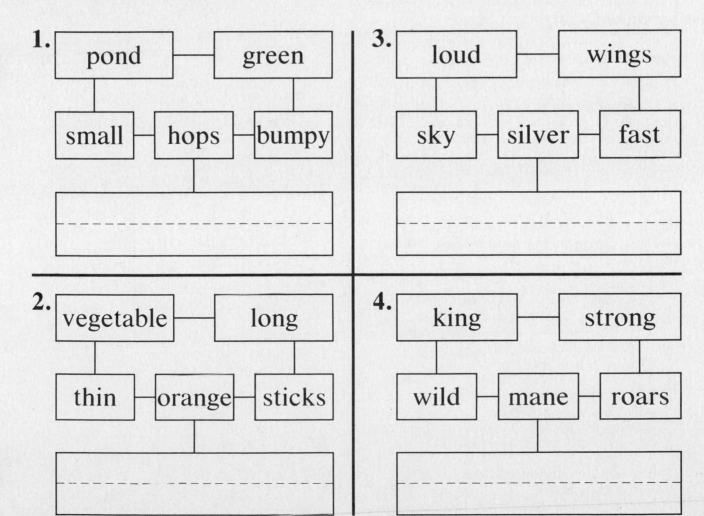

**1.**

| pond | green |
|------|-------|

| small | hops | bumpy |
|-------|------|-------|

_____

**3.**

| loud | wings |
|------|-------|

| sky | silver | fast |
|-----|--------|------|

_____

**2.**

| vegetable | long |
|-----------|------|

| thin | orange | sticks |
|------|--------|--------|

_____

**4.**

| king | strong |
|------|--------|

| wild | mane | roars |
|------|------|-------|

_____

# Critical Thinking: Connotations

**Focus:** It is important to understand that words that mean almost the same thing can carry different feelings to the reader.

**Model:** This activity gives you a choice of two words below a blank in a sentence. You must choose the more exciting word and write it in the sentence.

**Practice:** Suppose you saw this sentence:

Rain _____ down.
came    poured

To decide which word is more exciting, you would try each word in the sentence. You would see which sentence has a more exciting feeling.

Here is the sentence with the first word: Rain came down. Here is the sentence with the second word: Rain poured down. The second sentence sounds like it is really raining hard. It sounds more active and exciting than the first sentence, so you would write **poured** in the blank.

**Apply:** Now work on page 197.

**1.** Read the sentence and the two words below it.

**2.** If you are not sure which word sounds more exciting, try reading the sentence with the first word in the blank and then with the second word.

**3.** Decide which word makes the sentence more exciting.

**4.** Write that word in the sentence.

**Monitor:** When students have finished, discuss their choices.

**1.** The wind blew all night long. The wind might blow hard or not so hard. That sentence is not very exciting. The wind roared all night long. The word *roared* makes the wind sound like a fierce lion. It tells you that the wind was blowing so hard that it made a roaring sound. That sentence is more exciting.

**2.** The ship moved to and fro. A ship might move just a tiny bit. The ship rocked to and fro. That sentence sounds like the ship is moving from one side to the other. That sentence is more exciting.

**3.** The word *large* is not very exciting. Many things might be large. The word *giant* is more exciting because it makes you feel that something is extremely large and unusual.

**4.** Something that is coming toward you might be moving slowly. Something that is tumbling toward you is rolling very, very fast. The word tumbling is more exciting.

**Summary:**

1. roared
2. rocked
3. giant
4. tumbling

# Critical Thinking: Connotations

It is important to think about the feelings
that words carry.

A storyteller is telling about a storm at
sea. Write the words that make her
story more exciting.

_____
- - - - - - - - - - - - - - - - - - - - - - - - - - -
**1.** The wind _____ all night long.

roared    blew

_____
- - - - - - - - - - - - - - - - - - - - - - - - - - -
**2.** The ship _____ to and fro.

rocked    moved

_____
- - - - - - - - - - - - - - - - - - - - - - - - -
**3.** Then the sailors saw a _____ wave.

large    giant

_____
- - - - - - - - - - - - - - - - - - - - - - -
**4.** The wave was _____ toward them.

coming    tumbling

**Reteaching**

## Words with Short a

The letter **a** can stand for the vowel sound you hear in **bag** and **mat**.

bag    mat

**A.** Look at each picture. Then circle the words that have the same vowel sound as in **bag** and **mat**.

1. fat  cat
4. big  bag
7. sad  bat

2. mad  man
5. see  bus
8. dog  rag

3. fan  off
6. sat  mat
9. Pat  cap

**B.** Name each picture. Color the picture that has the same vowel sound as in **bag** and **mat**. Then write **a** next to the picture that has the vowel sound you hear in **bag** and **mat**.

10. color _____
    a

11. _____

---

**Reteaching**

## Words with Short a

The letter **a** can stand for the vowel sound you hear in **map** and **jam**.

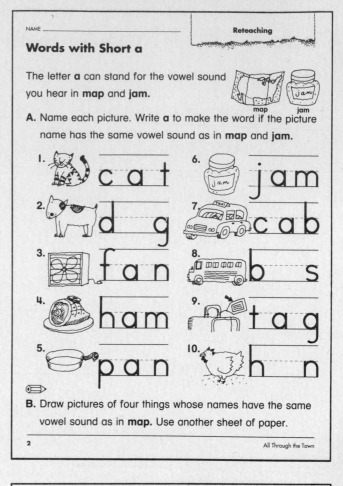
map    jam

**A.** Name each picture. Write **a** to make the word if the picture name has the same vowel sound as in **map** and **jam**.

1. c a t
6. j a m

2. d _ g
7. c a b

3. f a n
8. b _ s

4. h a m
9. t a g

5. p a n
10. h _ n

**B.** Draw pictures of four things whose names have the same vowel sound as in **map**. Use another sheet of paper.

---

**Reteaching**

## Words with Long a

The letter **a** can stand for the vowel sound you hear in **rake** and **cane**. Look for the **e** marker at the end of a short word. It often points out that the first vowel in the word stands for a long sound.

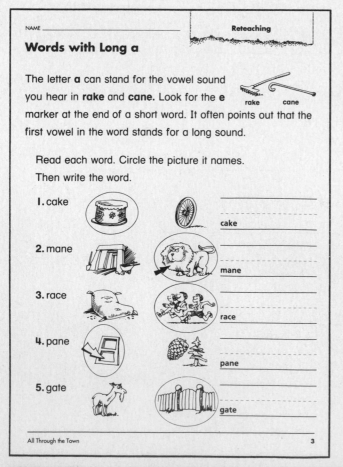
rake    cane

Read each word. Circle the picture it names. Then write the word.

1. cake _____ cake

2. mane _____ mane

3. race _____ race

4. pane _____ pane

5. gate _____ gate

---

**Reteaching**

## Words with Long a

The letter **a** can stand for the vowel sound you hear in **cave** and **rake**. Look for the **e** marker at the end of a short word. It often points out that the first vowel in the word stands for a long sound.

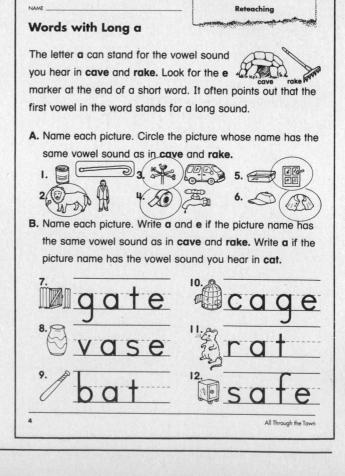
cave    rake

**A.** Name each picture. Circle the picture whose name has the same vowel sound as in **cave** and **rake**.

1.
2.
3.
4.
5.
6.

**B.** Name each picture. Write **a** and **e** if the picture name has the same vowel sound as in **cave** and **rake**. Write **a** if the picture name has the vowel sound you hear in **cat**.

7. g a t e
10. c a g e

8. v a s e
11. r a t

9. b a t
12. s a f e

**198**

## Sequence

Things happen in a certain order.
These pictures are in order.

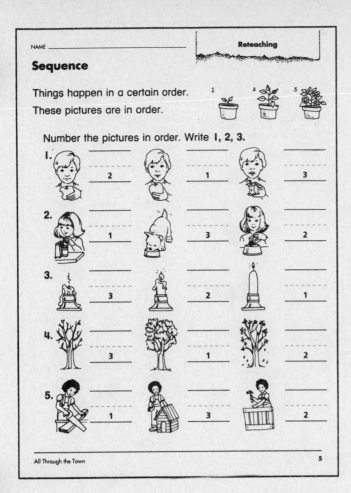

Number the pictures in order. Write **1, 2, 3.**

1. ___ **2**    ___ **1**    ___ **3**

2. ___ **1**    ___ **3**    ___ **2**

3. ___ **3**    ___ **2**    ___ **1**

4. ___ **3**    ___ **1**    ___ **2**

5. ___ **1**    ___ **3**    ___ **2**

---

## Sequence

Things happen in a certain order.
These pictures are in order.

Look at the first two pictures. What will happen next?
Circle the picture that shows what will happen next.

1.
2.
3.
4.
5.

---

## Words with Short e

The letter **e** can stand for the vowel sound
you hear in **well** and **jet.**

well    jet

**A.** Underline the words that have the same vowel sound as in
**well** and **jet.**

| | | | | | |
|---|---|---|---|---|---|
| get | hat | red | web | rid | fed |
| hen | bed | win | let | pet | we |
| me | bell | men | come | den | be |

**B.** Name each picture. Write **e** to make a word if the picture
name has the same vowel sound as in **well** and **jet.** Write
**a** if the picture name has the same vowel sound as in **can**
and **cat.**

1. p e g    4. v a n

2. h a t    5. n e t

3. 10 t e n    6. m e n

---

## Words with Short e

The letter **e** can stand for the vowel sound
you hear in **ten** and **bed.**

10 ten    bed

Write **e** to make a word. Say the word.
Then draw a line to the picture that shows the word.

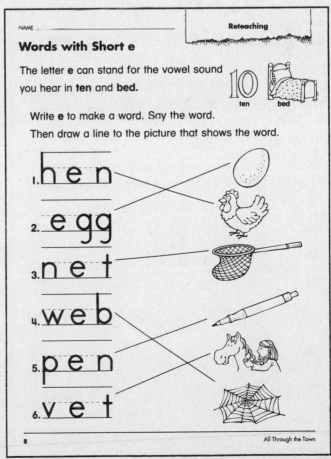

1. h e n

2. e gg

3. n e t

4. w e b

5. p e n

6. v e t

## Words with Long e

The letter **e** at the end of a word can stand for the sound you hear in **he** and **she**. Sometimes two letters stand for one sound. The letters **ee** stand for the vowel sound you hear in **bee**.

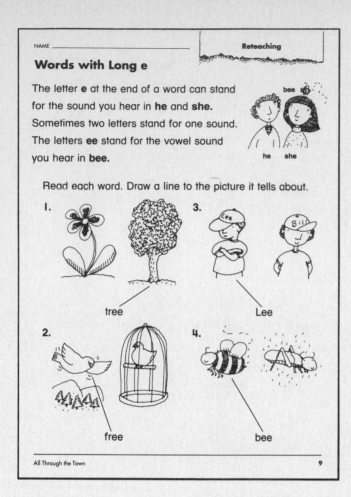

bee

he    she

Read each word. Draw a line to the picture it tells about.

1.

tree

3.

Lee

2.

free

4.

bee

---

## Words with Long e

The letter **e** at the end of a word can stand for the vowel sound you hear in **she** and **be**. Sometimes two letters stand for one sound. The letters **ee** stand for the vowel sound you hear in **see**.

she    see

Look at each picture. Write its name.

1.

| Lee | Len |
|-----|-----|

_____

**Lee**

| see | bee |
|-----|-----|

2.

_____

**bee**

| trim | tree |
|------|------|

3.

_____

**tree**

| we | when |
|----|------|

4.

_____

**we**

---

## Words with Long e

The letter **e** at the end of a word can stand for the sound you hear in **he** and **she**. Sometimes two letters stand for one sound. The letters **ee** stand for the vowel sound you hear at the end of **tree**.

he    she    tree

Draw a picture of each word in its box.

| | |
|---|---|
| we | he |
| she | me |

---

## Comprehending Relationships:
### Rhyming Words

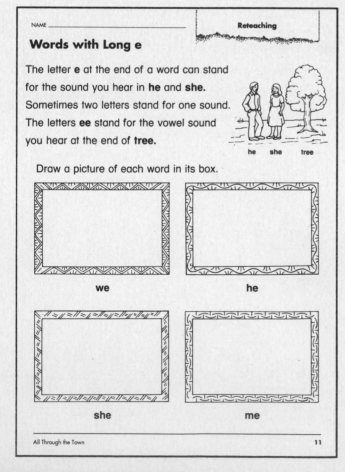

Color the first picture whose name rhymes with **wish** yellow.
Color the other picture whose name rhymes with **wish** green.

2. Find the two things whose names rhyme with the word **float**.
   With your pencil, circle the two pictures.
   Color the first picture whose name rhymes with **float** brown.
   Color the other picture whose name rhymes with **float** purple.

3. Find the two things whose names rhyme with the word **sail**.
   With your pencil, circle the two pictures.
   Color the first picture whose name rhymes with **sail** black.
   Color the other picture whose name rhymes with **sail** orange.

4. Find the two things whose names rhyme with the word **pan**.
   With your pencil, circle the two pictures.
   Color the first picture whose name rhymes with **pan** red.
   Color the other picture whose name rhymes with **pan** blue.

5. Find the two things whose names rhyme with the word **noon**.
   With your pencil, circle the two pictures.
   Color the first picture whose name rhymes with **noon** brown.
   Color the other picture whose name rhymes with **noon** yellow.

6. Find the two things whose names rhyme with the word **lock**.
   With your pencil, circle the two pictures.
   Color the first picture whose name rhymes with **lock** green.
   Color the other picture whose name rhymes with **lock** orange.

7. Find the two things whose names rhyme with the word **rain**.
   With your pencil, circle the two pictures.
   Color the first picture whose name rhymes with **rain** black.
   Color the other picture whose name rhymes with **rain** purple.

**Procedure:**

On the chalkboard, draw a picture of a flower, a cat, and a baseball bat.

*Say to the children:*  Take out your crayons or markers because you will need them for this lesson. Look at the pictures of the flower, the cat, and the bat on the chalkboard. Which two things have names that rhyme with the word *hat*? (cat, bat).

Now look at the first row of pictures on your paper. I am going to say another word. You will look at the pictures in the row and find the two pictures whose names rhyme with the word that I say. You will circle the two pictures with your pencil. Then I will ask you to do something to each of the two pictures.

1. Find the two things whose names rhyme with the word **wish**.
   With your pencil, circle the two pictures.

## Comprehending Relationships:
### Rhyming Words

13

---

## Comprehension:
### Following Directions

**Focus:** It is important to read and think carefully in order to follow directions correctly.

**Model:** This activity gives you a set of directions to read and then follow.

**Practice:*** Suppose a direction told you to make an **X** in the middle of your paper. You would find the middle of your paper and make an **X** there.

Now suppose a direction said this: If you are six years old, write 6 at the top of your paper. First, you would have to ask yourself, "Am I six years old?" If the answer is yes, you would write 6 at the top of your paper. If the answer is no, you would not write anything. You would go on to the next direction.

**Apply:** Now work on page 15.

1. First, read all the directions.

2. Then go back and read each direction.

3. Follow each direction as you read it. If you have to ask yourself a question, be sure you know the answer before you follow the direction.

4. Remember that sometimes you will go on to the next direction without writing anything.

**Monitor:** When students have finished, discuss their results.

1. There should be a D in the circle.

2. The dog's name is Bam, so there should be a B in the circle.

3. The cat's name is not Bam, so there should not be a B in the square.

4. The cat's name is not Bam, so the cat's name (Mab) should be in the square.

5. A cat is not a dog, so there should not be a C in the circle.

6. A cat is not a dog, so there should be a C in the square.

* Frequently there are diagrams, charts, or examples in **Practice** which the teacher should place on the chalkboard before the lesson begins.

**Summary:**

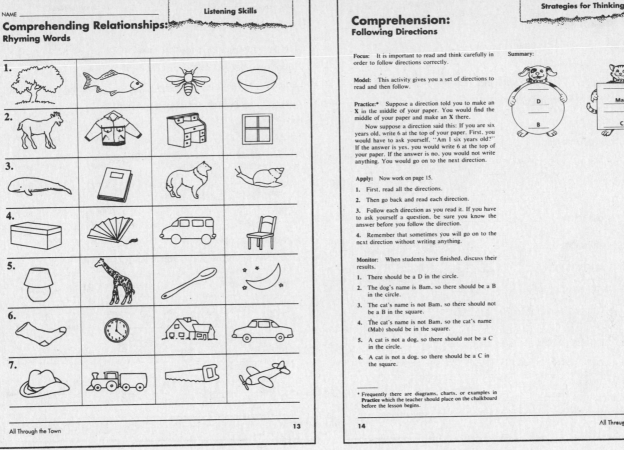

14

---

## Comprehension:
### Following Directions

It is important to follow directions carefully.

Then what you do will turn out right.

Read all the directions. Do what they say.

1. Write D in the dog's ◯.

2. Is the dog's name Bam? If it is, write B in the ◯.

3. Is the cat's name Bam? If it is, write B in the ☐.

4. If the cat's name is <u>not</u> Bam, write the cat's name in the ☐.

5. If a cat is a dog, write C in the ◯.

6. If a cat is <u>not</u> a dog, write C in the ☐.

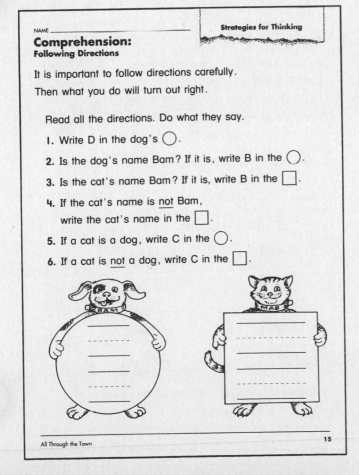

15

---

## Main Idea/Details

Sentences tell about a story.

Underline the sentence that tells the main idea of the story.

Then circle the best answer to each question.

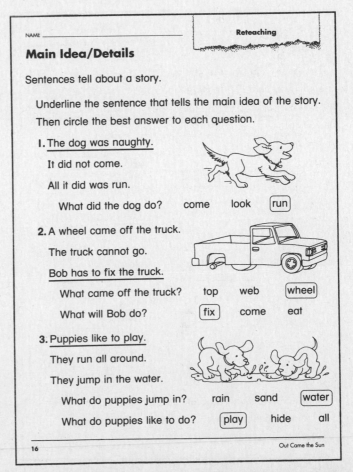

1. <u>The dog was naughty.</u>

It did not come.

All it did was run.

What did the dog do?　come　look　[run]

2. A wheel came off the truck.

The truck cannot go.

<u>Bob has to fix the truck.</u>

What came off the truck?　top　web　[wheel]

What will Bob do?　[fix]　come　eat

3. <u>Puppies like to play.</u>

They run all around.

They jump in the water.

What do puppies jump in?　rain　sand　[water]

What do puppies like to do?　[play]　hide　all

16

**201**

NAME _____

## Main Idea/Details

A story is always about something.
All the sentences tell about it.

Read the story. Circle the word that tells what the whole story is about. Then write the word.

1. Tim has a big cap.

He has an umbrella.

He has to jump over the water.

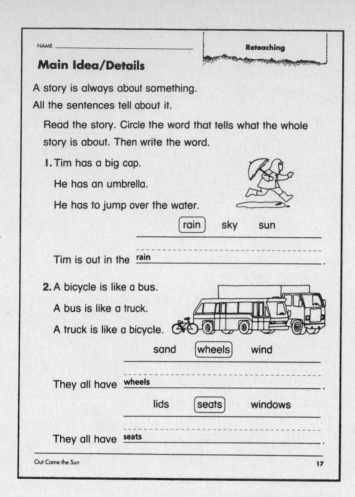

(rain)    sky    sun

Tim is out in the ___rain___ .

2. A bicycle is like a bus.

A bus is like a truck.

A truck is like a bicycle.

sand    (wheels)    wind

They all have ___wheels___ .

lids    (seats)    windows

They all have ___seats___ .

---

NAME _____

## Words with Short i

The letter **i** can stand for the vowel
sound you hear in **mitt**.

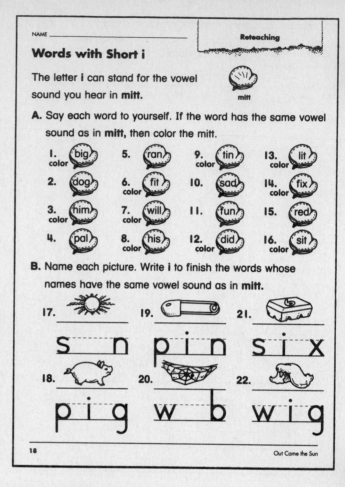

mitt

**A.** Say each word to yourself. If the word has the same vowel
sound as in **mitt**, then color the mitt.

1. color (big)    5. (ran)    9. color (tin)    13. color (lit)

2. (dog)    6. color (fit)    10. (sad)    14. color (fix)

3. color (him)    7. color (will)    11. (fun)    15. (red)

4. (pal)    8. color (his)    12. color (did)    16. color (sit)

**B.** Name each picture. Write **i** to finish the words whose
names have the same vowel sound as in **mitt**.

17.    19.    21.

s _ n    p i n    s i x

18.    20.    22.

p i g    w _ b    w i g

---

NAME _____

## Short i

The letter **i** can stand for the vowel
sound you hear in **bib** and **sit**.

bib    sit

**A.** Name each picture. Write **i** to make the word if the picture
name has the same vowel sound as in **bib** and **sit**.

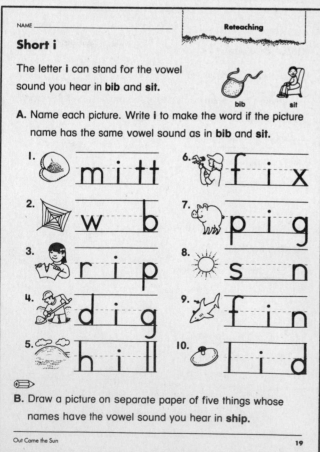

1. m i t t    6. f i x

2. w _ b    7. p i g

3. r i p    8. s _ n

4. d i g    9. f i n

5. h i l l    10. l i d

**B.** Draw a picture on separate paper of five things whose
names have the vowel sound you hear in **ship**.

---

NAME _____

## Words with Long i

The letter **i** can stand for the vowel sound
you hear in **line** and **ride**.

Look for the **e** marker at the end of a word.
It often points out that the first vowel in the
word stands for a long sound.

line

ride

**A.** Read the words. Circle and color the picture they tell
about. Then underline the words that have the same vowel
sound as in **line** and **ride**.

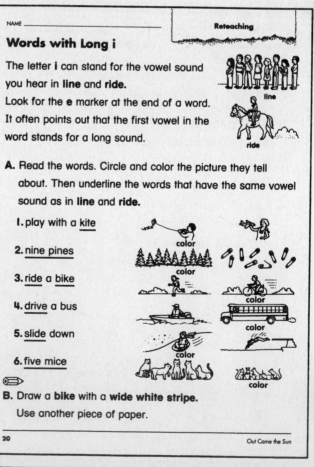

1. play with a <u>kite</u>

2. <u>nine pines</u>

3. <u>ride</u> a <u>bike</u>

4. drive a bus

5. <u>slide</u> down

6. <u>five mice</u>

**B.** Draw a **bike** with a **wide white stripe**.
Use another piece of paper.

## Words with Long i

The letter **i** can stand for the vowel sound you hear in **dime** and **vine.** Look for the **e** at the end of a short word. It often points out that the first vowel in the word stands for a long sound.

**A.** Name each picture. Circle the picture whose name has the same vowel sound as in **dime** and **vine.**

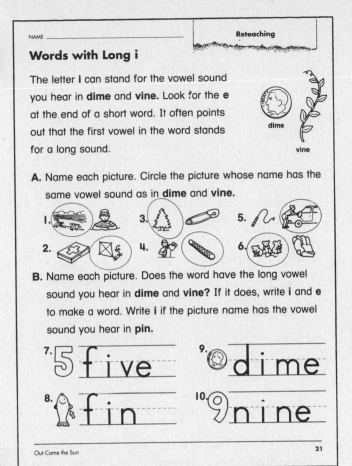

**B.** Name each picture. Does the word have the long vowel sound you hear in **dime** and **vine?** If it does, write **i** and **e** to make a word. Write **i** if the picture name has the vowel sound you hear in **pin.**

7. five    9. dime

8. fin    10. nine

---

## Cause/Effect

One thing can make another thing happen.

Read each sentence. Draw a line to the picture that shows what will happen because of this.

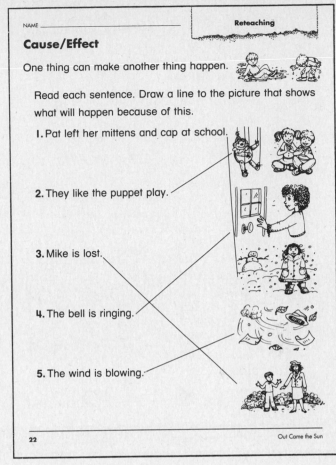

1. Pat left her mittens and cap at school.

2. They like the puppet play.

3. Mike is lost.

4. The bell is ringing.

5. The wind is blowing.

---

## Cause/Effect

One thing can make another thing happen.

Read the sentences. Write what caused the thing to happen.

Example:
School is out. Dave can play.

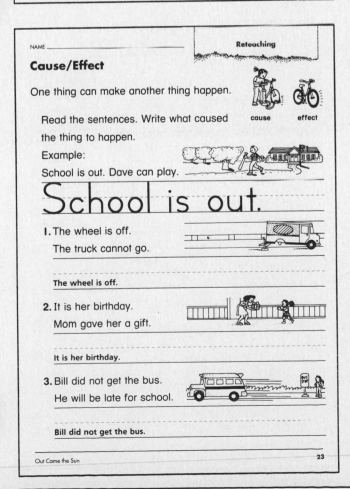

School is out.

1. The wheel is off.
   The truck cannot go.

   The wheel is off.

2. It is her birthday.
   Mom gave her a gift.

   It is her birthday.

3. Bill did not get the bus.
   He will be late for school.

   Bill did not get the bus.

---

## Words with Short o

The letter **o** can stand for the vowel sound you hear in **on** and **cot.**

**A.** Color each picture whose name has the same vowel sound as in **on** and **cot.**

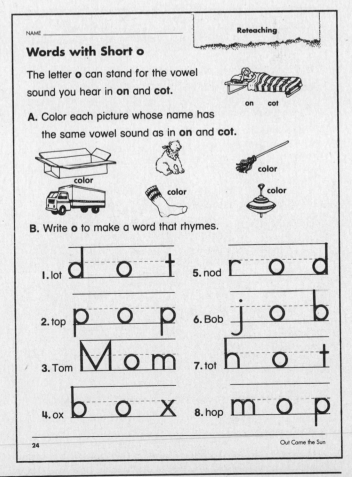

**B.** Write **o** to make a word that rhymes.

1. lot  dot    5. nod  rod

2. top  pop    6. Bob  job

3. Tom  Mom    7. tot  hot

4. ox  box    8. hop  mop

## Words with Short o

The letter **o** can stand for the vowel sound you hear in **top** and **box**.

top    box

**A.** Underline the words that have the same vowel sound as in **top** and **box**.

| cone | Bob | pup | cot | not | tot |
|------|-----|-----|-----|-----|-----|
| on   | Mom | box | mob | go  | top |
| lap  | so  | lot | pop | hot | so  |

**B.** Name each picture. Write **o** to make a word if the picture name has the same vowel sound as in **top** and **box**.

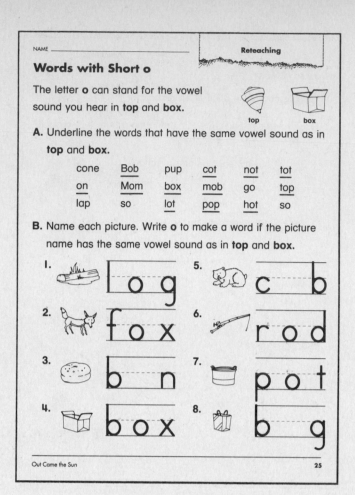

1. l o g
2. f o x
3. b _ n
4. b o x
5. c _ b
6. r o d
7. p o t
8. b _ g

---

## Words with Long o

The letter **o** at the end of a word can stand for the vowel sound you hear in **go** and **no**.

no

**A.** Underline the words that have the same vowel sound as in **go** and **no**.

| for | ho | too | go  | pro | you   |
|-----|----|-----|-----|-----|-------|
| so  | no | who | you | on  | yo-yo |

**B.** Read each question. Underline the words that have the vowel sound you hear in **go** and **no**. Then circle **yes** or **no** to answer each question.

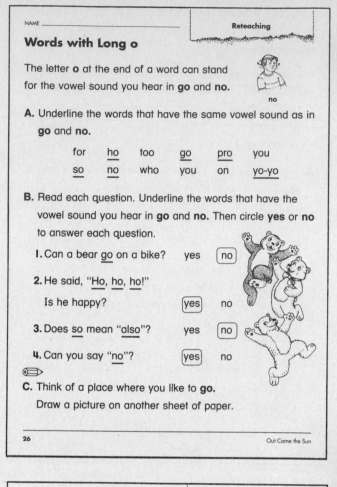

1. Can a bear go on a bike?    yes    [no]

2. He said, "Ho, ho, ho!"
   Is he happy?    [yes]    no

3. Does so mean "also"?    yes    [no]

4. Can you say "no"?    [yes]    no

**C.** Think of a place where you like to **go**. Draw a picture on another sheet of paper.

---

## Words with Long o

The letter **o** at the end of a word can stand for the vowel sound you hear in **so** and **go**.

**A.** Circle the correct word to finish each sentence. Then write the word.

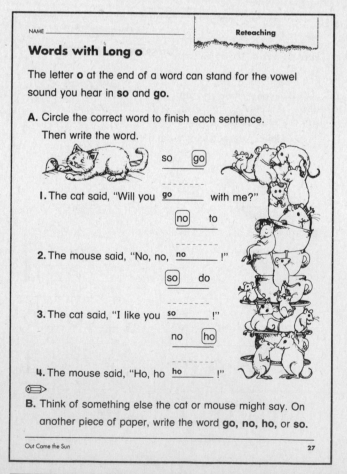

so    [go]

1. The cat said, "Will you go _____ with me?"
   [no]    to

2. The mouse said, "No, no, no _____ !"
   [so]    do

3. The cat said, "I like you so _____ !"
   no    [ho]

4. The mouse said, "Ho, ho ho _____ !"

**B.** Think of something else the cat or mouse might say. On another piece of paper, write the word **go, no, ho,** or **so**.

---

## Sequence

Things happen in a certain order. These pictures are in order.

Look at the first two pictures in each row. What will happen next? Draw a picture that shows what happens next.

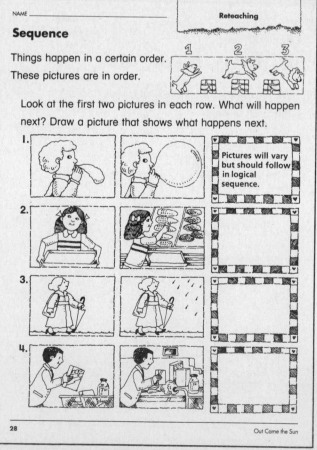

Pictures will vary but should follow in logical sequence.

1.
2.
3.
4.

© Silver Burdett Ginn Inc.

# Sequence

**Procedure:**

*Say to the children:* When you listen to a story, the order in which things happen is important. If things are out of order, the story will not make sense.

I will tell you about something a person wants to do. Then I will ask you about the order in which the person should do that thing.

Page 31

1. Look at the first row of pictures.
   Listen carefully.

   Pam wants to shovel the snow.
   What must Pam do first?

   Write a number **1** in the box in the picture that tells the right answer. (If children cannot write the numerals, substitute a direction—**circle, X, underline, box**—of your choice.)

What must Pam do next?

Write a number **2** in the box in the picture that tells the right answer.

What will Pam do last?

Write a number **3** in that box in the picture that tells the right answer.

2. Look at the second row of pictures.
   Listen carefully.

   Joe is going to school.
   What must Joe do first?

   Write a number **1** in the box in the picture that tells the right answer.

   What must Joe do next?

   Write a number **2** in that box.

   What will Joe do last?

   Write a number **3** in that box.

3. Look at the third row of pictures.
   Listen carefully.

   Kerry wants to wash her dog.
   What must Kerry do first?

   Write **1** in the box in the picture that tells the right answer.

   What must Kerry do second?

   Write **2** in that box.

   What will Kerry do third?

   Write **3** in that box.

4. Look at the fourth row of pictures.
   Listen carefully.

   Bill wants to make a sandwich.
   What must Bill do first?

   Write **1** in the box in the picture that tells the right answer.

   What must Bill do next?

   Write **2** in that box.

   What will Bill do last?

   Write **3** in that box.

---

Page 32

1. Look at the first row of pictures.
   Listen carefully.

   Paul wants to draw a picture.
   What must he do first?

   Write a number **1** in the box in the picture that tells the right answer.

   What must Paul do second?

   Write a number **2** in that box.

   What will Paul do last?

   Write a number **3** in that box.

2. Look at the second row of pictures.
   Listen carefully.

   Tina wants to fly a kite.
   What must Tina do first?

   Write **1** in the box in the picture that tells the right answer.

   What must Tina do next?

   Write **2** in that box.

   What will Tina do last?

   Write **3** in that box.

3. Look at the third row of pictures.
   Listen carefully.

   Rick wants to grow a plant.
   What must Rick do first?

   Write **1** in the box in the picture that tells the right answer.

   What must Rick do second?

   Write **2** in that box.

   What will happen last?

   Write **3** in that box.

4. Look at the last row of pictures.
   Listen carefully.

   Sue wants to give a present to her friend.
   What must Sue do first?

   Write **1** in the box in the picture that tells the right answer.

   What must Sue do second?

   Write **2** in that box.

   What will happen last?

   Write **3** in that box.

---

NAME _____

# Sequence

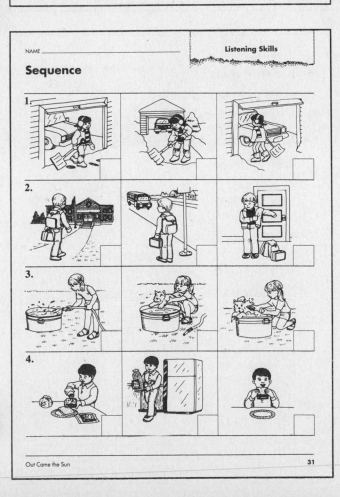

---

NAME _____

# Sequence

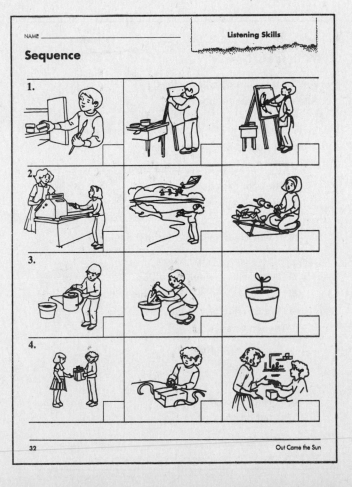

## Critical Thinking:
**Making Statements True**

**Focus:** Learning to choose the right words is important. Changing a word can change what a sentence means.

**Summary:**
1. Some
2. Some
3. Some
4. All
5. Some

**Model:** This activity gives you some sentences that are not complete. You will pick the best word to make each sentence true.

**Practice:** Suppose you saw this sentence:

_____ dogs are tan.

No   Some

Try the sentence with the first word in the blank—"No dogs are tan." That is not a true statement because dogs can be tan. Try the sentence with the other word—"Some dogs are tan." That is a true statement, so you would write the word *Some* in the blank.

Here are some words that are important because they can make a sentence true or not true.

All        Most        Some        No

**Apply:** Now work on page 34.
1. Read each sentence carefully.
2. Look at the two words below the sentence.
3. Try both words in the sentence.
4. Pick the best word to make the sentence true.
5. Write that word in the blank.
6. Read the sentence again to be sure it is true.

**Monitor:** When students have finished, discuss their choices.
1. It would not be true to say that no people ride bicycles. It is true that some people ride bicycles.
2. It is not true that all wheels are on trucks; some wheels are on cars, buses, and so on. It is true that some wheels are on trucks.
3. It is true that some bicycles are red. It is not true to say that no bicycles are red.
4. It is true that all wheels are round; Wheels would not go well if they were not round.
5. It cannot be true to say that most people ride on the bus. Some people ride in cars, trains, or bicycles. It is true that some people ride on the bus.

Out Came the Sun                                                   33

---

## Critical Thinking:
**Making Statements True**

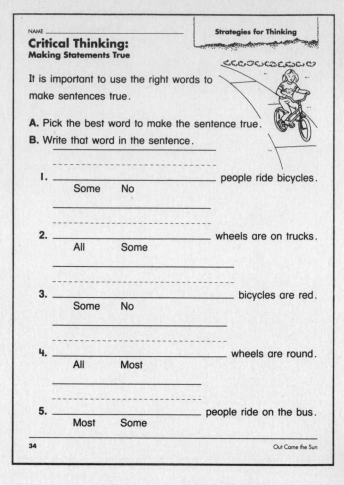

It is important to use the right words to make sentences true.

**A.** Pick the best word to make the sentence true.
**B.** Write that word in the sentence.

1. _____ people ride bicycles.
   Some    No

2. _____ wheels are on trucks.
   All    Some

3. _____ bicycles are red.
   Some    No

4. _____ wheels are round.
   All    Most

5. _____ people ride on the bus.
   Most    Some

34                                                   Out Came the Sun

---

## Main Idea/Details

A story is always about something.
All the sentences tell about it.

Read each story title. Color the box beside each sentence that tells about what is in the story.

1. **The Bear and the Cave**
   □ The bear likes honey.
   ■ The bear came to a cave.
   ■ It went in the cave.
   ■ "I will live in this cave," said the bear.

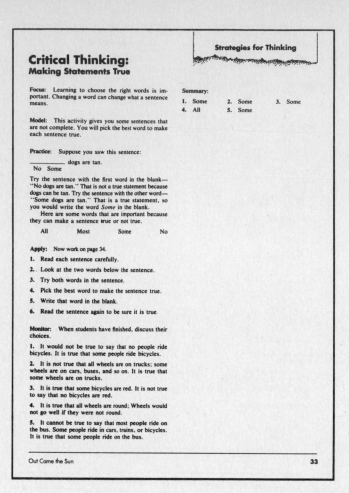

2. **The Ride**
   ■ "What will we ride?" said Dad.
   ■ "We can ride in the truck," said Bob.
   ■ "We can ride on the bus," said Mom.
   □ The sun was out.

3. **The Hat**
   ■ I see a hat.
   ■ It is a big hat.
   ■ I will put on the hat.
   □ I put on a wig.

Morning Bells                                                   35

---

## Main Idea/Details

A story is always about something.
All the sentences tell about it.

Read the story. Write the word that finishes each sentence.

**Jane and Bingo**
Jane has a dog.
The dog is Bingo.
Jane and Bingo run.
They play in the water.

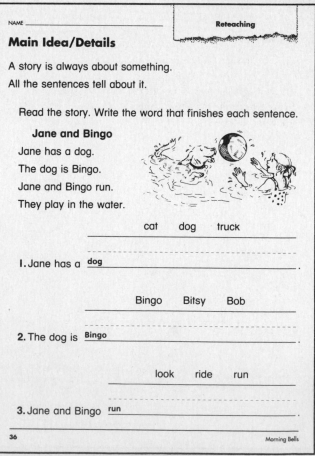

cat    dog    truck

1. Jane has a  dog                                    .

Bingo    Bitsy    Bob

2. The dog is  Bingo                                   .

look    ride    run

3. Jane and Bingo  run                                .

36                                                   Morning Bells

© Silver Burdett Ginn Inc.

**206**

## Words with Short u

The letter **u** can stand for the vowel sound you hear in **bug** and **tub**.

bug    tub

Name each picture. Then write **u** or **o** to make the picture name.

1. bun
2. mop
3. hut
4. nut
5. bus
6. pot
7. cup
8. sun
9. pup
10. fox
11. hug
12. cub

---

## Words with Short u

The letter **u** can stand for the vowel sound you hear in **bus** and **jug**.

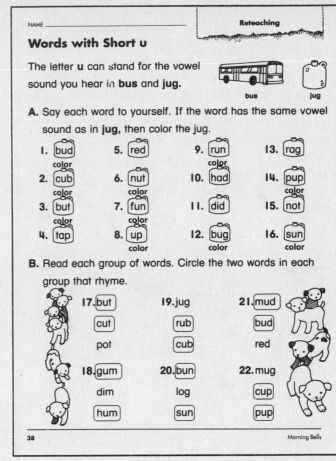

bus    jug

**A.** Say each word to yourself. If the word has the same vowel sound as in **jug**, then color the jug.

1. bud
2. cub — color
3. but — color
4. tap
5. red
6. nut — color
7. fun — color
8. up — color
9. run — color
10. had
11. did
12. bug — color
13. rag
14. pup — color
15. not
16. sun — color

**B.** Read each group of words. Circle the two words in each group that rhyme.

17. but / cut / pot
18. gum / dim / hum
19. jug / rub / cub
20. bun / log / sun
21. mud / bud / red
22. mug / cup / pup

---

## Words with Long u

The letter **u** can stand for the vowel sound you hear in **cube** and **flute**. Look for the letter **e** at the end of a short word. It often points out that the first vowel in the word stands for a long sound.

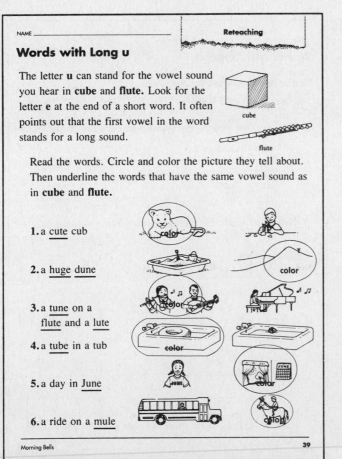

cube

flute

Read the words. Circle and color the picture they tell about. Then underline the words that have the same vowel sound as in **cube** and **flute**.

1. a cute cub
2. a huge dune
3. a tune on a flute and a lute
4. a tube in a tub
5. a day in June
6. a ride on a mule

color

---

## Words with Long u

The letter **u** can stand for the vowel sound you hear in **huge** and **cute**. Look for the letter **e** at the end of a short word. It often points out that the first vowel in the word stands for a long sound.

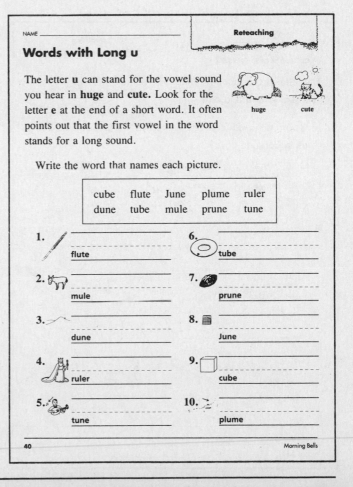

huge    cute

Write the word that names each picture.

| cube | flute | June | plume | ruler |
| dune | tube | mule | prune | tune |

1. flute
2. mule
3. dune
4. ruler
5. tune
6. tube
7. prune
8. June
9. cube
10. plume

## Words with Final g, m

The letters **g** and **m** can stand for the
sounds you hear at the end of **dog** and **ham.**

ham   dog

Name each picture. Then circle the letter that stands for the
ending sound. Write the letter below the picture.

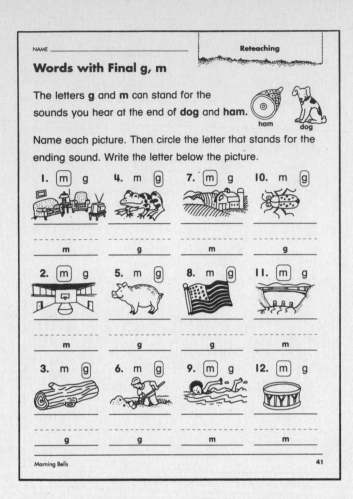

1. (m)  g        4. m  (g)       7. (m)  g      10. m  (g)

        m            g              m             g

2. (m)  g        5. m  (g)       8. m  (g)      11. (m)  g

        m            g              g             m

3. m  (g)        6. m  (g)       9. (m)  g      12. (m)  g

        g            g              m             m

## Words with Final g, m

The letters **g** and **m** can stand for the
sounds you hear at the end of **jug** and **ram.**

jug   ram

**A.** Write **m** to make a word. Say the word. Then draw a line
to the picture that shows the word.

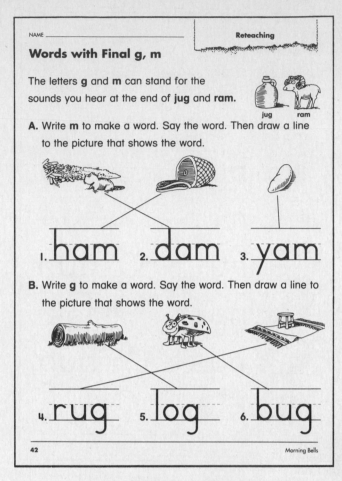

1. ham    2. dam    3. yam

**B.** Write **g** to make a word. Say the word. Then draw a line to
the picture that shows the word.

4. rug    5. log    6. bug

## Words with Short a

The letter **a** can stand for the vowel sound
you hear in **can** and **cat.**

can   cat

**A.** Color each picture whose name has the same vowel sound
as in **can** and **cat.**

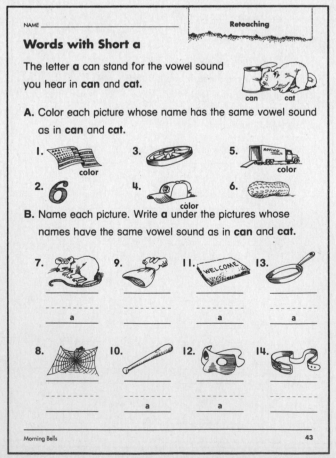

1. ___        3. ___       5. ___
   color                      color

2. ___        4. ___       6. ___
                 color

**B.** Name each picture. Write **a** under the pictures whose
names have the same vowel sound as in **can** and **cat.**

7. ___    9. ___    11. ___    13. ___

    a               a            a

8. ___   10. ___   12. ___    14. ___

              a        a

## Words with Short a

The letter **a** can stand for the vowel sound
you hear in **rat** and **van.**

rat   van

**A.** Underline the words that have the same vowel sound as in
**rat** and **van.**

| Dad | tan | fall | has | and | ate |
|------|------|------|------|------|------|
| was | cat | play | pat | can | sand |
| am | what | pal | cave | sad | fat |

**B.** Write **a** to make a word that rhymes. Read your words.

1. can    pan       5. bag    wag

2. Pat    sat       6. tan    man

3. am     ham       7. cat    rat

4. Dad    mad       8. sad    bad

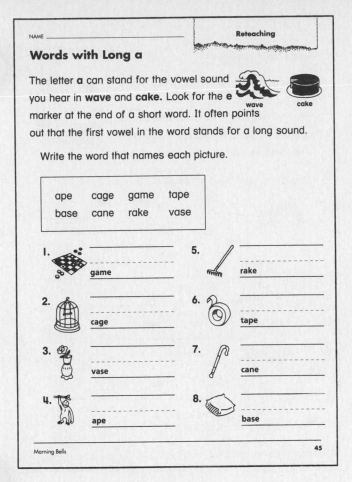

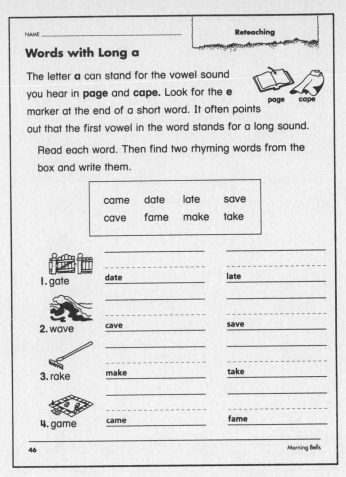

## Words with Long a

The letter **a** can stand for the vowel sound you hear in **wave** and **cake.** Look for the **e** marker at the end of a short word. It often points out that the first vowel in the word stands for a long sound.

Write the word that names each picture.

| ape | cage | game | tape |
|-----|------|------|------|
| base | cane | rake | vase |

1. game
2. cage
3. vase
4. ape

5. rake
6. tape
7. cane
8. base

---

## Words with Long a

The letter **a** can stand for the vowel sound you hear in **page** and **cape.** Look for the **e** marker at the end of a short word. It often points out that the first vowel in the word stands for a long sound.

Read each word. Then find two rhyming words from the box and write them.

| came | date | late | save |
|------|------|------|------|
| cave | fame | make | take |

1. gate — date — late
2. wave — cave — save
3. rake — make — take
4. game — came — fame

---

## Words with Short e

The letter **e** can stand for the vowel sound you hear in **well.**

Find the word that has the same vowel sound as in **well.** Circle the word. Then write it.

1. pin  (men)  tan — men
2. bit  truck  (net) — net
3. (bed)  had  rod — bed
4. fat  win  (pen) — pen
5. what  hit  (jet) — jet
6. (pet)  lid  fun — pet

---

## Words with Short e

The letter **e** can stand for the vowel sound you hear in **bell** and **pen.**

**A.** Color each picture whose name has the same vowel sound as in **bell** and **pen.**

1.
2. color
3. color
4. color
5. color
6.

**B.** Name each picture. Write **e** under the pictures whose names have the same vowel sound as in **bell** and **pen.**

7. _____
8. _____ e
9. _____ e
10. _____ e
11. _____ e
12. _____
13. _____ e
14. _____ e

## Words with Long e

The letter **e** at the end of a word can stand for the vowel sound you hear in **he** and **she**. Sometimes two letters stand for one sound. The letters **ee** stand for the vowel sound you hear in **jeep**.

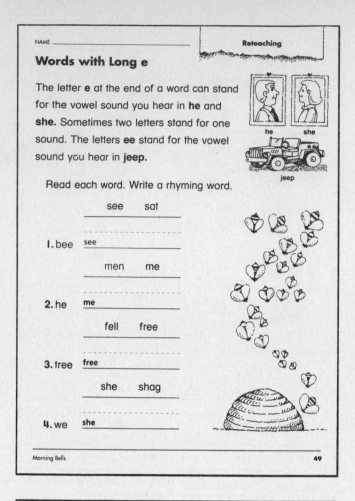

jeep

Read each word. Write a rhyming word.

see    sat

1. bee  _see_

men    me

2. he  _me_

fell    free

3. tree  _free_

she    shag

4. we  _she_

---

## Words with Long e

The letter **e** at the end of a word can stand for the sound you hear in **me** and **we**. Sometimes two letters stand for one sound. The letters **ee** stand for the vowel sound you hear in **Lee**.

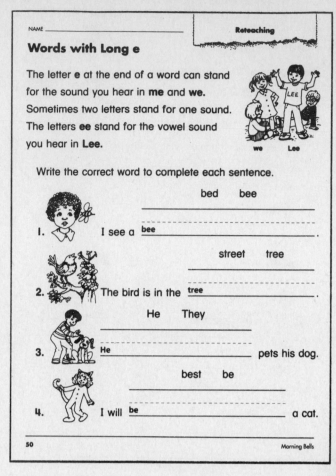

we    Lee

Write the correct word to complete each sentence.

bed    bee

1. I see a _bee_ .

street    tree

2. The bird is in the _tree_ .

He    They

3. _He_ pets his dog.

best    be

4. I will _be_ a cat.

---

## Predicting Outcomes

When you read a story, think ahead and try to tell what will happen next.

clue    clue

What will happen next

**Example:**
**Clue 1:** The bicycle tire has a hole.
**Clue 2:** Gail wants to ride her bicycle.
What will happen next? Gail will fix the wheel.

Look at the first two pictures.
Circle the picture that shows what will happen next.

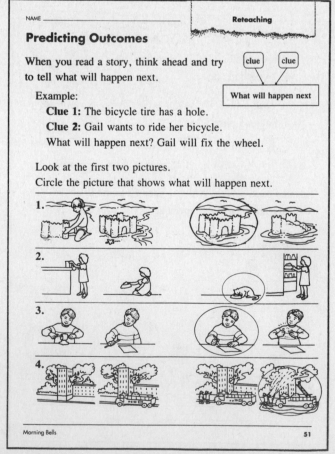

1.
2.
3.
4.

---

## Predicting Outcomes

When you read a story, think ahead and try to tell what will happen next.

clue    clue

What will happen next

**Example:**
**Clue 1:** John put on his hat.
**Clue 2:** He opened the door.
What will happen next? He will go outside.

Circle the right word. Write what **happens** next.
Then draw a picture to show what **happens** next.

1. The wind blows. Jeff runs with the kite.

back    down    (up)

The kite will go _up_ .

2. Coral is very tired. She is in bed.

eat    play    (sleep)

Coral will _sleep_ .

3. We can put this together. It is a plane.

(fly)    ride    walk

Now we will _fly_ it.

## Words with Short i

The letter **i** can stand for the vowel sound you hear in **Tim** and **fix**.

Tim    fix

**A.** Underline the words that have the same vowel sound as in **Tim** and **fix**.

| rid | it  | kit | in  | his  | kite |
| den | big | is  | ran | lip  | tin  |
| mix | lap | Jim | win | Bill | fit  |

**B.** Look at each picture. Then circle the words that have the same vowel sound as in **Tim** and **fix**.

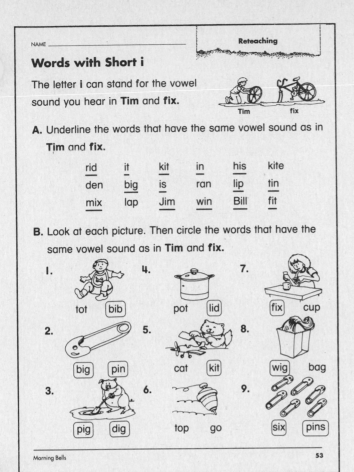

1. tot  bib
4. pot  lid
7. fix  cup
2. big  pin
5. cat  kit
8. wig  bag
3. pig  dig
6. top  go
9. six  pins

---

## Words with Short i

The letter **i** can stand for the vowel sound you hear in **pin** and **sit**.

pin    sit

**A.** Find the word that has the same vowel sound as in **pin** and **sit**. Circle the word. Then write it.

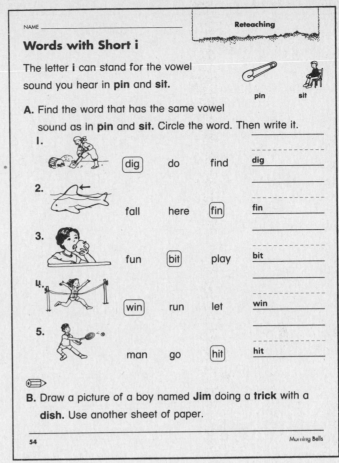

1. dig   do    find    _dig_
2. fall  here  fin     _fin_
3. fun   bit   play    _bit_
4. win   run   let     _win_
5. man   go    hit     _hit_

**B.** Draw a picture of a boy named **Jim** doing a **trick** with a **dish**. Use another sheet of paper.

---

## Words with Long i

The letter **i** can stand for the vowel sound you hear in **dice** and **pine**. Look for the **e** at the end of a short word. It often points out that the first vowel in the word stands for a long sound.

dice    pine

Read each word. Circle the picture it names. Then write the word.

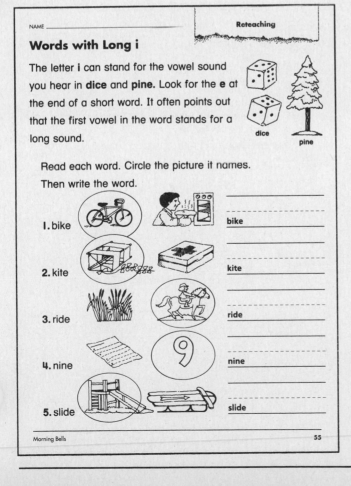

1. bike    _bike_
2. kite    _kite_
3. ride    _ride_
4. nine    _nine_
5. slide   _slide_

---

## Words with Long i

The letter **i** can stand for the vowel sound you hear in **five** and **nine**. Look for the **e** at the end of a word. It often points out that the first vowel in the word stands for a long sound.

five    nine

Read each word. Then find two rhyming words. Write them.

| hide | mine | rice | wide |
| line | nice | ripe | wipe |

1. mice    _nice_    _rice_
2. vine    _line_    _mine_
3. pipe    _ripe_    _wipe_
4. bride   _hide_    _wide_

## Panel 1 (top left)

NAME _____                   Reteaching

### Words with Short o

The letter **o** can stand for the vowel
sound you hear in **hot** and **pot**.

hot   pot

Find the word that has the same vowel
sound as in **hot** and **pot**. Circle the word. Then write it.

1. toy  (box)  up          box

2. (dots)  ten  big        dots

3. (mop)  go  look         mop

4. get  off  (pop)         pop

5. fun  (hop)  den         hop

6. (fox)  bug  went        fox

Morning Bells                    57

## Panel 2 (top right)

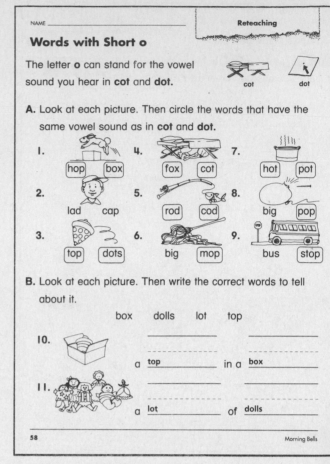

NAME _____                   Reteaching

### Words with Short o

The letter **o** can stand for the vowel
sound you hear in **cot** and **dot**.

cot   dot

**A.** Look at each picture. Then circle the words that have the
same vowel sound as in **cot** and **dot**.

1. (hop)  box      4. (fox)  cot      7. (hot)  pot

2. lad  cap        5. (rod)  cod      8. big  (pop)

3. (top)  dots     6. big  (mop)      9. bus  (stop)

**B.** Look at each picture. Then write the correct words to tell
about it.

box    dolls    lot    top

10. a  top  in a  box

11. a  lot  of  dolls

58                    Morning Bells

## Panel 3 (bottom left)

NAME _____                   Reteaching

### Words with Long o

The letter **o** at the end of a word can stand for the vowel
sound you hear in **go**, **no**, and **so**.

Read each question. Underline the words that have the
vowel sound you hear in **go**, **no**, and **so**. Then write **yes** or
**no** to answer the question.

1. Do they g<u>o</u>?          yes

2. Can you do this?            no

3. Is she s<u>o</u> happy?      yes

4. Did he g<u>o</u> in water?   yes

5. Will she g<u>o</u>?          yes

6. Will she stay?             no

Morning Bells                    59

## Panel 4 (bottom right)

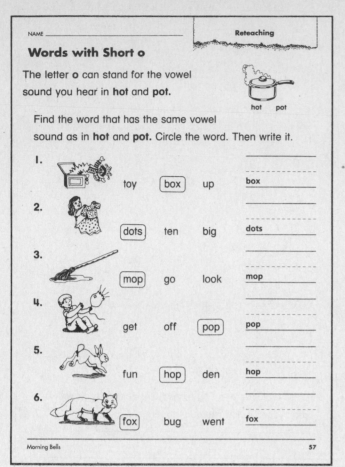

NAME _____                   Reteaching

### Words with Long o

The letter **o** at the end of a word can stand for the vowel
sound you hear in **no** and **so**.

**A.** Finish the sentence that tells about each picture.

1. The bus can  go  .          ho
                               go

2. She said, " No ."           No
                               So

3. He said, "I told you  so  !"   so
                                  go

4. She will  go  .             no
                               go

**B.** Answer the question.

5. Can you turn left?  No       Yes
                               No

60                    Morning Bells

212

## Main Idea

**Main Idea** (student worksheet reproduced)

| | | | |
|---|---|---|---|
| 1. ___ | Some of the cars had four doors, and some had two doors. | _X_ | There were many different kinds of cars in the parking lot. |
| 2. _X_ | Polly's room was a mess. | ___ | Papers were all over her bed. |
| 3. ___ | Then they played on the slide. | _X_ | The children played on three things at the park. |
| 4. _X_ | It was a wet week. | ___ | It rained hard on Sunday and Monday. |
| 5. ___ | Lou can shake hands. | _X_ | Lou the dog can do tricks. |
| 6. _X_ | Ted likes green more than any other color. | ___ | Ted has a green bike. |
| 7. _X_ | There are four seasons. | ___ | Fall means a new school year. |
| 8. ___ | *Caps* means almost the same thing as *hats*. | _X_ | Some words mean almost the same thing. |
| 9. _X_ | Sally and Joyce are best friends. | ___ | They walk to school and eat lunch together. |

**Procedure:**

Write the following sentences on the chalkboard:

1. Jack just read a story about mice.
2. Jack likes animal stories.

*Say to the children:* I will read a short story to you. Listen carefully for what the story is mostly about.

Jack likes animal stories. He reads stories about cats and horses. He reads stories about rabbits. Jack just read a story about mice.

Look at the sentences that I have written on the chalkboard. Which one tells what the story is mostly about? (Elicit that the second sentence tells what the story is mostly about; the first sentence tells only about one kind of animal story that Jack has read. The second sentence, however, includes all animal stories.)

Now I will read another story. Listen carefully for what the story is mostly about. Then, on your paper, you will mark an X next to the sentence that tells what the story is mostly about.

**Story Number 1**

Some were new cars, and some were old cars. There were big cars and little cars. Some of the cars had four doors, and some had two doors. There were many different kinds of cars in the parking lot.

**Story Number 2**

Polly's room was a mess. Papers were all over her bed. Toys were all over the floor. Polly's desk was covered with dust.

**Story Number 3**

First, the children played on the merry-go-round. Then they played on the slide. Next, they played on the swings. The children played on three things at the park.

**Story Number 4**

It was a wet week. It rained hard on Sunday and Monday. It sprinkled on Tuesday, Wednesday, and Thursday. On Friday and Saturday, it rained hard again.

**Story Number 5**

Lou the dog can do tricks. Lou can shake hands. He can bring the newspaper to the back door. Lou can roll over, too.

**Story Number 6**

Ted has a green bike. His room is painted green, and he likes green clothes. When he grows up, Ted wants his house to be painted green. Ted likes green more than any other color.

**Story Number 7**

There are four seasons. Summer is usually warm, and people go on vacations. Fall means a new school year. In some places, winter brings snow and cold weather. In spring, many people plant gardens.

**Story Number 8**

*Caps* means almost the same thing as *hats*. *Evening* means almost the same thing as *night*. *Strange* means almost the same thing as *odd*. Some words mean almost the same thing.

**Story Number 9**

Sally and Joyce are best friends. They walk to school together and eat lunch together. After school, Sally and Joyce walk to the same babysitter's house where they do their homework together. On Saturdays, Sally and Joyce go to the park together.

---

## Main Idea

1. ___ Some of the cars had four doors, and some had two doors.　　___ There were many different kinds of cars in the parking lot.

2. ___ Polly's room was a mess.　　___ Papers were all over her bed.

3. ___ Then they played on the slide.　　___ The children played on three things at the park.

4. ___ It was a wet week.　　___ It rained hard on Sunday and Monday.

5. ___ Lou can shake hands.　　___ Lou the dog can do tricks.

6. ___ Ted likes green more than any other color.　　___ Ted has a green bike.

7. ___ There are four seasons.　　___ Fall means a new school year.

8. ___ *Caps* means almost the same thing as *hats*.　　___ Some words mean almost the same thing.

9. ___ Sally and Joyce are best friends.　　___ They walk to school and eat lunch together.

---

## Elaboration: Creating Inventions

**Focus:** Using the imagination is important in solving real or imagined problems.

**Model:** This activity gives you ideas about situations that can be real or imaginary. You will choose one idea and draw an invention that would help people in that situation.

**Practice:** Suppose you read this idea: All raindrops are as hard as rocks. Draw a new thing that people will need. First, you would imagine a problem that people would have if raindrops were as hard as rocks. You might imagine that people would get hurt when they went out in the rain.

Then you would imagine an invention to solve the problem. You might imagine building roofs over the sidewalks. Then you would draw a picture of your invention.

**Apply:** Now work on page 64.

1. Read all four ideas.
2. Think about the ideas and choose the one you like best. Circle that idea.
3. Read again the idea that you circled. Think of a problem that people would have.
4. Imagine an invention to solve the problem.
5. Draw a picture of your invention at the bottom of the page.

**Monitor:** When students have finished, have them display and explain their drawings. Help them to focus on the problems they identified and on how they thought of their solutions.

---

## Elaboration: Creating Inventions

You can use your imagination to think of new things.

**A.** Read all the ideas.

**B.** Pick the one you like best and circle it.

**C.** Draw the picture.

1. Draw a new thing to help people ride bicycles in the rain.

2. Draw an umbrella you can use when the wind blows hard.

3. Rain does not fall from the sky any more. It comes up from the ground! Draw a new thing that people need.

4. The wind does not blow at all any more. Draw a new thing that people need.

**213**

## Reality/Fantasy

Some things you read about are **real** and can happen. Other things are not real. They are **make-believe**.

This is real. ——————→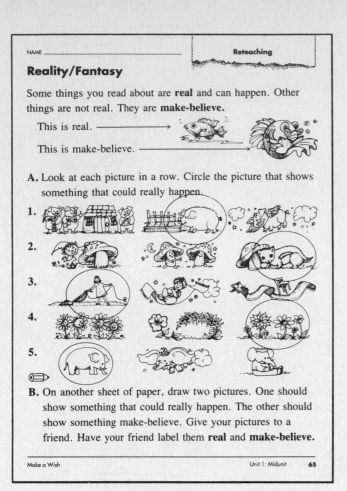

This is make-believe. ——————→

**A.** Look at each picture in a row. Circle the picture that shows something that could really happen.

1.
2.
3.
4.
5.

**B.** On another sheet of paper, draw two pictures. One should show something that could really happen. The other should show something make-believe. Give your pictures to a friend. Have your friend label them **real** and **make-believe**.

---

## Classification

Some words belong in the same group. These words belong together.

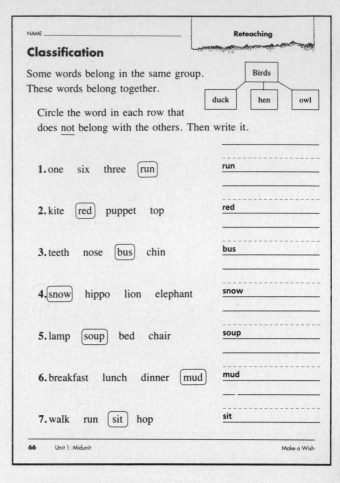

Circle the word in each row that does <u>not</u> belong with the others. Then write it.

1. one   six   three   [run]          run

2. kite   [red]   puppet   top        red

3. teeth   nose   [bus]   chin        bus

4. [snow]   hippo   lion   elephant   snow

5. lamp   [soup]   bed   chair        soup

6. breakfast   lunch   dinner   [mud] mud

7. walk   run   [sit]   hop           sit

---

## Words with ea

Sometimes two letters stand for one sound. The letters **ea** can stand for the vowel sound you hear in **eat** and **read**.

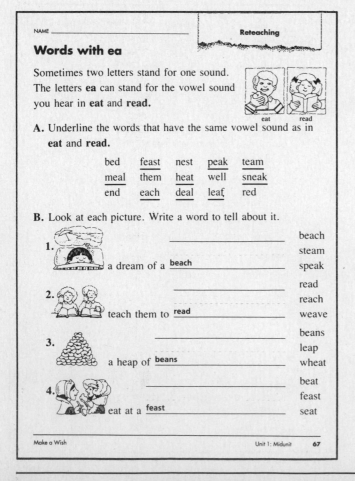

eat   read

**A.** Underline the words that have the same vowel sound as in **eat** and **read**.

| bed | feast | nest | peak | team |
| meal | them | heat | well | sneak |
| end | each | deal | leaf | red |

**B.** Look at each picture. Write a word to tell about it.

1. a dream of a __beach__          beach
                                    steam
                                    speak

2. teach them to __read__          read
                                    reach
                                    weave

3. a heap of __beans__             beans
                                    leap
                                    wheat

4. eat at a __feast__              beat
                                    feast
                                    seat

---

## Predicting Outcomes

When you read a story, think ahead and try to tell what will happen next.

Write the sentence that tells what will happen next.

| Greg will win the race.    Susan will be late for school. |

1. Susan takes the bus to school.
   This morning she got up late.
   The bus was gone.

   **Susan will be late for school.**

2. Dave can run very fast.
   He can run faster than everyone but Greg.
   Dave and Greg will have a race.

   **Greg will win the race.**

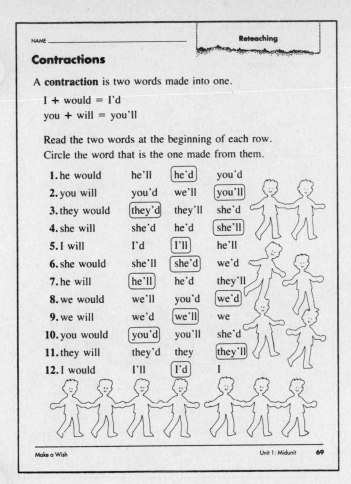

## Contractions

A **contraction** is two words made into one.

I + would = I'd
you + will = you'll

Read the two words at the beginning of each row.
Circle the word that is the one made from them.

1. he would — he'll — (he'd) — you'd
2. you will — you'd — we'll — (you'll)
3. they would — (they'd) — they'll — she'd
4. she will — she'd — he'd — (she'll)
5. I will — I'd — (I'll) — he'll
6. she would — she'll — (she'd) — we'd
7. he will — (he'll) — he'd — they'll
8. we would — we'll — you'd — (we'd)
9. we will — we'd — (we'll) — we
10. you would — (you'd) — you'll — she'd
11. they will — they'd — they — (they'll)
12. I would — I'll — (I'd) — I

---

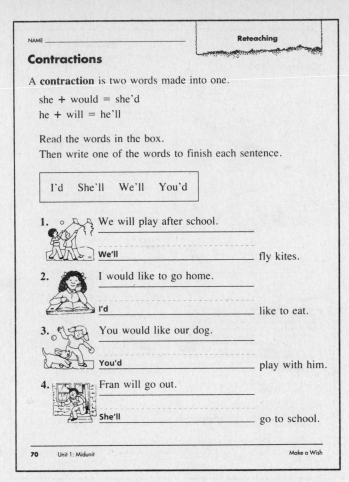

## Contractions

A **contraction** is two words made into one.

she + would = she'd
he + will = he'll

Read the words in the box.
Then write one of the words to finish each sentence.

| I'd   She'll   We'll   You'd |

1. We will play after school.

   **We'll** _____ fly kites.

2. I would like to go home.

   **I'd** _____ like to eat.

3. You would like our dog.

   **You'd** _____ play with him.

4. Fran will go out.

   **She'll** _____ go to school.

---

## Context Clues

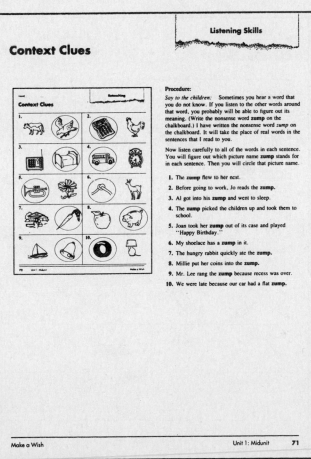

Procedure:

*Say to the children:* Sometimes you hear a word that you do not know. If you listen to the other words around that word, you probably will be able to figure out its meaning. (Write the nonsense word *zump* on the chalkboard.) I have written the nonsense word *zump* on the chalkboard. It will take the place of real words in the sentences that I read to you.

Now listen carefully to all of the words in each sentence. You will figure out which picture name *zump* stands for in each sentence. Then you will circle that picture name.

1. The *zump* flew to her nest.
2. Before going to work, Jo reads the *zump*.
3. Al got into his *zump* and went to sleep.
4. The *zump* picked the children up and took them to school.
5. Joan took her *zump* out of its case and played "Happy Birthday."
6. My shoelace has a *zump* in it.
7. The hungry rabbit quickly ate the *zump*.
8. Millie put her coins into the *zump*.
9. Mr. Lee rang the *zump* because recess was over.
10. We were late because our car had a flat *zump*.

---

## Context Clues

1.   2.

3.   4.

5.   6.

7.   8.

9.   10.

## Comparison

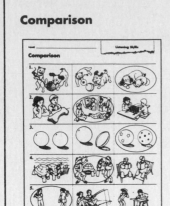

**Procedure:**

*Say to the children:* People often compare things by telling how the things are alike or how they are different. Let's compare your desk to my desk. How are your desk and my desk alike? (Possible responses: flat tops, used for writing, have a place to store things) How are they different? (Possible responses: size, made of different materials) I am going to read some short stories. In some of the stories, you will have to listen for how certain things are alike. In the other stories, you will have to listen for how certain things are different.

Now I will read the first story. In this story, listen for how two pets are **alike**.

1.  Mert the cat likes to play with yarn. Bert the dog likes to chase balls. Mert *and* Bert like to take naps.

Look at the first row of pictures on your paper. Circle the picture that shows how Mert and Bert are alike.

As I read the next story, listen for how two people are **alike**.

2.  Tim rides his bike to his art class every Saturday, but Jan draws at home. Tim and Jan want to be artists when they grow up. Tim lives in the city, and Jan lives in the country.

Look at the row of pictures next to Number 2. Circle the picture that shows how Tim and Jan are alike.

As I read the next story, listen for how two things are **different**.

3.  Rob got two beach balls for his birthday. Rob thought that he would share the beach balls with his sister. The beach balls are the same size and the same shape, but one of the beach balls is decorated with stars, and the other is decorated with spots.

Look at the row of pictures next to Number 3. Circle the picture of the pair that shows how Rob's beach balls are different.

As I read the next story, listen for how two things are **different**.

4.  Two turtles, Tillie and Tom, enjoy taking walks around the pond. They also like to visit with their neighbors, Fred and Fay Frog. When Fred starts to sing, Tom goes into his shell, but Tillie could listen to Fred for hours.

Look at the row of pictures next to Number 4. Circle the picture that shows how Tillie and Tom are different.

As I read the next story, listen for how two people are **alike**.

5.  Kathy and Lenny go to different schools. Kathy lives in an apartment, and Lenny lives in a trailer. Kathy met Lenny when their baseball teams held a championship game.

Look at the last row of pictures and circle the picture that shows how Kathy and Lenny are alike.

---

## Comparison

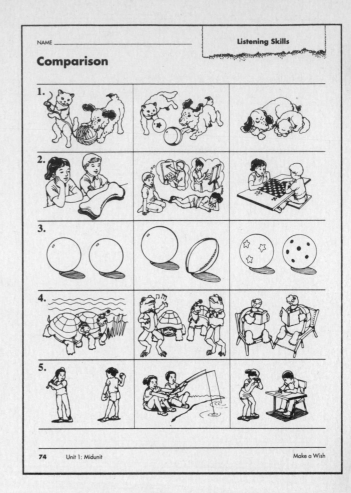

---

## Classification

**Procedure:**

On the chalkboard, draw a large rectangle; add a doorway and two windows. Write the words **cat, hen, train,** and **pig** under the rectangle.

*Say to the children:* The drawing is a house for animals. There are four words written under the house. I will read the words to you. (Read the four words to the children.) Three of the four words name things that are alike in some way. They are *cat, hen,* and *pig.* (Write *cat, hen,* and *pig* "inside" the house.) The words *cat, hen,* and *pig* are alike and belong in the house because they are animals. The word *train* does not belong with the other words because a train is not an animal. What is another word that belongs to the same group as *cat, hen,* and *pig*? (Accept any word that names an animal.) What is another word that does **not** belong to the same group as *cat, hen,* and *pig*? (Accept any word that does not name an animal.)

Write the numerals **6, 7,** and **8** on the chalkboard. Draw a square to the right of the numerals. Then say to the children: I will read three words. You must decide which of the four things on the chalkboard does not belong to the same group of words that I read. (Read the words *one, two,* and *three.* Ask a volunteer to come to the chalkboard and mark an X on the thing that does not belong to the group. Elicit that *6, 7,* and *8* belong to the same group as *one, two,* and *three* because they are numbers, but the square is a shape and does not belong to the group "Numbers.") Now look at your paper. I will read three words that are alike in some way. They belong to the same group. After you hear the three words, you will look at the pictures and mark an X on the picture that *does not* belong to the group of words that I have read. We'll do the first one together. The three words are *carrot, potato,* and *beet.* Now mark an X on the picture that *does not* belong to the group. Which picture should have an X on it? (Elicit that the picture of the umbrella should have an X on it because an umbrella is not a vegetable; *celery, lettuce,* and *corn* belong to the same group as *carrot, potato,* and *beet* because all six are vegetables.)

Now we will move to number 2. Again, I will read three words that are alike in some way. You will listen carefully to the three words and then you will mark an X on the picture that does **not** belong to the group of words that I read.

1.  carrot, potato, beet
2.  piano, guitar, violin
3.  robin, sparrow, crow
4.  cab, van, car
5.  bowl, cup, fork
6.  pajamas, suit, sweater
7.  desk, chair, table

---

## Classification

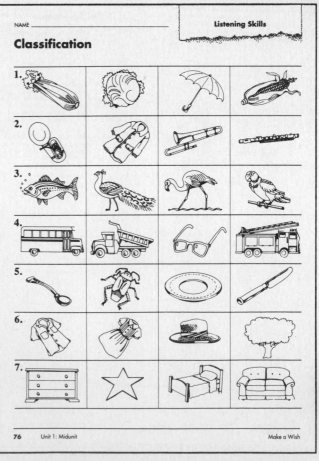

216

© Silver Burdett Ginn Inc.

## Comprehension: Classification

**Focus:** It is important to figure out how things are alike in order to put things in the right groups.

**Model:** This activity shows you figures that are different in some ways but that are all alike in one way. You must find another figure that belongs with them.

**Practice:** Suppose you were shown these two faces:

You can see that they have different noses and different mouths. They are the same in these ways: both are round and both have round eyes.

Now suppose you were shown these two faces:

You want to figure out which one of these faces goes with the other two. Remember how the other faces are alike—they are round and they have round eyes. Both of these faces are round, so either one could go with the others. But look at the eyes. Only one of these faces has round eyes. That is the one that goes with the others.

**Apply:** Now work on page 78.

1. Look at the first three figures in the row.
2. Decide how the three are alike.
3. Look at the other two figures. Figure out which one is like the first three.
4. Write on the line the name of the one that is like the others.

**Monitor:** When students have finished, discuss their choices.

1. The first three figures have hair. Tim has hair, so Tim is like them.

2. The first three have shoes. Mike has shoes, so Mike is like the others.

3. The first three have their left arms (the arms on your right) raised. Jane has her left arm raised, so Jane is like them.

4. The first three are leaning to their left (your right) Nat is leaning the same way, so Nat is like them.

5. The first three have their right legs up. Bitsy has her right leg up, so Bitsy is like them.

**Summary:**

1. Tim
2. Mike
3. Jane
4. Nat
5. Bitsy

---

## Comprehension: Classification

It is important to know how things are alike.

Then you can put the things that are alike together.

### Do The Hokeypokey

**A.** Find the one that goes with the others.

**B.** Write the name.

1. Tim    Tom _____

2. May    Mike _____

3. Jane    Fran _____

4. Nat    Pat _____

5. Becky    Bitsy _____

---

## Problem-Solving:
### Reasoning from Clues

**Focus:** Knowing how to combine information from several different clues to reach a solution is an important reasoning skill.

**Model:** This activity gives you a problem and some clues. You can solve the problem by putting the clues together.

**Practice:** Suppose you are trying to answer the question "Where is Jerry?" Jane and Joe are standing near a cave. Jane gives you this clue: I saw Jerry go into the cave. Joe gives you this clue: I did not see Jerry come out of the cave. You can put the two clues together to figure out where Jerry is—Jerry is in the cave.

**Apply:** Now work on page 80.

1. Read the problem on the sign.
2. Then read all the clues and look carefully at the picture. Look at where each bear is standing and what each bear said.
3. Draw a line to show where B.B. went. The clues will help you figure it out.
4. Make an X on the place where you think B.B. is.

**Monitor:** When students have finished, discuss their answers.

1. Betty saw B.B. go up the mountain, so he must have started at the bottom of the mountain.
2. Ben saw B.B. play in the water, so B.B. must have been near the stream.
3. Bitsy saw B.B. at the top of the mountain, near the fir trees.
4. Bob did not see B.B. come down the mountain, so B.B. must still be on the mountain.
5. Draw a line from Betty to Ben (across the bridge) to Bitsy, and into the fir trees where Bitsy is pointing. B.B. did not pass Bob, and we can't see B.B. coming down the mountain, so he must still be in the fir trees. The X should be on the fir trees.

**Summary:**

---

## Problem-Solving:
### Reasoning from Clues

It is important to think about how clues fit together.

That will help you figure out things for yourself.

> B.B. Bear is lost! Help us find him.

**A.** Read the clues and look at the picture.

**B.** Draw a line to show where B.B. went.

**C.** Make an **X** where you think B.B. is.

**Clues:** 1. **Betty:** I saw B.B. go up the mountain.

2. **Ben:** I saw B.B. play in the water.

3. **Bitsy:** I saw B.B. over there.

4. **Bob:** I did not see B.B. at all.

**217**

## Words with -er, -est

The ending **-er** can compare two things.
The ending **-est** can compare three things.

long
longer
longest

Look at the pictures.
Add **-er** or **-est** to each to compare all three things.

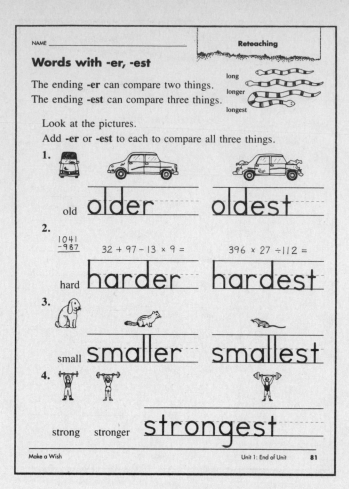

1. old **older**  **oldest**

2. $$\begin{array}{r} 1041 \\ -987 \end{array}$$   $32 + 97 - 13 \times 9 =$   $396 \times 27 \div 112 =$

   hard **harder**  **hardest**

3. small **smaller**  **smallest**

4. strong  stronger  **strongest**

---

## Contractions

A **contraction** is two words made into one.

we + would = we'd
they + will = they'll

Write the contraction for each set of words.

| he'd | I'd | she'd | they'd | you'd |
| he'll | I'll | she'll | we'll | you'll |

1. she + would

   she'd

2. you + will

   you'll

3. I + would

   I'd

4. we + will

   we'll

5. I + will

   I'll

6. they + would

   they'd

7. he + will

   he'll

8. you + would

   you'd

---

## Main Idea/Details

A main idea tells about the whole story. All the sentences tell about the main idea. These sentences are details.

Round things are all around you. → Main Idea
The sun is round. → Detail
Wheels are round. → Detail

Read each main idea. Color the circle before each detail that tells about the main idea.

1. Balloons are nice.
   - ● Balloons are pretty colors.
   - ● Balloons are fun to blow up.
   - ○ Balloons are stretchy.
2. Maud is a good dog.
   - ● Maud can do tricks.
   - ○ Maud digs holes.
   - ● Maud carries the paper.
   - ○ Maud eats a lot.
3. The park is fun.
   - ○ The park is far away.
   - ● The park has swings.
   - ● The park has a little pool.

---

## Classification

Some words belong in the same group.

These words belong together.

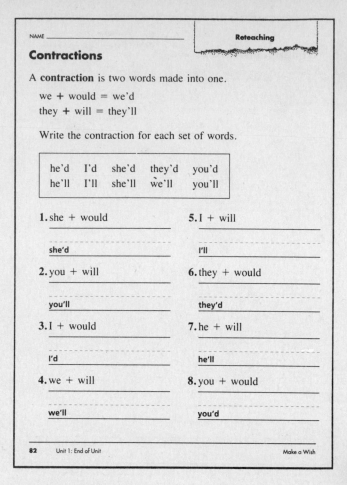

Things to Ride
bicycle   truck   bus

Circle the word in each row that does not belong with the others. Then write it.

1. red        green      six      yellow      six

2. elephant   kitchen    giraffe  monkey      kitchen

3. feet       arms       nose     snow        snow

4. bell       den        nest     house       bell

5. game       puppet     orange   kite        orange

6. five       warm       three    one         warm

© Silver Burdett Ginn Inc.

218

## Alphabetical Order

The letters of the alphabet come in a certain order. This is called **ABC order.**

ABC

A B C D E F G H I J K L M N O P Q R S T U V W X Y Z
a b c d e f g h i j k l m n o p q r s t u v w x y z

Draw a line from one letter to another. Follow ABC order.

bear   dog   pig

What picture did you make?   bear

---

## Action Words with -ing

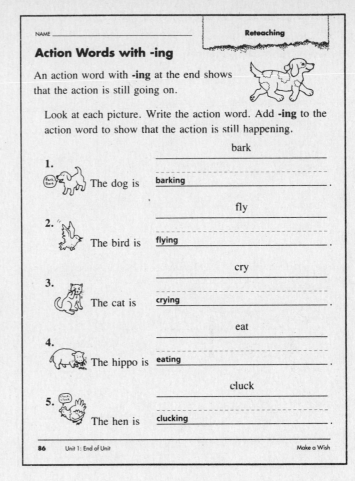

An action word with **-ing** at the end shows that the action is still going on.

Look at each picture. Write the action word. Add **-ing** to the action word to show that the action is still happening.

1.                                          bark
   The dog is    barking                        .

2.                                          fly
   The bird is   flying                         .

3.                                          cry
   The cat is    crying                         .

4.                                          eat
   The hippo is  eating                         .

5.                                          cluck
   The hen is    clucking                       .

---

## Comprehending Fiction

**Procedure:**

*Say to the children:*  I am going to read the story ''Willy the Walrus'' to you. After I have read the story, I will ask you some questions about it.

### Willy the Walrus

Willy the Walrus was good at swimming, but he was not very good at telling what time it was. Each day, his mom told him not to stay out too long. Each day, Willy came home late. After a while, Willy's mom was upset.

"If you do not start coming home on time," said his mom, "I will not let you go out at all. I worry when you are late."

"I do not want to stay out late," said Willy. "It's just that I do not have a way of telling time."

Mom said, "If you want to go out, you are just going to have to find a way of telling time."

That afternoon, Willy turned on the TV set. When the TV came on, he saw a man holding up a watch.

"Good afternoon, friends," said the man. "Today I am selling a wonderful watch. It's made just for creatures of the sea. This watch works under water. You can wear it when you swim! Hurry and get one today!"

"I'll send away for that watch," said Willy. "A watch that works under water is really good. I can tell time when I'm swimming."

The very next day, Willy's watch came. He took it out of the box and put it on. It was a beautiful watch. There was

just one thing wrong with it. It was very loud. It went TICK-TICK, TICK-TICK, TICK-TICK.

"If you want to wear that watch, you must go outside," said Willy's mom. "It's much too loud to wear inside."

"I was just on my way out," said Willy. "I'm going to swim in the sea with my friends, the seals. Now I have a wonderful watch. I'll know when it's time to come home."

When Willy reached the sea, his friends, the seals, were not in the water. The seals were sitting on some rocks.

"Look at my new watch," said Willy. "It's loud, but it works under water. I can wear it when I swim."

"We do not care if you can wear it when you swim," said one seal. "All we care about is that you do not wear it around us. We have a lot of thinking to do. We can't think if you are wearing that loud watch!"

"What is it you have to think about?" asked Willy. "Maybe I can help you."

"There is a big fish out in the water," said one of the seals. "He hides behind rocks. Then when we are not looking, he swims out to chase us. He makes us worry so much, we can't have any fun. We have to find a way to tell when he is around."

Willy sat down to think. All the while, his watch was going TICK-TICK, TICK-TICK, TICK-TICK. "I have it!" said Willy. "I'll give this watch to the big fish and get a quiet underwater watch for myself."

The next day, Willy got his quiet watch. He took the loud watch to the sea and gave it to the big fish. The big fish was very happy; he put the watch on his tail. Now when Willy and his friends hear the loud TICK-TICK, TICK-TICK, TICK-TICK, they jump out of the water because they know that the big fish is nearby.

---

**Comprehending Fiction**

1. a walrus     a duck        a cow
2. sing         swim          run
3. make friends think         get home on time
4. happy        upset         sleepy
5. in a book    from his mom  from TV
6. quiet        funny         loud
7. inside       outside       in school
8. dogs         fish          seals
9. on some rocks on chairs    on the grass
10. talked to them chased them gave them fish
11. behind rocks behind trees behind snails
12. loud        pretty        quiet
13. the seals   Willy's mom   Willy

**Comprehending Fiction**

The children should draw a picture of Willy giving the big fish his watch or the big fish with a watch on his tail.

The children should draw the seals jumping out of the water.

Now I will ask some questions about the story ''Willy the Walrus.'' Underline the correct answer on your paper.

1. What kind of animal is Willy?
2. What did Willy do well?
3. What didn't Willy do well?
4. How did Willy's mother feel about Willy's problem?
5. Where did Willy hear about the first watch?
6. How did Willy's first watch sound?
7. Where did Willy's mother tell him to wear his watch?
8. Who are Willy's friends?
9. When Willy reached the sea, where were his friends sitting?
10. What did the big fish do to the seals?
11. Where did the big fish hide?
12. How did Willy's second watch sound?
13. Who solved the seals' problem with the big fish?

(Reread the story ''Willy the Walrus.'') *Say to the children:* There are two boxes on your paper. In the first box, draw a picture of what happened to the loud watch. In the second box, draw a picture of what the seals do now when the big fish is nearby.

## Comprehending Fiction

1. a walrus      a duck      a cow

2. sing      swim      run

3. make friends      think      get home on time

4. happy      upset      sleepy

5. in a book      from his mom      from TV

6. quiet      funny      loud

7. inside      outside      in school

8. dogs      fish      seals

9. on some rocks      on chairs      on the grass

10. talked to them      chased them      gave them fish

11. behind rocks      behind trees      behind snails

12. loud      pretty      quiet

13. the seals      Willy's mom      Willy

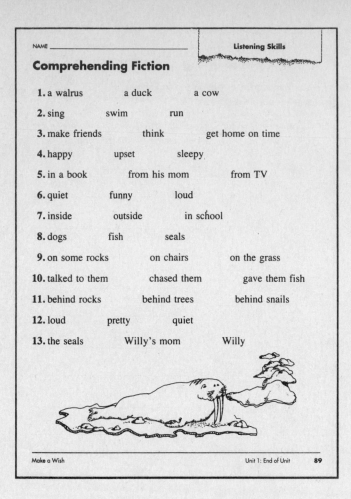

---

## Comprehending Fiction

---

## Elaboration: Imagining

**Focus:** Imagining is an important kind of thinking.

**Model:** This activity asks you to imagine what some different animals might do.

**Practice:** Suppose you read this question: What pet would an alligator have? You know that alligators do not have pets, so you must use your imagination to think of what kind of pet an alligator would have if alligators did have pets.

Since alligators like to be in water, you might think that an alligator would like a pet elephant. The alligator could train the elephant to squirt water with its trunk so the alligator could stay wet when it is on dry land.

You could write your answer: elephant, or you could draw a picture of an elephant.

**Apply:** Now work on page 92.

1. Read the question.

2. Imagine the best answer you can. Think of reasons why your answer is good.

3. You can write your answer, or draw your answer, or do both.

**Monitor:** When students have finished, discuss their ideas.

Ask children to share what they wrote or drew. In discussing their work, focus on the reasons they had for their answers, and the process of imagining.

---

## Elaboration: Imagining

Using your imagination is an important way of thinking.

**A.** Think of the best answer you can.

**B.** Write or draw your answer.

1. What gift will a 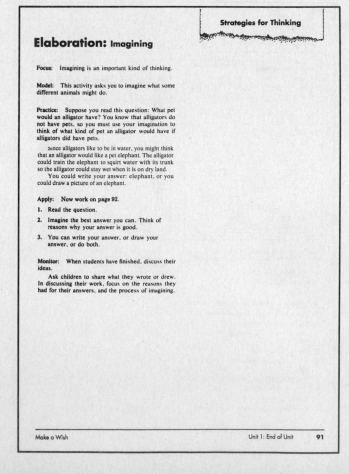 give his brother?

   _____
   - - - - - - - - - - - - - - - - - - -

2. What game does a 🦘 play with her sister?

   _____
   - - - - - - - - - - - - - - - - - - -

3. What toy will Mother give 🐻 ?

   _____
   - - - - - - - - - - - - - - - - - - -

4. What surprise will Father give 🐤🐤 ?

   _____
   - - - - - - - - - - - - - - - - - - -

**220**

## Problem-Solving:
### Logical Thinking

**Focus:** It is important to think about facts you know in order to figure out other facts.

**Summary:**
1. Bob    2. blue    3. Jane

**Model:** This activity gives you a set of facts and then asks a question. You can answer the question by using the facts.

**Practice:** Suppose you read these facts:

Max has only one brother.
Nat is Max's brother.

Now you have to answer this question:

Who is Nat's brother?

To answer the question, think about the facts. You know from the first fact that Max has one brother. You know from the second fact that Max's brother is named Nat. Now you know that Max and Nat are brothers, so you know the answer to the question Who is Nat's brother? The answer is Max.

**Apply:** Now work on page 94.

1. Read the facts and the question.

2. Think about each fact and the information it gives you.

3. When you have figured out the answer, write it in the space.

**Monitor:** When students have finished, discuss their answers.

1. The first fact tells you that Bob has a sister. The next fact tells you that his sister's name is Ann. Now you know that Bob and Ann are brother and sister. The question asks what Ann's brother is named. You know that Bob and Ann are brother and sister, so you know that Ann's brother is named Bob.

2. The first fact tells you that Becky's mother has a red car. The next fact says that Becky's father has a blue car. The next fact says that Fran is Becky's sister. If Fran and Becky are sisters, they have the same father. Fran's father is the same person as Becky's father, so his car is blue.

3. The first fact tells you that Jane has a brother. Her brother is either John or Tim. The next fact tells you that John's sister is not Jane. If John's sister is not Jane, then John is not Jane's brother. That means that Tim must be Jane's brother and Jane is Tim's sister. The answer to the question Who is Tim's sister? is Jane.

---

## Problem-Solving:
### Logical Thinking

It is helpful to think about facts and how they fit together.

**A.** Read the facts.

**B.** Read each question.

**C.** Write your answer to the question.

1. Bob has a sister.

   Her name is Ann.

   What is Ann's brother named? _____

   _____

2. Becky's mother has a red car.

   Becky's father has a blue car.

   Fran is Becky's sister.

   What color is Fran's father's car?

   _____

3. Jane's brother is John or Tim.

   John's sister is not Jane.

   Who is Tim's sister? _____

   John   Jane   Tim   Pat

   _____

---

## Cause/Effect

One thing can make another thing happen. An **effect** is what happens. A **cause** is what makes it happen.

cause   effect

**A.** Read the sentences. Underline the sentence that tells what made something happen.

1. Pat slipped on the ice. She fell down.

2. Billy left the door open. The cat ran away.

**B.** Read the sentences. Circle the part that tells what happened because of something else.

3. The dog played in the mud. Max gave it a bath.

4. It was Peter's birthday. He got a nice surprise.

---

## Words with -es

When **-es** is added to a naming word, it means **more than one thing**. Add **-es** to words that end in **s, ch, tch, sh, x,** or **z.**

45¢ each

peach + es    peaches

**A.** Write four words from the box that mean **more than one thing.**

| benches | boxes | bus | grass | lunches | watches |
|---|---|---|---|---|---|

1. benches _____     3. lunches _____

2. boxes _____     4. watches _____

**B.** Write a word you wrote in one of the sentences.

5. We ate our lunches _____ in the yard.

6. Joe used two watches _____ to time the race.

7. I keep my shoes in boxes _____

## Action Words with -ing

An action word with **-ing** at the end shows that the action is still going on.

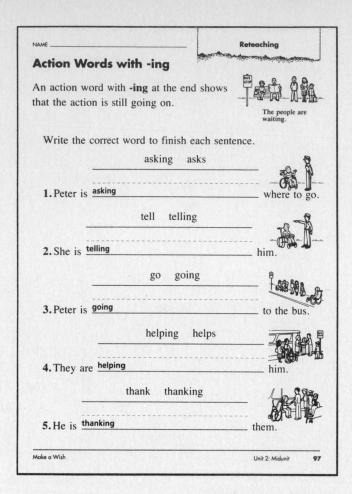

The people are waiting.

Write the correct word to finish each sentence.

asking   asks

1. Peter is _asking_ where to go.

tell   telling

2. She is _telling_ him.

go   going

3. Peter is _going_ to the bus.

helping   helps

4. They are _helping_ him.

thank   thanking

5. He is _thanking_ them.

---

## Sequence

Things in a story happen in a certain order.   1 → 2 → 3

These sentences are in order.

It was raining.
The sun came out.
We saw a rainbow!

Number the sentences in order. Write **1, 2, 3**.

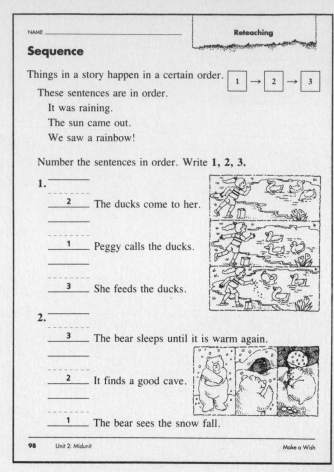

1.
_2_ The ducks come to her.

_1_ Peggy calls the ducks.

_3_ She feeds the ducks.

2.
_3_ The bear sleeps until it is warm again.

_2_ It finds a good cave.

_1_ The bear sees the snow fall.

---

## Words with ey, y

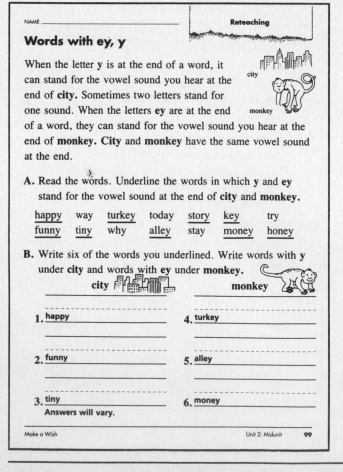

city

monkey

When the letter **y** is at the end of a word, it can stand for the vowel sound you hear at the end of **city**. Sometimes two letters stand for one sound. When the letters **ey** are at the end of a word, they can stand for the vowel sound you hear at the end of **monkey**. City and monkey have the same vowel sound at the end.

A. Read the words. Underline the words in which **y** and **ey** stand for the vowel sound at the end of **city** and **monkey**.

<u>happy</u>  way  <u>turkey</u>  today  <u>story</u>  <u>key</u>  try
<u>funny</u>  <u>tiny</u>  why  <u>alley</u>  stay  <u>money</u>  <u>honey</u>

B. Write six of the words you underlined. Write words with **y** under **city** and words with **ey** under **monkey**.

city                    monkey

1. happy          4. turkey

2. funny          5. alley

3. tiny           6. money
Answers will vary.

---

## Predicting Outcomes

When you read a story, think ahead and try to tell what will happen next.

clue   clue
What will happen next

Example:
**Clue 1:** Terry looked down at the water.
**Clue 2:** She closed her eyes.
What will happen next? She will jump into the water.

Read each story. Write the word that tells what will happen next.

1. I like to feed the ducks.
   I give them bits of sandwich.
   My sandwiches are all gone.

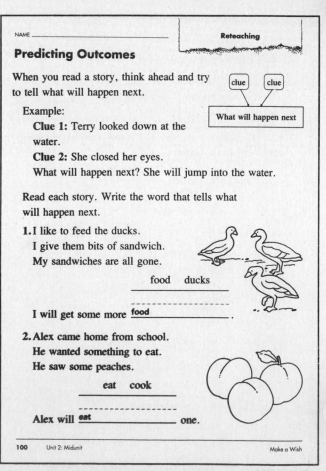

food   ducks

I will get some more _food_

2. Alex came home from school.
   He wanted something to eat.
   He saw some peaches.

eat   cook

Alex will _eat_ one.

© Silver Burdett Ginn Inc.

## Words with ai, ay

Sometimes two letters stand for one sound. The letters **ai** and **ay** can stand for the vowel sound you hear in **rain** and **ray**. The words **rain** and **ray** have the same vowel sound.

rain

ray

Circle the word that names each picture. Then write it.

1. hail (hay)

___hay___

6. claim (clay)

___clay___

2. trait (tray)

___tray___

7. (pail) pay

___pail___

3. (sail) say

___sail___

8. sprain (spray)

___spray___

4. plain (play)

___play___

9. (braid) bray

___braid___

5. (mail) may

___mail___

10. (train) tray

___train___

---

## Alphabetical Order

The letters of the alphabet come in a certain order. This is called **ABC order**.

ABC

A B C D E F G H I J K L M N O P Q R S T U V W X Y Z
a b c d e f g h i j k l m n o p q r s t u v w x y z

Write the letters in ABC order.

1. q   r   p   o   t   s

___o___  ___p___  ___q___  ___r___  ___s___  ___t___

2. b   e   d   c   g   f

___b___  ___c___  ___d___  ___e___  ___f___  ___g___

3. y   u   z   v   x   w

___u___  ___v___  ___w___  ___x___  ___y___  ___z___

4. k   m   h   j   i   l

___h___  ___i___  ___j___  ___k___  ___l___  ___m___

5. i   f   j   g   e   h

___e___  ___f___  ___g___  ___h___  ___i___  ___j___

---

## Problem-Solving: Logic Matrix

**Focus:** Examining clues in an orderly way is an important method of solving problems.

**Model:** This activity gives you a problem and some clues. It also gives you a special kind of chart, or matrix. You can solve the problem by writing information from the clues in the boxes on the chart.

**Practice:** Suppose you want to solve this problem: Hi and Ho are a dog and a cat. Which animal has which name?

Here is the chart, or matrix, that you would use to solve this problem:

|    | dog | cat |
|----|-----|-----|
| Hi |     |     |
| Ho |     |     |

The top row across is Hi's row. If Hi is the dog, it will say Yes in the first box in Hi's row, under the word dog. If Hi is not the dog, it will say No in that box. If Hi is the cat, it will say Yes in the other box in Hi's row, the one under the word cat. If Hi is not the cat, it will say No in that box.

Now suppose you have this clue: Hi can bark. You can tell from that clue that Hi is the dog. You would write Yes in the box under the word dog in Hi's row.

Then you can write No in the next box because Hi is the name of only one of the animals. If you know that one animal is named Hi, you know that the other animal or animals in that row cannot be named Hi.

You can also write No in the box under the word dog in Ho's row. If Hi is the dog, then Ho cannot be a dog. That leaves just one empty box in Ho's row. The other box says No, so this box must say Yes.

Here is how the chart will look when you are finished writing the information from the clues:

|    | dog | cat |
|----|-----|-----|
| Hi | Yes | No  |
| Ho | No  | Yes |

The chart tells you that Hi is the dog and Ho is the cat.

**Apply:** Now work on page 104.

1. Read the problem and the clues.

2. Read the first clue again. Write Yes or No in every box you can.

3. Read the second clue again and write Yes or No in every box you can.

4. Remember that each name belongs to one of the animals. If two boxes in a row say No, the other box must say Yes.

**Monitor:** When students have finished, discuss the solution.

1. The first clue tells you that Happy can fly. Rabbits and turtles cannot fly, so you know that Happy is the bird. The word Yes goes in the box in Happy's row under the word bird.

2. Since Happy is the bird, Huffy and Hokey are not birds. You can write No in the boxes for Huffy and Hokey under the word bird.

3. You also know that Happy is not a rabbit or a turtle; write No in those boxes in Happy's row.

4. The next clue tells you that Huffy is not a rabbit; write No in the box under rabbit in Huffy's row.

5. Now you know that Huffy is not a bird or a rabbit, so Huffy must be the turtle. Write Yes in the box under turtle in Huffy's row.

6. Since Huffy is the turtle, Hokey cannot be the turtle. Write No under turtle in Hokey's row.

7. Since Hokey is not a bird or a turtle, Hokey must be the rabbit. Write Yes under rabbit in Hokey's row.

**Summary:**

|       | bird | rabbit | turtle |
|-------|------|--------|--------|
| Happy | Yes  | No     | No     |
| Huffy | No   | No     | Yes    |
| Hokey | No   | Yes    | No     |

Happy is the bird; Huffy is the turtle; Hokey is the rabbit.

---

## Problem-Solving: Logic Matrix

Writing clues on a chart can help you solve a problem.

**A.** Read the problem and the clues.
**B.** Write **Yes** or **No** in each box.

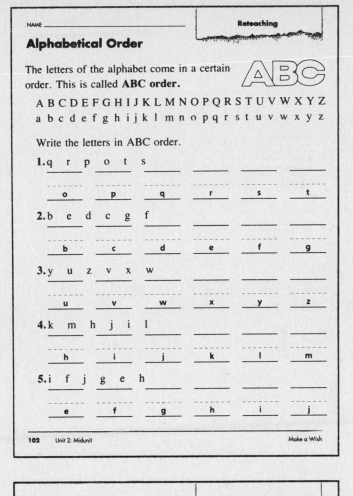

**Problem:** Happy, Huffy, and Hokey are animals. One is a bird. One is a rabbit. One is a turtle. Find out which animal has which name.

**Clues:** 1. Happy can fly.
2. Huffy is not a rabbit.

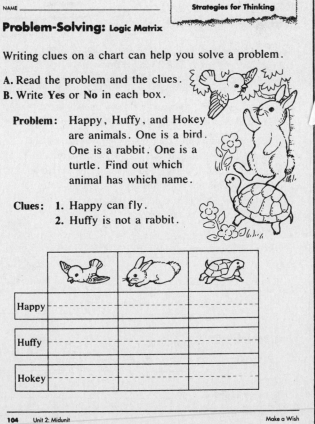

|       |     |     |     |
|-------|-----|-----|-----|
| Happy |     |     |     |
| Huffy |     |     |     |
| Hokey |     |     |     |

## Elaboration: Imagining

**Focus:** Imagining is an important way to think of new ideas.

**Model:** This activity asks you to imagine different ideas and draw pictures to show what you imagine.

**Practice:** Suppose you read this: Pretend you are a mouse. Draw a picture of your house. You would have to imagine what it would be like to be a mouse. You would imagine where you would live. Maybe you would imagine that you live in a little hole in the wall of a house. You might have a nest made from something you found in the house.

Maybe you would imagine that you are a field mouse. You might imagine your home in a hole under the ground with a nest of grass and weeds.

Then you would draw a picture of what you imagined.

**Apply:** Now work on page 106.

**1.** Read the sentences for number 1. Take some time to imagine. Swim around for a while. Find your favorite place. Take time to imagine it. Try to see it clearly in your mind.

**2.** Then draw your picture.

**3.** Do the numbers 2 and 3 the same way.

**Monitor:** When students have finished, discuss their ideas. Have them show and explain their pictures. Focus on the imagining process that helped them get a picture in their minds before they drew on their papers.

---

## Elaboration: Imagining

One important way to think is to use your imagination.

Draw a picture in each space.

**1.** Pretend you are a fish.
Draw a picture of your favorite place to hide.

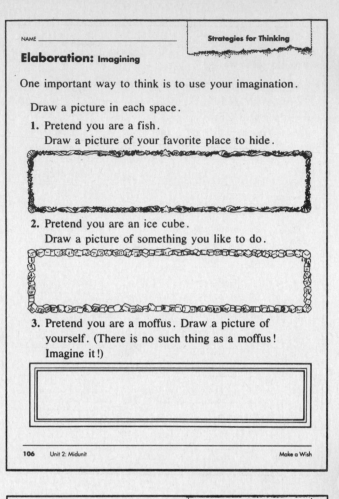

**2.** Pretend you are an ice cube.
Draw a picture of something you like to do.

**3.** Pretend you are a moffus. Draw a picture of yourself. (There is no such thing as a moffus! Imagine it!)

---

## Drawing Conclusions

Sometimes you need to figure out things that are not told in a story. This is called drawing a **conclusion**.

Clue    Clue

Conclusion

Read the story. Use clues and what you already know. Circle the best answer to complete each sentence. Then write it.

Betsy sat under a tree. She put on her new skates. She stood up and walked onto the ice. She began to move her feet. She fell down! Betsy stood up again. She moved one foot. She put out her arms. She fell down again! Betsy got right back up. She tried to skate again.

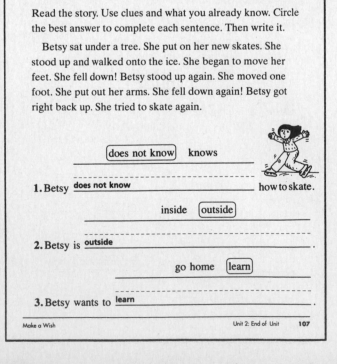

does not know    knows

**1.** Betsy does not know how to skate.

inside    outside

**2.** Betsy is outside .

go home    learn

**3.** Betsy wants to learn

---

## Words with ai, ay

Sometimes two letters stand for one sound. The letters **ai** and **ay** can stand for the vowel sound you hear in **jail** and **jay**. The words **jail** and **jay** have the same vowel sound.

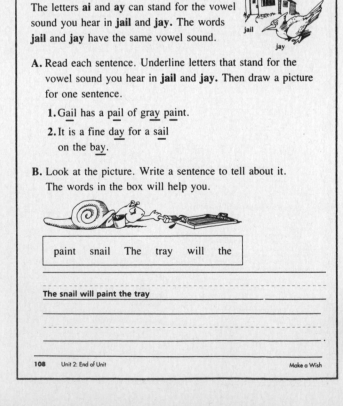

jail

jay

**A.** Read each sentence. Underline letters that stand for the vowel sound you hear in **jail** and **jay**. Then draw a picture for one sentence.

1. Gail has a pail of gray paint.

2. It is a fine day for a sail on the bay.

**B.** Look at the picture. Write a sentence to tell about it. The words in the box will help you.

| paint | snail | The | tray | will | the |

The snail will paint the tray

**224**

## Words with ey, y

The letters **y** and **ey** as in **puppy** and **donkey** have the same sound.

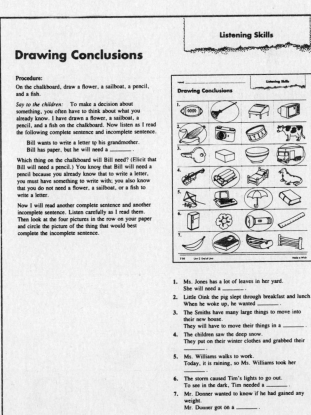

puppy    donkey

Read each clue. Write the word that fits it.

1. a space between buildings

   alley    every    only    **alley**

2. make something exactly alike

   chimney    country    copy    **copy**

3. the place between two hills

   very    valley    volley    **valley**

4. why you laugh at something

   family    funny    furry    **funny**

5. your mother, father, and you

   family    many    happy    **family**

6. something to read or tell

   sorry    story    sunny    **story**

7. how a rabbit feels

   silly    furry    turkey    **furry**

---

## Comprehending Nonfiction

**Procedure:**

*Say to the children:* I am going to read the article "Four Kinds of Wild Animals" to you. After I have read the article, I will ask you some questions about it.

### Four Kinds of Wild Animals

Wild rabbits live all over the world. They usually are gray or brown. Some rabbits that live where it snows in the winter have fur that changes from brown to white. The white fur helps this kind of rabbit hide from its enemies. Wild rabbits live in the ground. They dig holes for their homes. Often, many rabbits will dig their homes next to one another. Rabbits like to eat plants.

A raccoon looks as if it is wearing a mask. It is about the size of a cat and has a long, bushy tail. Most raccoons sleep during the day and look for food at night. Some people think raccoons are pests because the animals get into people's garbage or eat corn from their fields.

Did you know that there are wild pigs? Most wild pigs live in wooded areas. They have short tusks that they use for digging up roots. Besides eating roots, wild pigs eat small animals, grasses, and leaves. Wild pigs can be very dangerous. Their tusks not only are used for digging but also for defending themselves. If a wild pig is disturbed, the animal's tusks become dangerous weapons.

Forests are homes for many deer. These wild animals eat leaves or grass. One kind of deer eats fruit that falls from trees in the forest. The deer has two relatives that you might have seen on a farm and a zoo. The relatives are the goat and the giraffe.

Now I will ask you some questions about the article "Four Kinds of Wild Animals." Underline the correct answer on your paper.

1. Where do wild rabbits make their homes?
2. When do raccoons look for food?
3. What do some people think about raccoons?
4. What do wild pigs use for digging up roots?
5. What does one kind of deer eat?
6. What are two relatives of the deer?

Listen to the part that tells what the raccoon looks like. (Reread paragraph 2.)

Now draw the raccoon and what it eats in box 1.

Listen to the part that tells about wild rabbits. (Reread paragraph 1.)

Now draw wild rabbits and where they live in box 2.

---

## Comprehending Nonfiction

1. in the ground    in trees    in rock piles
2. in the morning    at noon    at night
3. They are big.    They are pests.    They are tired.
4. their noses    their feet    their tusks
5. fruit    meat    peanut butter
6. goats and giraffes    fish and frogs    dogs and cats

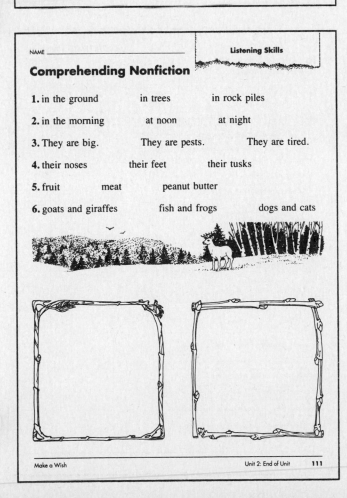

---

## Drawing Conclusions

**Procedure:**

On the chalkboard, draw a flower, a sailboat, a pencil, and a fish.

*Say to the children:* To make a decision about something, you often have to think about what you already know. I have drawn a flower, a sailboat, a pencil, and a fish on the chalkboard. Now listen as I read the following complete sentence and incomplete sentence.

Bill wants to write a letter to his grandmother. Bill has paper, but he will need a _____.

Which thing on the chalkboard will Bill need? (Elicit that Bill will need a pencil.) You know that Bill will need a pencil because you already know that to write a letter, you must have something to write with; you also know that you do not need a flower, a sailboat, or a fish to write a letter.

Now I will read another complete sentence and another incomplete sentence. Listen carefully as I read them. Then look at the four pictures in the row on your paper and circle the picture of the thing that would best complete the incomplete sentence.

1. Ms. Jones has a lot of leaves in her yard.
   She will need a _____.
2. Little Oink the pig slept through breakfast and lunch.
   When he woke up, he wanted _____.
3. The Smiths have many large things to move into their new house.
   They will have to move their things in a _____.
4. The children saw the deep snow.
   They put on their winter clothes and grabbed their _____.
5. Ms. Williams walks to work.
   Today, it is raining, so Ms. Williams took her _____.
6. The storm caused Tim's lights to go out.
   To see in the dark, Tim needed a _____.
7. Mr. Donner wanted to know if he had gained any weight.
   Mr. Donner got on a _____.

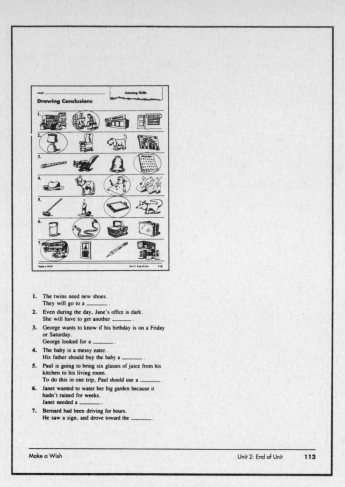

**Drawing Conclusions**

1. The twins need new shoes.
   They will go to a _____.
2. Even during the day, Jane's office is dark.
   She will have to get another _____.
3. George wants to know if his birthday is on a Friday or Saturday.
   George looked for a _____.
4. The baby is a messy eater.
   His father should buy the baby a _____.
5. Paul is going to bring six glasses of juice from his kitchen to his living room.
   To do this in one trip, Paul should use a _____.
6. Janet wanted to water her big garden because it hadn't rained for weeks.
   Janet needed a _____.
7. Bernard had been driving for hours.
   He saw a sign, and drove toward the _____.

---

**Drawing Conclusions**

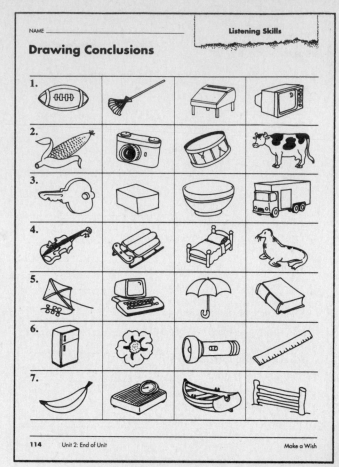

---

**Drawing Conclusions**

---

**Problem-Solving:**
**Figural Sequences**

**Focus:** By thinking about the order in which things are shown, you can often figure out what will come next.

**Model:** This activity gives you a set of pictures and asks you to draw the picture that comes next in each set.

**Practice:** Suppose you saw this set of pictures:

You have to draw the picture that comes next.

Look at the pictures in the set. The first one is a circle, the next is a circle with a line through the middle. The next picture is a plain circle, and the next is another circle with a line through it. The next picture is a plain circle again.

You can see this pattern in the set: circle/ circle with line/circle/circle with line. Since the last picture is a circle, you know that the next one will be a circle with a line. You would draw a circle with a line.

**Apply:** Now work on page 117.

1. Look at the pictures in each row.
2. Try to see how each picture is the same as or different from the others.
3. Figure out the pattern.
4. Draw the next picture in the set.

**Monitor:** When children have finished, discuss their results.

1. The pattern is little circle at the top/two little circles at the bottom/circles at all three points. The next figure in the set has circles at all three points.

2. The pattern is stripe in one corner/two stripes in the same corner. The next picture will have two stripes in the same corner as the last picture in the row.

3. The pattern is no tail/tail/tail. The next cat in the set should have a tail.

4. The pattern is circle in one corner/circles in two corners/circles in three corners. The next picture should have circles in all four corners.

5. The pattern is little shape up high/ little shape in big shape/little shape down low. The next picture should be a little circle on the line.

6. The pattern is big fir tree and little shade tree/little shade tree and big shade tree/little fir tree and big fir tree. The next picture should be a big shade tree and a little shade tree.

**Summary:**

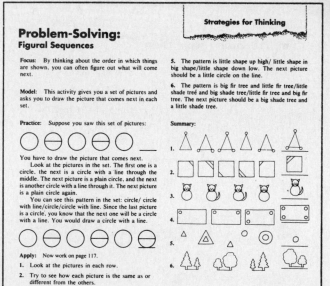

© Silver Burdett Ginn Inc.

**226**

## Problem-Solving:
### Figural Sequences

Looking at the order of things can help you know what comes next.

Pretend you are an artist.
Draw the picture that comes next in each line.

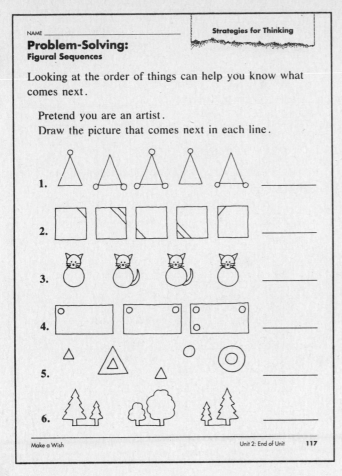

1.
2.
3.
4.
5.
6.

Make a Wish    Unit 2: End of Unit    **117**

---

## Critical Thinking:
### Making Judgments

**Focus:** It is good to be able to judge how important different things are.

**Model:** This activity gives you some choices in a box. You look at a picture and pretend to be the animal or thing in the picture. Then you choose the thing from the box that is most important to you.

**Practice:** Suppose you have these two things in the box:

> fur
> water

You are supposed to pretend you are a fish. Now you have to choose the thing from the box that is most important to you. You know that fur is important to many different kinds of animals, but it is not important to a fish. Water is very important to a fish, so you would write **water** next to the picture of the fish.

**Apply:** Now work on page 119.

1. Look at all the words in the box.

2. Look at each picture and pretend to be the thing that the picture shows.

3. Try to figure out which thing in the box would be most important to you.

4. When you have picked the thing from the box, cross off that word in the box.

5. Write the word next to the picture.

6. If you cannot decide what is most important, skip that picture and go on to the next one. You can come back to the one you skipped later. You may be able to figure it out when more of the words in the box have been crossed out.

**Monitor:** When students have finished, discuss their answers. The answers that follow are reasonable; accept other answers as well if students can justify them.

1. Horses eat hay, so hay is probably most important to the horse.

2. Kites need wind in order to fly, so wind is probably most important to the kite.

3. Most books have words in them, so words are probably most important to the book.

4. A bus needs wheels in order to run, so wheels are probably most important to the bus.

5. A bee drinks nectar from flowers, so flowers are probably most important to a bee.

6. A tree needs rain in order to grow, so rain is probably most important to the tree.

Summary:

1. hay        4. wheels
2. wind       5. flowers
3. words      6. rain

118    Unit 2: End of Unit    Make a Wish

---

## Critical Thinking:
### Making Judgments

It is good to know what things are most important and why.

A. Pretend you are the animal or thing in the picture.
B. Pick the most important thing from the box.
C. Write it.

| flowers   hay   rain   wheels   wind   words |

1.
2.
3.
4.
5.
6.

Make a Wish    Unit 2: End of Unit    **119**

---

## Comprehension:
### Story Coherence and Sequence

**Focus:** Understanding how the parts of a story go together and the order they go in is an important skill.

**Model:** This activity gives you six sentences to read. Three of the sentences belong in one story, and the other three sentences belong in another story. The sentences are all mixed up.

**Practice:** Suppose you had to show what stories these sentences belong in:

> Two wings popped out on the horse's back.
> A mouse helped an elephant.
> A horse wished it had wings.
> Then the mouse and the elephant were friends.

First you would read all the sentences. You would find out that two of the sentences tell about a horse and wings. The other two sentences tell about a mouse and an elephant. You would know then that the sentences about the horse and its wings are both part of one of the stories. You would underline the first sentence and the third sentence to show that they are parts of the same story.

You would also know that the second sentence and the fourth sentence are parts of another story, about a mouse and an elephant. You would circle those sentences.

Now you would read the two sentences you underlined and decide what order they should be in. It wouldn't make sense for the wings to pop out and then for the horse to wish that it had wings. It makes sense for the horse first to wish for wings, so you would write 1 by that sentence. You would write 2 by the other sentence. Then you would read the sentences you circled and put them in order.

**Apply:** Now work on page 121.

1. Read all the sentences carefully.

2. Underline the first sentence. Figure out which two other sentences go in the same story as this sentence. Underline them, too.

3. Make sure the other three sentences also go together in a story. Circle those sentences.

4. Read the underlined sentences again. Write 1 by the sentence that tells what happened first. Write 2 by the sentence that tells what happened next. Write 3 by the sentence that tells what happened last.

5. In the same way, read the circled sentences and write 1, 2, and 3 to show the right order.

**Monitor:** Discuss children's answers.

1. The first sentence tells about some rabbits. It is underlined.

2. The next sentence does not tell about rabbits. It tells about a bear and is part of a different story. It is circled.

3. The next sentence also tells about the bear, so it is also circled.

4. The next sentence tells about more than one animal (*they*) hopping home. This might be about the rabbits, but you cannot tell for sure yet.

5. The next sentence is about some rabbits, as the first sentence is. This sentence is underlined.

6. This sentence tells about a ladder. You cannot tell from the sentence who it is about. Looking back at the other sentences, you see one that tells about the bear coming up a ladder. Now you know that this last sentence is about the bear. This sentence is circled.

7. Now three sentences are circled and two are underlined. The other sentence must be part of the underlined story because it tells about hopping.

8. The underlined sentence that tells what happened first in that story is about the three rabbits setting out to see the world. That is Number 1. Number 2 tells that they heard a loud noise. Number 3 tells that they hopped home as fast as they could go.

9. In the circled story, sentence Number 1 tells how the bear fell in the hole. Number 2 tells about his friends making a ladder. Number 3 tells that the bear came up the ladder.

Summary:

2   The rabbits heard a loud noise.
1   (A bear went walking and fell in a hole.)
3   (The bear came up the ladder.)
3   They hopped back home as fast as they could go.
1   Three rabbits set out to see the world.
2   (His friend made a ladder out of branches.)

120    Unit 2: End of Unit    Make a Wish

---

## Comprehension:
### Story Coherence and Sequence

It is important to know how the parts of a
story go together.

Two stories are all mixed up!

**A.** Underline the sentences that go in one story.
**B.** Circle the sentences that go in the other story.
**C.** Put each story in order. Write 1, 2, 3 for each story.

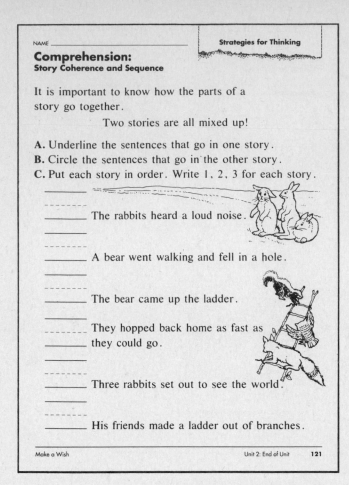

_____ The rabbits heard a loud noise.

_____ A bear went walking and fell in a hole.

_____ The bear came up the ladder.

_____ They hopped back home as fast as
they could go.

_____ Three rabbits set out to see the world.

_____ His friends made a ladder out of branches.

---

## Characterization

A **character** is a person or animal
in a story. You can know what
characters are like by what they
say and do.

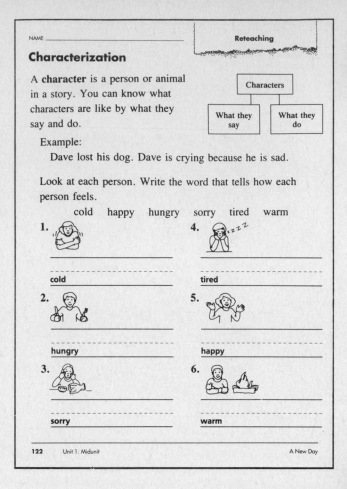

Example:

Dave lost his dog. Dave is crying because he is sad.

Look at each person. Write the word that tells how each
person feels.

    cold   happy   hungry   sorry   tired   warm

**1.**
_____
cold

**4.**
_____
tired

**2.**
_____
hungry

**5.**
_____
happy

**3.**
_____
sorry

**6.**
_____
warm

---

## Compound Words

Two small words can be put together to make
a longer word. The longer word is called a
**compound word.** The new word has some of
the meaning of both small words.

dog + house = doghouse

Put the two small words together. Write the new long word.

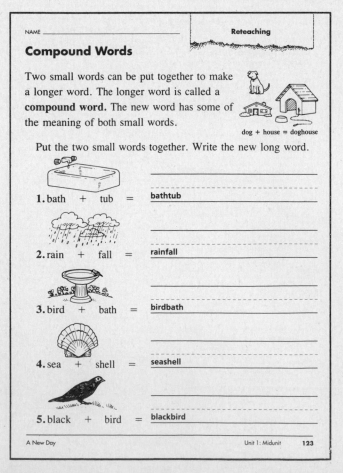

**1.** bath + tub = **bathtub**

**2.** rain + fall = **rainfall**

**3.** bird + bath = **birdbath**

**4.** sea + shell = **seashell**

**5.** black + bird = **blackbird**

---

## Making Inferences

Use story clues and what you already know to figure
out things that the story doesn't tell you.

Story Clues
+ What I Know
Inference

Read each story. Then draw a line
under the best answer to each question.

**1.** The girls climbed higher and higher. There was no more grass under
their feet. Now there was only rock. They looked up. They would have
to climb even higher to get to the top. What were the girls climbing?

a ladder        a mountain        some stairs

**2.** Terry looked out the window at the nice spring day. He wanted to
play baseball after he finished his work. Then his teacher asked him to
write on the board. Where was Terry?

at a game        at school        in his bedroom

**3.** Susan looked at all of the displays. She saw food and animals and
clothes. She heard some loud music. Where was Susan?

at a game        at a fair        on a mountain

**4.** William looked up. The trees were very tall. There were a lot of
them, too. He could hardly see the sky. Where was William?

in a forest        in his school        on a big lake

**5.** The only sound Kit heard was of birds singing. There were no people.
There was only the water and trees and sky. Where was Kit?

in a building        in a city        in the country

## Contractions

A **contraction** is a short way of writing two words.

| I + am = I'm |
|---|
| they + are = they're |
| you + have = you've |

**A.** Look at the two words at the beginning of each row. Circle the word that is the contraction of the two words.

1. I have    I've    we've    they've
2. you are    we're    you've    you're
3. we have    I've    we're    we've
4. they have    they're    they've    you've
5. I am    I've    I'm    we're
6. they are    they've    you're    they're
7. we are    we're    they're    we've
8. you have    you're    we've    you've

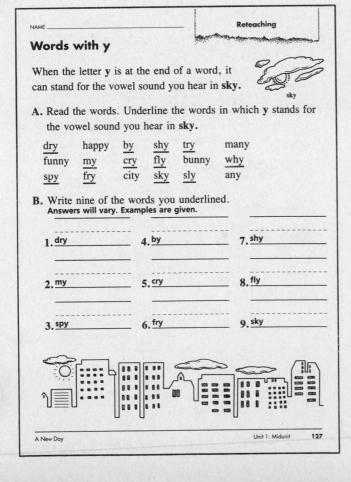

**B.** Write the two words that make the contraction.

9. they've   they have
10. I'm   I am

---

## Words with Long u

The letter **u** can stand for the vowel sound you hear in **tube** and **mule**. Look for the letter **e** at the end of a short word. It often points out that the first vowel in the word stands for a long sound.

tube    mule

**A.** Underline the words that have the same vowel sound as in **tube** and **mule**.

| rule | but | up | dune | cube | use |
|---|---|---|---|---|---|
| prune | June | bus | huge | pull | tune |
| put | run | rude | flute | us | fuse |

**B.** Look at each picture. Circle the picture whose name has the vowel sound you hear in **tube** and **mule**. Then write the word that names the picture.

1.    cub    cube

     cube

2.    tub    tube

     tube

---

## Words with y

When the letter **y** is at the end of a word, it can stand for the vowel sound you hear in **sky**.

sky

**A.** Read the words. Underline the words in which **y** stands for the vowel sound you hear in **sky**.

| dry | happy | by | shy | try | many |
|---|---|---|---|---|---|
| funny | my | cry | fly | bunny | why |
| spy | fry | city | sky | sly | any |

**B.** Write nine of the words you underlined.
**Answers will vary. Examples are given.**

1. dry      4. by      7. shy
2. my      5. cry      8. fly
3. spy      6. fry      9. sky

---

## Words with -igh

Sometimes many letters stand for one sound. The letters *igh* stand for the vowel sound you hear in **night**.

| igh → night |
|---|

Read the story. Draw a line under the words that have the vowel sound you hear in **night**.

Nick saw a strange sight one night. Some very bright lights were high in the sky. "It might be a strange ship," he said. He was frightened and ran home. Soon his dad came home. "Did you see any bright lights tonight?" he asked. "My airplane flight went right over our house." Nick sighed to himself. "Dad was my scary thing tonight."

Read the sentences. Draw a circle around the word with the vowel sound you hear in *night* that finishes each sentence.

1. Nick saw a strange ——— .
    fight   sight   bright

2. There were very ——— lights.
    light   frightened

3. He was ——— .
    lightning   lights

4. His dad asked if Nick had seen ——— .
    might

5. The airplane ——— had gone over the house.
    fight   flight

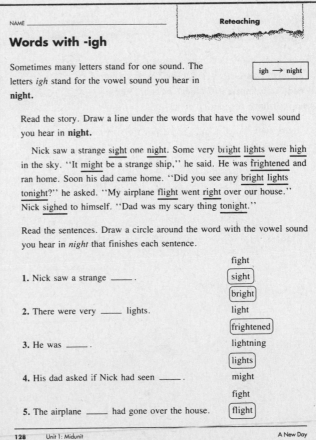

## Synonyms

**Synonyms** are words that mean almost the same thing.

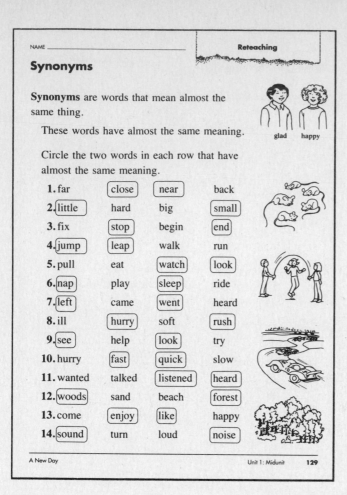
glad    happy

These words have almost the same meaning.

Circle the two words in each row that have almost the same meaning.

1. far (close) (near) back
2. (little) hard big (small)
3. fix (stop) begin (end)
4. (jump) (leap) walk run
5. pull eat (watch) (look)
6. (nap) play (sleep) ride
7. (left) came (went) heard
8. ill (hurry) soft (rush)
9. (see) help (look) try
10. hurry (fast) (quick) slow
11. wanted talked (listened) (heard)
12. (woods) sand beach (forest)
13. come (enjoy) (like) happy
14. (sound) turn loud (noise)

---

## Words with oa

Sometimes two letters stand for one sound. The letters **oa** can stand for the vowel sound in **boat** and **soap.**

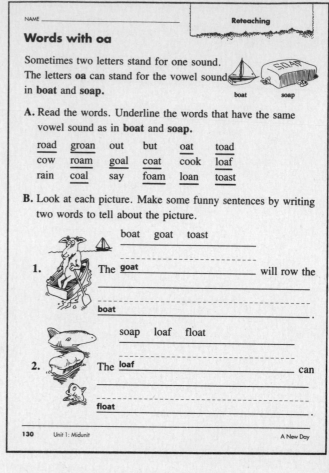
boat    soap

**A.** Read the words. Underline the words that have the same vowel sound as in **boat** and **soap.**

| | | | | | |
|---|---|---|---|---|---|
| road | groan | out | but | oat | toad |
| cow | roam | goal | coat | cook | loaf |
| rain | coal | say | foam | loan | toast |

**B.** Look at each picture. Make some funny sentences by writing two words to tell about the picture.

boat    goat    toast

1. The <u>goat</u> _____ will row the _____ <u>boat</u> .

soap    loaf    float

2. The <u>loaf</u> _____ can _____ <u>float</u> .

---

## Words with oa

Sometimes two letters stand for one sound. The letters **oa** can stand for the vowel sound you hear in **home** and **loaf.** The words **home** and **loaf** have the same vowel sound.

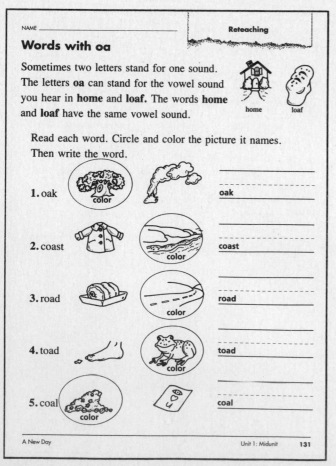
home    loaf

Read each word. Circle and color the picture it names. Then write the word.

1. oak       oak _____
2. coast     coast _____
3. road      road _____
4. toad      toad _____
5. coal      coal _____

---

## Making Inferences

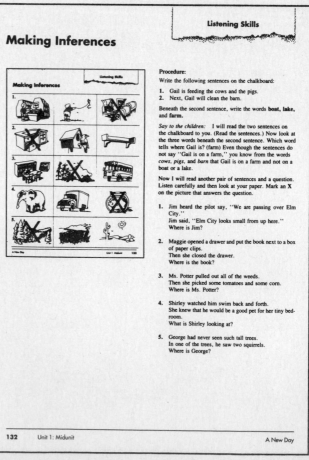

**Procedure:**
Write the following sentences on the chalkboard:

1. Gail is feeding the cows and the pigs.
2. Next, Gail will clean the barn.

Beneath the second sentence, write the words **boat, lake,** and **farm.**

*Say to the children:*   I will read the two sentences on the chalkboard to you. (Read the sentences.) Now look at the three words beneath the second sentence. Which word tells where Gail is? (farm) Even though the sentences do not say "Gail is on a farm," you know from the words *cows, pigs,* and *barn* that Gail is on a farm and not on a boat or a lake.

Now I will read another pair of sentences and a question. Listen carefully and then look at your paper. Mark an X on the picture that answers the question.

1. Jim heard the pilot say, "We are passing over Elm City."
   Jim said, "Elm City looks small from up here."
   Where is Jim?

2. Maggie opened a drawer and put the book next to a box of paper clips.
   Then she closed the drawer.
   Where is the book?

3. Ms. Potter pulled out all of the weeds.
   Then she picked some tomatoes and some corn.
   Where is Ms. Potter?

4. Shirley watched him swim back and forth.
   She knew that he would be a good pet for her tiny bedroom.
   What is Shirley looking at?

5. George had never seen such tall trees.
   In one of the trees, he saw two squirrels.
   Where is George?

**230**

## Making Inferences

## Making Inferences

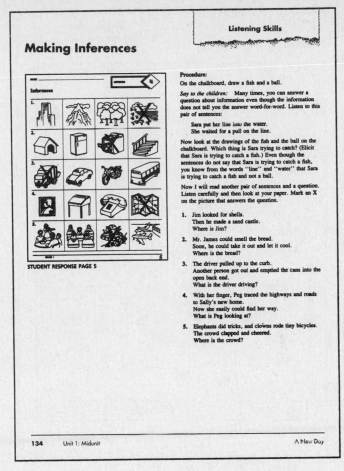

STUDENT RESPONSE PAGE 5

**Procedure:**
On the chalkboard, draw a fish and a ball.

*Say to the children:*   Many times, you can answer a question about information even though the information does not tell you the answer word-for-word. Listen to this pair of sentences:

> Sara put her line into the water.
> She waited for a pull on the line.

Now look at the drawings of the fish and the ball on the chalkboard. Which thing is Sara trying to catch? (Elicit that Sara is trying to catch a fish.) Even though the sentences do not say that Sara is trying to catch a fish, you know from the words "line" and "water" that Sara is trying to catch a fish and not a ball.

Now I will read another pair of sentences and a question. Listen carefully and then look at your paper. Mark an **X** on the picture that answers the question.

**1.**  Jim looked for shells.
Then he made a sand castle.
Where is Jim?

**2.**  Mr. James could smell the bread.
Soon, he could take it out and let it cool.
Where is the bread?

**3.**  The driver pulled up to the curb.
Another person got out and emptied the cans into the open back end.
What is the driver driving?

**4.**  With her finger, Peg traced the highways and roads to Sally's new home.
Now she easily could find her way.
What is Peg looking at?

**5.**  Elephants did tricks, and clowns rode tiny bicycles.
The crowd clapped and cheered.
Where is the crowd?

## Making Inferences

## Following Directions

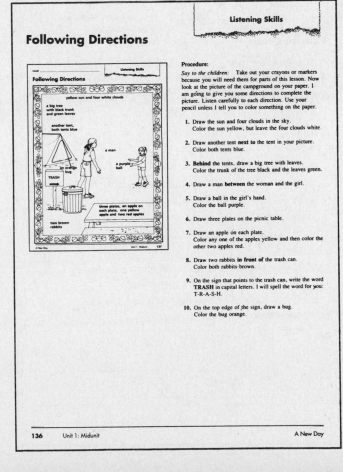

**Procedure:**
*Say to the children:*   Take out your crayons or markers because you will need them for parts of this lesson. Now look at the picture of the campground on your paper. I am going to give you some directions to complete the picture. Listen carefully to each direction. Use your pencil unless I tell you to color something on the paper.

**1.**  Draw the sun and four clouds in the sky.
Color the sun yellow, but leave the four clouds white.

**2.**  Draw another tent **next to** the tent in your picture.
Color both tents blue.

**3.**  **Behind** the tents, draw a big tree with leaves.
Color the trunk of the tree black and the leaves green.

**4.**  Draw a man **between** the woman and the girl.

**5.**  Draw a ball in the girl's hand.
Color the ball purple.

**6.**  Draw three plates on the picnic table.

**7.**  Draw an apple on each plate.
Color any one of the apples yellow and then color the other two apples red.

**8.**  Draw two rabbits **in front of** the trash can.
Color both rabbits brown.

**9.**  On the sign that points to the trash can, write the word **TRASH** in capital letters. I will spell the word for you: T-R-A-S-H.

**10.**  On the top edge of the sign, draw a bug.
Color the bug orange.

## Following Directions

---

## Comprehension:
### Following Directions

**Focus:** The ability to follow directions correctly is an important skill.

**Model:** This activity gives you a set of directions to read and follow.

**Practice:** Suppose a direction said this: If an apple is not an orange, write I. You know that an apple is not an orange, so you would write I on your paper.

Then suppose the next direction said this: If you wrote I, write H before the I. You did write I, so now you would write H before it. Here is what you would have if you followed directions correctly:

HI

**Apply:** Now work on page 139.

1. First, read all the directions.

2. Then go back and follow each direction in the right order.

3. Pay careful attention to what each direction says. You may have to write or draw something, or you may not have to do anything.

**Monitor:** When students have finished, discuss their results.

1. The first direction tells you to write an E in the middle of the box.

2. The next direction says to do something if day is night. You know that day is not night, so you should not do what the direction says; you should not draw a flower in the top left corner.

3. This direction says to write ND after the E if red is not blue. You know that red is not blue, so you should write ND after E.

4. This direction says to draw a sun in the top right corner.

5. This direction says to write OK before the E if you drew a flower in Step 2. However, you did not draw a flower in Step 2, so you should not write OK.

6. This direction says to write something if you did not draw a flower. You did not draw a flower, so you should write RI before the E.

7. This direction tells you to draw two happy faces if you wrote RI before the E. You did write RI, so you should draw the happy faces in the bottom left corner.

8. The last direction tells you to write S at the end of the word and F at the beginning.

**Summary:** If you followed directions correctly, you should have written the word FRIENDS, with a sun in the upper right corner and two happy faces in the lower left corner.

---

## Comprehension:
### Following Directions

It is important to follow directions carefully to get the results you want.

Do what the directions tell you. Work in the box.

1. Write **e** right in the middle of the box.

2. If day is night, draw a flower in the top left corner.

3. If red is not blue, write **nd** after the **e**.

4. Draw a sun in the top right corner.

5. If you drew a flower in Step 2, write **ok** before the **e**.

6. If you did not draw a flower, write **ri** before the **e**.

7. If you wrote **ri** before the **e**, draw two happy faces in the bottom left corner. ☺ ☺

8. Write **s** at the end of the word and **f** at the beginning.

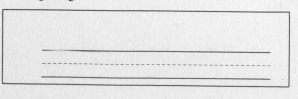

---

## Comprehension: Visualizing

**Focus:** Creating pictures in your mind as you read is an important way to understand what you read.

**Model:** This activity gives you two short stories to read. You must form pictures in your mind as you read and then draw the pictures.

**Practice:** Suppose you read this:
A small brown dog ran with a huge orange cat.

You would see a picture in your mind of a dog that is small and brown running with a cat that is orange and very big. Maybe the cat in your picture is even bigger than the dog.

The cat and dog in your picture might be running down a city street or across a grassy field. You will see the picture your own way, but it should match what you read in the story.

**Apply:** Now work on page 141.

1. Read the story for Number 1. As you read, try to see a picture in your mind.

2. Draw your picture in the box below the story.

3. Now do the same for Number 2.

**Monitor:** When children have finished, discuss their pictures.

1. Each person's picture may look different, but every picture should show these things from the story: a large gray elephant, a red ball under a bush, the elephant either trying to reach the ball or looking sad because the ball is out of reach.

2. Each picture should show these things from the story: Three little pigs either in a puddle or next to it. They should all be wearing sneakers that are wet and muddy. The smallest pig is looking in the direction from which Mother Pig is coming toward them.

## Comprehension: Visualizing

It is good to make pictures in your mind when you read.

**A.** Read each story and make a picture in your mind.

**B.** Draw your picture.

1. A large gray elephant played with a red ball. The ball rolled under a bush. Poor Elephant wants the ball.

2. Three little pigs fell in a puddle. Their new sneakers are all wet and muddy. The smallest pig sees Mother Pig coming.

A New Day  Unit 1: Midunit  **141**

---

## Elaboration: Creative Thinking

**Focus:** You can use your imagination to think of other uses for everyday things.

**Model:** This activity shows you pictures of some things you see every day. You have to imagine what an animal would do if it found one of these things.

**Practice:** Suppose you read this: A bird finds a pencil. What will he do with it? You must draw a picture to answer the question.

You know that birds do not write, so the bird will probably not use the pencil the same way a person would. You may imagine that the bird would put the pencil across two branches of a tree to make a bridge. You could draw a picture of the bird sitting on the pencil that it has placed across the branches.

You might imagine that the bird would use the pencil as a flagpole. Maybe the flag could be a leaf. You could draw a picture of the bird standing next to its new flagpole.

**Apply:** Now work on page 143.

1. Read each sentence and each question.

2. Use your imagination to think of a good answer to the question.

3. Think of how you can show your answer in a picture.

4. Draw the picture.

**Monitor:** When children have finished, discuss their ideas, having them display and explain their pictures. Help them focus on the thinking processes they used, such as imagining that they were the animal, imagining how the object would look to that animal, and so on.

**142**  Unit 1: Midunit  A New Day

---

## Elaboration: Creative Thinking

Using your imagination is an important kind of thinking.

Draw a picture to answer each question.

1. A pig finds a 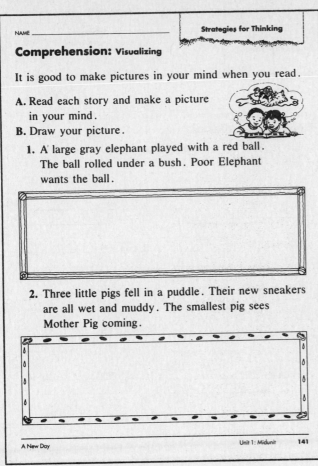 in her pen. What will she do with it?

2. A duck finds a 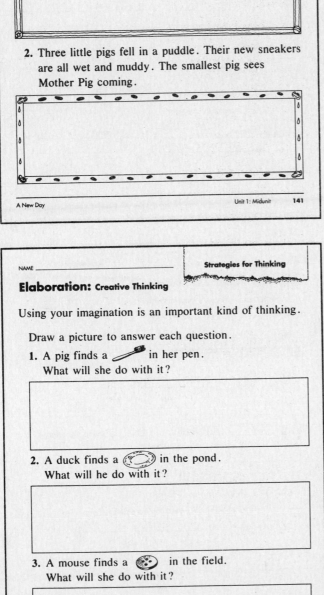 in the pond. What will he do with it?

3. A mouse finds a 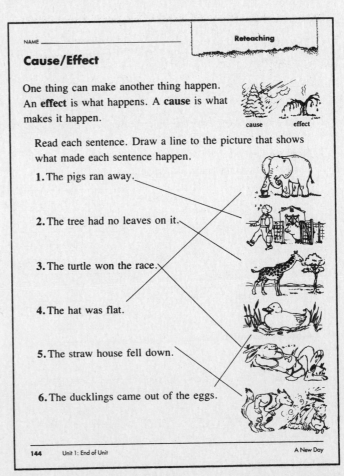 in the field. What will she do with it?

A New Day  Unit 1: Midunit  **143**

---

## Cause/Effect

One thing can make another thing happen. An **effect** is what happens. A **cause** is what makes it happen.

cause   effect

Read each sentence. Draw a line to the picture that shows what made each sentence happen.

1. The pigs ran away.

2. The tree had no leaves on it.

3. The turtle won the race.

4. The hat was flat.

5. The straw house fell down.

6. The ducklings came out of the eggs.

**144**  Unit 1: End of Unit  A New Day

---

**233**

**Cause/Effect**

One thing can make another thing happen.
An **effect** is what happens. A **cause** is what
makes it happen.

cause    effect

Read the sentences. Write what caused something to happen.

1. The farmer does not want rabbits in the garden because
   they eat the beans.    they work very hard.

   _____
   **they eat the beans.**

2. Emily eats lots of spinach because
   she does not like it.    it is good for her.

   _____
   **it is good for her.**

3. John was late for school because
   he got up on time.    he missed the bus.

   _____
   **he missed the bus.**

4. The work was done fast because
   everyone helped.    Grandfather came to visit.

   _____
   **everyone helped.**

---

**Synonyms**

**Synonyms** are words that mean almost the
same thing.

race    dash

Read each numbered word. Write a word
from the list that has almost the same meaning.

call    end    left    mom    sick    start
cook    glad    many    nap    small    think

1. begin  start          7. lots  many

2. ill  sick             8. stop  end

3. happy  glad           9. went  left

4. believe  think        10. sleep  nap

5. mother  mom           11. bake  cook

6. little  small         12. yell  call

---

**Synonyms**

**Synonyms** are words that mean almost the
same thing.

These words have almost the same meaning.    nap    sleep

Read the first word in each row. Find the word that has
almost the same meaning. Underline the word. Then write it.

1. **boat**    bus    truck    ship̲     ship

2. **yellow**    red    gold̲    green    gold

3. **call**    yell̲    wait    sit     yell

4. **beetle**    bird    bug̲    plant    bug

5. **father**    dad̲    mom    brother    dad

6. **looked**    found    saw̲    heard    saw

---

**Words with *r*-Controlled Vowels**

When the letter **r** follows a vowel, it changes the
sound that the vowel letter usually stands for.

ir → bird
ur → hurt

Read the sentences. Draw a circle around the word that best
finishes each sentence. Then write the word.

1. A bear has thick _____ fur _____ .
   fur    girl    sir

2. She _____ heard _____ a sound far away.
   burned    heard    learn

3. A _____ gerbil _____ is a small animal.
   gerbil    nurse    turn

4. He began to _____ stir _____ the soup.
   first    hurt    stir

5. We sat on the floor in a _____ circle _____ .
   certainly    circle    surprise

6. We _____ turned _____ on the TV.
   heard    surprised    turned

© Silver Burdett Ginn Inc.

**234**

## Compound Words

Two small words can be put together to
make a longer word. The longer word is
called a **compound word.** The new word
has some of the meaning of both small words.

rain + coat = raincoat

Choose a word from List 1. Draw a line to a word in List 2
that goes with it. Put the two words together to make a
compound word. Write the word. The first one is done.

| 1 | 2 |
|------|------|
| farm | book |
| day | boat |
| cook | house |
| sail | time |
| bread | water |
| rain | box |

1. farmhouse

2. daytime

3. cookbook

4. sailboat

5. breadbox

6. rainwater

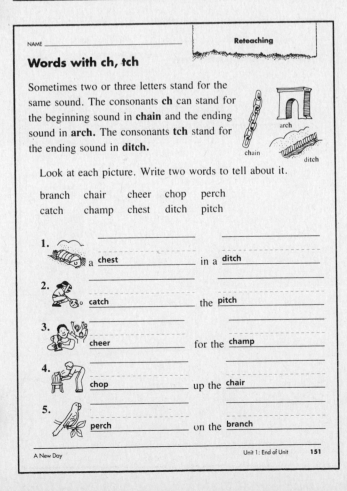

---

## Comparison

When we **compare** things, we think about how they
are alike and how they are different.

Alike and Different

Think about the two things. Then answer the questions.
Draw a line under each answer.

kite—airplane

1. How are they alike?
   a. They both fly.
   b. They have wheels.
   c. They both have wings.
   d. They go up.
   e. They can be used for fun.
   f. They are both used by adults only.
   g. They are the same shape.
   h. They are both flown by someone.
   i. They can be seen in the sky.

2. How are they different?
   a. One has wings. One does not have wings.
   b. One needs wind to fly. One needs an engine to fly.
   c. One is used only by children. One is used only by adults.
   d. One has many colors. One has only one color.
   e. One has seats. One does not have seats.
   f. One is very big. One is small.
   g. One is very quiet. One makes a lot of noise.
   h. One is held to the ground. One is not.

---

## Words with ch, tch

Sometimes two or three letters stand for the
same sound. The consonants **ch** can stand for
the beginning sound in **chain** and the ending
sound in **arch.** The consonants **tch** stand for
the ending sound in **ditch.**

chain    arch    ditch

Look at each picture. Write two words to tell about it.

branch    chair    cheer    chop    perch
catch     champ    chest    ditch   pitch

1. a chest _____ in a ditch

2. _____ catch _____ the pitch

3. _____ cheer _____ for the champ

4. _____ chop _____ up the chair

5. _____ perch _____ on the branch

---

## Antonyms

Some words mean the opposite.

Up    Down

Circle the words in each row that have opposite meanings.

1. over     across    under     between

2. saw      found     closed    lost

3. back     left      right     side

4. old      warm      tall      new

5. glad     sad       good      tired

6. run      stop      sleep     start

7. looked   opened    pulled    pushed

8. give     win       take      hide

9. come     go        could     line

10. we      me        yes       no

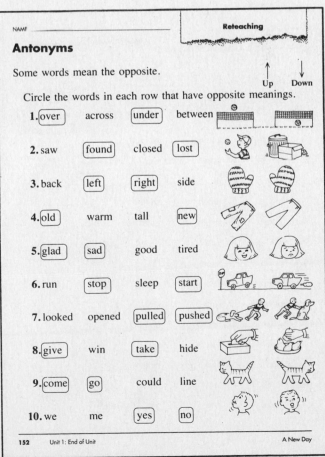

**235**

## Synonyms and Antonyms

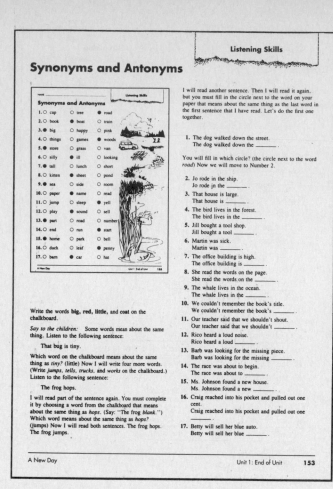

**Synonyms and Antonyms**

1. ○ cap  ● tree  ● road
2. ● book  ● boat  ○ train
3. ● big  ○ happy  ○ pink
4. ○ things  ● games  ○ woods
5. ● store  ○ grass  ○ van
6. ● silly  ● ill  ○ looking
7. ● tall  ● lunch  ○ short
8. ● kitten  ● sheet  ● pond
9. ● sea  ○ side  ○ room
10. ● paper  ● name  ○ read
11. ○ jump  ● sleep  ● yell
12. ● play  ● sound  ○ sell
13. ● part  ● road  ○ number
14. ● end  ○ run  ● start
15. ● home  ○ park  ● bell
16. ○ duck  ● leaf  ● penny
17. ○ barn  ● car  ○ hat

Unit 1: End of Unit  **153**

Write the words **big, red, little,** and **coat** on the chalkboard.

*Say to the children:* Some words mean about the same thing. Listen to the following sentence:

That bug is tiny.

Which word on the chalkboard means about the same thing as *tiny?* (little) Now I will write four more words. (Write *jumps, tells, trucks,* and *works* on the chalkboard.) Listen to the following sentence:

The frog hops.

I will read part of the sentence again. You must complete it by choosing a word from the chalkboard that means about the same thing as *hops.* (Say: "The frog *blank.*") Which word means about the same thing as *hops?* (jumps) Now I will read both sentences. The frog hops. The frog jumps.

I will read another sentence. Then I will read it again, but you must fill in the circle next to the word on your paper that means about the same thing as the last word in the first sentence that I have read. Let's do the first one together.

1. The dog walked down the street.
The dog walked down the _____.

You will fill in which circle? (the circle next to the word *road*) Now we will move to Number 2.

2. Jo rode in the ship.
Jo rode in the _____.
3. That house is large.
That house is _____.
4. The bird lives in the forest.
The bird lives in the _____.
5. Jill bought a tool shop.
Jill bought a tool _____.
6. Martin was sick.
Martin was _____.
7. The office building is high.
The office building is _____.
8. She read the words on the page.
She read the words on the _____.
9. The whale lives in the ocean.
The whale lives in the _____.
10. We couldn't remember the book's title.
We couldn't remember the book's _____.
11. Our teacher said that we shouldn't shout.
Our teacher said that we shouldn't _____.
12. Rico heard a loud noise.
Rico heard a loud _____.
13. Barb was looking for the missing piece.
Barb was looking for the missing _____.
14. The race was about to begin.
The race was about to _____.
15. Ms. Johnson found a new house.
Ms. Johnson found a new _____.
16. Craig reached into his pocket and pulled out one cent.
Craig reached into his pocket and pulled out one _____.
17. Betty will sell her blue auto.
Betty will sell her blue _____.

A New Day  Unit 1: End of Unit  **153**

---

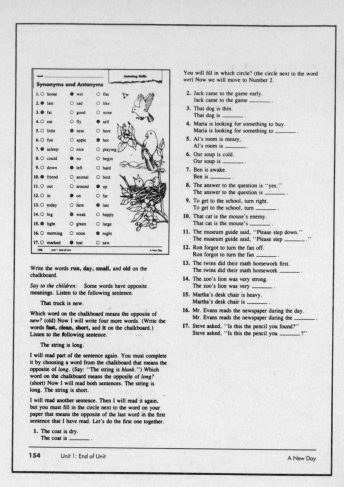

**Synonyms and Antonyms**

1. ○ home  ● wet  ○ flat
2. ● late  ○ sad  ○ like
3. ● fat  ○ good  ○ mine
4. ○ eat  ● fly  ● sell
5. ○ little  ● neat  ○ here
6. ● fun  ● apple  ● hot
7. ● asleep  ○ nice  ○ playing
8. ● could  ● no  ○ begin
9. ● down  ● left  ● hard
10. ● friend  ○ animal  ● bird
11. ○ out  ● around  ● up
12. ● in  ● on  ○ far
13. ○ today  ● here  ● last
14. ○ big  ● weak  ● happy
15. ● light  ● green  ● large
16. ○ morning  ● noon  ● night
17. ○ marked  ● lost  ○ saw

Unit 1: End of Unit  **188**  A New Day

Write the words **run, day, small,** and **old** on the chalkboard.

*Say to the children:* Some words have opposite meanings. Listen to the following sentence.

That truck is new.

Which word on the chalkboard means the opposite of *new?* (old) Now I will write four more words. (Write the words **fast, clean, short,** and **lt** on the chalkboard.) Listen to the following sentence.

The string is long.

I will read part of the sentence again. You must complete it by choosing a word from the chalkboard that means the opposite of *long.* (Say: "The string is *blank.*") Which word on the chalkboard means the opposite of *long?* (short) Now I will read both sentences. The string is long. The string is short.

I will read another sentence. Then I will read it again, but you must fill in the circle next to the word on your paper that means the opposite of the last word in the first sentence that I have read. Let's do the first one together.

1. The coat is dry.
The coat is _____.

You will fill in which circle? (the circle next to the word *wet*) Now we will move to Number 2.

2. Jack came to the game early.
Jack came to the game _____.
3. That dog is thin.
That dog is _____.
4. Maria is looking for something to buy.
Maria is looking for something to _____.
5. Al's room is messy.
Al's room is _____.
6. Our soup is cold.
Our soup is _____.
7. Ben is awake.
Ben is _____.
8. The answer to the question is "yes."
The answer to the question is _____.
9. To get to the school, turn right.
To get to the school, turn _____.
10. That cat is the mouse's enemy.
That cat is the mouse's _____.
11. The museum guide said, "Please step down."
The museum guide said, "Please step _____."
12. Ron forgot to turn the fan off.
Ron forgot to turn the fan _____.
13. The twins did their math homework first.
The twins did their math homework _____.
14. The zoo's lion was very strong.
The zoo's lion was very _____.
15. Martha's desk chair is heavy.
Martha's desk chair is _____.
16. Mr. Evans reads the newspaper during the day.
Mr. Evans reads the newspaper during the _____.
17. Steve asked, "Is this the pencil you found?"
Steve asked, "Is this the pencil you _____?"

**154**  Unit 1: End of Unit  A New Day

---

NAME _____

## Synonyms and Antonyms

1. ○ cap  ○ tree  ○ road
2. ○ book  ○ boat  ○ train
3. ○ big  ○ happy  ○ pink
4. ○ things  ○ games  ○ woods
5. ○ store  ○ grass  ○ van
6. ○ silly  ○ ill  ○ looking
7. ○ tall  ○ lunch  ○ short
8. ○ kitten  ○ sheet  ○ pond
9. ○ sea  ○ side  ○ room
10. ○ paper  ○ name  ○ read
11. ○ jump  ○ sleep  ○ yell
12. ○ play  ○ sound  ○ sell
13. ○ part  ○ road  ○ number
14. ○ end  ○ run  ○ start
15. ○ home  ○ park  ○ bell
16. ○ duck  ○ leaf  ○ penny
17. ○ barn  ○ car  ○ hat

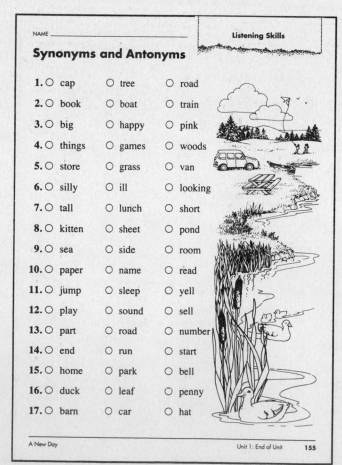

A New Day  Unit 1: End of Unit  **155**

---

NAME _____

## Synonyms and Antonyms

1. ○ home  ○ wet  ○ flat
2. ○ late  ○ sad  ○ like
3. ○ fat  ○ good  ○ mine
4. ○ eat  ○ fly  ○ sell
5. ○ little  ○ neat  ○ here
6. ○ fun  ○ apple  ○ hot
7. ○ asleep  ○ nice  ○ playing
8. ○ could  ○ no  ○ begin
9. ○ down  ○ left  ○ hard
10. ○ friend  ○ animal  ○ bird
11. ○ out  ○ around  ○ up
12. ○ in  ○ on  ○ far
13. ○ today  ○ here  ○ last
14. ○ big  ○ weak  ○ happy
15. ○ light  ○ green  ○ large
16. ○ morning  ○ noon  ○ night
17. ○ marked  ○ lost  ○ saw

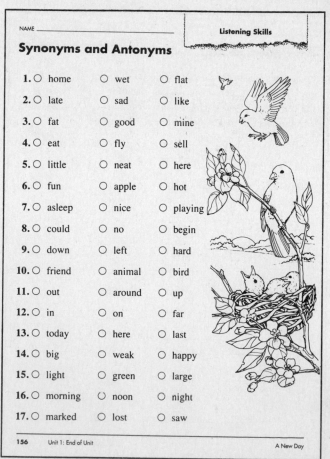

**156**  Unit 1: End of Unit  A New Day

## Cause and Effect

© Silver Burdett Ginn Inc.

**Procedure:**

*Say to the children:* When you listen to a story, you often will hear how one thing in the story causes another thing to happen. I will read a short story. Listen for how one thing in the story causes another thing to happen.

Fox carefully took two eggs from his refrigerator. He set them on a little table. As Fox turned around to close the refrigerator door, his tail brushed the eggs off the table, and they broke.

Why did the eggs break? (Fox's tail brushed them off the table.) Fox's tail movement *caused* the eggs to fall off the table and break.

I will read another short story. Then I will ask a question. After I have asked the question, you will read the two sentences on your paper and mark an X next to the sentence that correctly answers the question.

**Number 1**
The first graders were playing on the playground. It started to rain. The first graders ran toward the school. Why did the first graders run toward the school?

**Number 2**
Mr. Hall got a beautiful plant for his office. After two weeks, all of the leaves had turned black. Mr. Hall was sad; he had given the plant too much water. Why did all of the plant's leaves turn black?

**Number 3**
Two pigs wanted to have a party. They decorated their pigpen and went to the cupboard where they kept their corn. When they opened the cupboard, they saw that mice had eaten all of the corn. "We can't serve corn at the party this time," said one of the pigs. Why couldn't the pigs serve corn at the party?

**Number 4**
Ken was watching a robin from his window. Ken wanted to hear the robin sing. Ken opened the window, but the sound scared the robin away. What scared the robin away?

**Number 5**
Mary and Denise were walking to the library. Suddenly, Denise ran back toward her house. "Where are you going?" shouted Mary. "I forgot two books," yelled Denise. Why was Denise running toward her house?

**Number 6**
A horse and a cow were going to a fair. The cow got to the horse's house on time and rang the doorbell. The horse answered the door and said, "I can't go to the fair looking like this. You'll have to wait until I have brushed myself." Why did the cow have to wait for the horse?

**Number 7**
Paul had one page in his reading workbook to finish and two pages in his math book to complete. He also had a science worksheet to finish. Paul had missed school for two days, so he had to catch up with his work. Why did Paul have schoolwork to finish?

**Number 8**
Maria was late for the play. Her puppy was missing, and Maria was looking for him. Maria looked under her bed and behind the sofa. She went outside and looked behind the trees and bushes. Finally, Maria saw her puppy in her neighbor's yard. Why was Maria late for the play?

**Number 9**
Victor did not like the city because it was too noisy. He was tired of the horns and sirens. Even though he had lived in the city for many years, Victor decided to move to the country. "I will find a job and I will plant a garden," he said. So Victor packed his belongings, hired some movers, and left the city for a more quiet life. Why did Victor leave the city?

**Number 10**
Bill was planning a party. He made a list of all the things that he would need. Bill wrote down "food," "balloons," and "prizes." He also wrote down "gift" because it was his sister's birthday, and he was planning the party for her. Why was Bill planning a party?

---

## Cause and Effect

1. _____ It was hot.          _____ It was raining.

2. _____ Mr. Hall didn't water it.          _____ Mr. Hall put too much water on it.

3. _____ Pigs ate the corn.          _____ Mice ate the corn.

4. _____ Ken opened the window.          _____ Ken was singing.

5. _____ She didn't want to go with Mary.          _____ She forgot two books.

6. _____ The horse had to brush himself.          _____ The cow was too early.

7. _____ He missed two days of school.          _____ He didn't like math.

8. _____ She looked outside.          _____ Her puppy was missing.

9. _____ It was too noisy.          _____ It had too many old buildings.

10. _____ He liked parties.          _____ It was his sister's birthday.

---

## Comprehension: Analogies

**Focus:** It is important to be able to see how parts of two different things can be alike.

**Model:** This activity shows you parts of two different things. You have to think about how each part of one is like a part of the other. Then you have to match the parts that are alike.

**Practice:** Suppose you read this: A girl pretends to be a car. You have to decide what parts are alike. Here are the parts of the girl: eyes, legs. Here are the parts of the car: wheels, headlights.

Think about a girl's eyes and a car's headlights. The girl uses her eyes to know where to go. A car uses its headlights to know where to go. Eyes and headlights are alike in that way, so you would draw a line from eyes to headlights.

A girl uses her legs to move from place to place. A car uses its wheels to move from place to place. Legs and wheels are alike in that way, so you would draw a line from legs to wheels.

Now suppose you had sentences with blanks in them. The sentences say this:

A girl's _____ are like a car's _____.
A girl's _____ are like a car's _____.

You would write eyes and headlights in one sentence. You would write legs and wheels in the other sentence. The completed sentences would say this:

A girl's eyes are like a car's headlights.
A girl's legs are like a car's wheels.

**Apply:** Now work on page 161.

1. Look at the pictures of the boy and the bird.

2. Look at the small pictures. Match each thing on the left with the thing on the right that is like it. Draw lines to show the things that match.

3. Write the names of the things that match from numbers 1–4 in sentences 5–8 so that the sentences are true.

**Monitor:** When children have finished, discuss their answers.

1. The boy's arm is at his side. He can move it and flap it up and down. The boy's arm is like the bird's wing, so you should have a line from the boy's arm to the bird's wing.

2. The boy opens his mouth to eat and to speak. The bird opens its mouth to eat and to chirp or sing. The boy's mouth is like the bird's beak, so the line should go from the mouth to the beak.

3. The boy rests and sleeps in his bed. The bird rests and sleeps in its nest. A line should go from the bed to the nest.

4. The apple is food for the boy. The worm is food for the bird. The apple and the worm are alike in that way, so the line should go from the apple to the worm.

5. The line from number 1, the boy's arm, goes to the bird's wing to show that they are alike. The words *arm* and *wing* make sense in the sentence.

6. The line from number 2, the boy's mouth, goes to the bird's beak to show that they are alike. The words *mouth* and *beak* make sense in the sentence.

7. The line from number 3, the boy's bed, goes to the bird's nest to show that they are alike. The words *bed* and *nest* make sense in the sentence.

8. The line from number 4, the apple, goes to the worm to show that they are alike. The words *apple* and *worm* make sense in the sentence.

**Summary:**

1. arm—c. wing
2. mouth—d. beak
3. bed—a. nest
4. apple—b. worm
5. A boy's *arm* is like a bird's *wing*.
6. A boy's *mouth* is like a bird's *beak*.
7. A boy's *bed* is like a bird's *nest*.
8. A boy's *apple* is like a bird's *worm*.

## Comprehension: Analogies

It is important to see ways that different things are alike.

**A.** Draw lines to show which things are alike.

A boy pretends to be a bird.

1. arm     a. nest
2. mouth     b. worm
3. bed     c. wing
4. apple     d. beak

**B.** Write the words that fit.

5. A boy's _____ is like a bird's _____ .

6. A boy's _____ is like a bird's _____ .

7. A boy's _____ is like a bird's _____ .

8. A boy's _____ is like a bird's _____ .

---

## Critical Thinking: Word Choices

**Focus:** It is important to think about the meanings of words so that others can understand exactly what you want to say.

**Model:** This activity gives you some sets of three words each. You are to write the word that best explains what you think a friend should do.

**Practice:** Suppose you saw these three words under a writing line:

swim     . draw     play

You would think about each word and whether it tells something that you think a friend should do. The first word is *swim*. If you really love to swim and do it all the time, it might be important to you to have a friend that swims. This would not be the word that most people would choose, however.

The next word is *draw*. It might be nice to have a friend who can draw, but that is probably not an important thing that you think friends should do.

The last word is *play*. When you are with your friends, it is probably important to you to play. You might decide that play tells best what you think friends should do. You would write the word **play**.

**Apply:** Now work on page 163.

1. Read each set of three words.

2. Think about each word. Decide which one tells best what you think friends should do.

3. Write that word.

4. At the bottom of the page, there are lines for you to write your own words. Think of four more words that tell what you think friends should do. Write those words.

**Monitor:** When children have finished, discuss their choices. The following are reasonable choices: the children, however, may have good reasons for choosing other words. Encourage them to discuss the reasons for their choices.

1. Many people think it is important for friends to help each other.

2. It is fun to be with people who smile and make you feel happy.

3. Many people think it is important for friends to share.

4. A friend is a person who will listen to you.

Have children share the words they wrote at the bottom of the page, focusing on how and why they thought of these words.

**Summary:** (Possible answers)

1. help     3. share
2. smile     4. listen

---

## Critical Thinking: Word Choices

It is important to choose the right words to tell what you think and feel.

WHAT FRIENDS DO

**A.** Choose the word in each set that tells what **you** think friends should do.

**B.** Write the word.

1. _____
    sing   run   help

3. _____
    trick   share   ask

2. _____
    push   smile   win

4. _____
    listen   shout   work

**C.** Write more words that tell what friends do.

_____     _____

_____     _____

---

## Critical Thinking: Evaluating Arguments

**Focus:** It is important to recognize arguments for and against a point of view.

**Model:** This activity lists sentences that two people might say. The two people disagree about something. You must decide which sentences each person would say.

**Practice:** Suppose you know that someone likes dogs and someone else likes cats. You read this sentence: Dogs make a lot of noise. You must decide which person said it.

You think about the sentence. Most people probably do not think it is good for pets to make a lot of noise. The person who likes dogs would probably not say that they are noisy. The person who likes cats might say this, though, to show why cats are better than dogs.

**Apply:** Now work on page 165.

1. Read what Lee and Pat say in the pictures.

2. Read each sentence on the rest of the page and decide whether Lee said it or Pat said it.

3. Write **Lee** or **Pat** to show who said each sentence.

**Monitor:** When children have finished, discuss their answers.

1. The first sentence says something good about a horse. Pat likes horses, so Pat would say this.

2. Sentence 2 sounds as if it is saying something bad about cows. It might be all right for an animal to be slow, but this person says that cows are too slow. Pat wants to show that horses are better than cows, so Pat probably said this.

3. Sentence 3 says that horses do not give us milk. Giving us milk is a good thing that cows do. The person who said this was probably trying to show that horses are not as good as cows. Lee likes cows, so Lee probably said this.

4. Sentence 4 tells something good about horses, so Pat must have said it.

5. Sentence 5 says that cows do not run away. It is not good for animals to run away, so this sentence is saying something good about cows. Lee must have said it.

**Summary:**

1. Pat     2. Pat     3. Lee
4. Pat     5. Lee

## Critical Thinking:
**Evaluating Arguments**

It is important to see the good and bad points
of something.

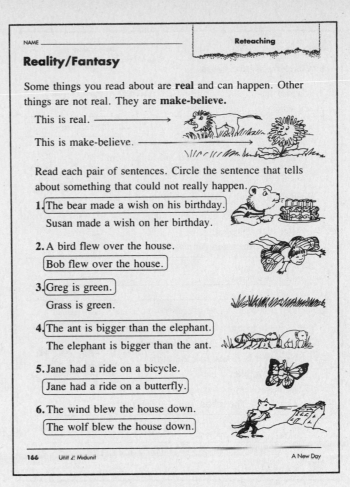

COWS ARE BETTER.

Lee

HORSES ARE BETTER.

Pat

Write the name of the one who will say each thing.

_____

1. _____ "You can ride a horse."
_____

2. _____ "Cows are too slow."
_____

3. _____ "Horses do not give us milk."
_____

4. _____ "A horse can pull a wagon."
_____

5. _____ "Cows do not run away."

---

## Reality/Fantasy

Some things you read about are **real** and can happen. Other
things are not real. They are **make-believe.**

This is real. ⟶

This is make-believe. ⟶

Read each pair of sentences. Circle the sentence that tells
about something that could not really happen.

1. (The bear made a wish on his birthday.)
   Susan made a wish on her birthday.

2. A bird flew over the house.
   (Bob flew over the house.)

3. (Greg is green.)
   Grass is green.

4. (The ant is bigger than the elephant.)
   The elephant is bigger than the ant.

5. Jane had a ride on a bicycle.
   (Jane had a ride on a butterfly.)

6. The wind blew the house down.
   (The wolf blew the house down.)

---

## Words with oa

Sometimes two letters stand for one sound.
The letters **oa** can stand for the vowel sound
you hear in **mole** and **toad.** The words **mole**
and **toad** have the same vowel sound.

mole

toad

Write the two words the sentence tells about.

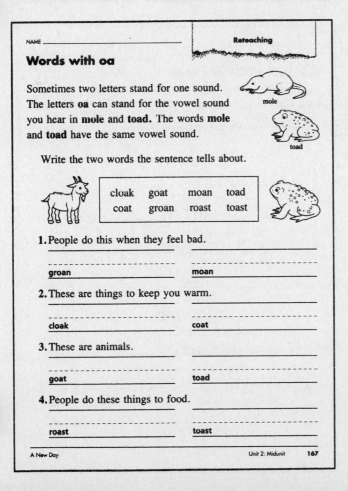

| cloak | goat | moan | toad |
|-------|-------|------|------|
| coat | groan | roast | toast |

1. People do this when they feel bad.

   **groan** _____     **moan** _____

2. These are things to keep you warm.

   **cloak** _____     **coat** _____

3. These are animals.

   **goat** _____     **toad** _____

4. People do these things to food.

   _____     _____

   **roast**     **toast**

---

## Words with ou, ow

Sometimes two letters stand for one sound. The letters
*ou* and *ow* may stand for the vowel sound you hear in
*shoulder* and *flow.*

ow ⟶ flow

ou ⟶ shoulder

Write the words in the box to match the riddles.

| bowl | dough | crowed | row | shoulder | snow |
|------|-------|--------|-----|----------|------|

1. What did a rooster do
   each day?                    crowed

2. What is white and cold
   and falls from the sky?      snow

3. What is the part of the
   body where the arms
   are fastened?                shoulder

4. What do you mix to
   bake bread?                  dough

5. What is a small deep
   dish for soup?               bowl

6. How do you move a
   boat in the water?           row

## Predicting Outcomes

When you read a story, think ahead and try to tell what will happen next.

clue   clue

**What will happen next**

Example:

**Clue 1:** Greg does not like the water.

**Clue 2:** His friends want to go for a swim.

What will happen next? Greg will stay at home.

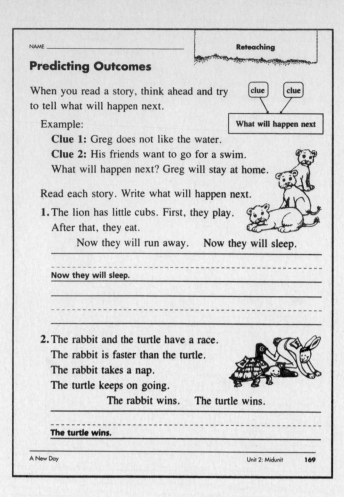

Read each story. Write what will happen next.

1. The lion has little cubs. First, they play.
   After that, they eat.
   Now they will run away.   Now they will sleep.

   _____
   **Now they will sleep.**
   _____
   _____

2. The rabbit and the turtle have a race.
   The rabbit is faster than the turtle.
   The rabbit takes a nap.
   The turtle keeps on going.
   The rabbit wins.   The turtle wins.

   _____
   **The turtle wins.**

---

## Classification

Some words belong in the same group. These words belong together.

**Things with Wheels**

bicycle   bus   truck

Read each list of words. Write the word that tells about the whole list.

| Animals   Colors   Days   Food   Plants   Times |
|---|

1. afternoon
   morning
   night
   _____
   **Times**

4. green
   orange
   purple
   _____
   **Colors**

2. flower
   grass
   tree
   _____
   **Plants**

5. goat
   mole
   pig
   _____
   **Animals**

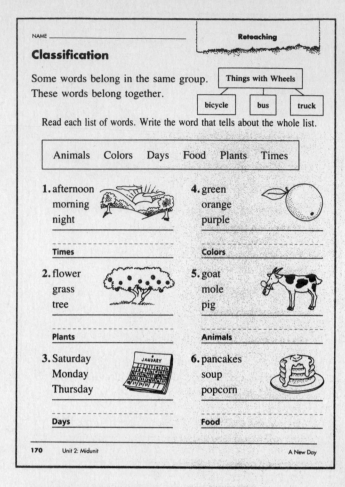

3. Saturday
   Monday
   Thursday
   _____
   **Days**

6. pancakes
   soup
   popcorn
   _____
   **Food**

---

## Contractions

A **contraction** is a short way of writing two words.

I + am = I'm
you + are = you're
we + have = we've

Write the correct contraction for each set of words.

|   |   |   |   |   |
|---|---|---|---|---|

I'm

1. I   +   have   **I've**    I've
                              you're

2. you   +   are   **you're**    you've
                                 they've

3. they   +   have   **they've**    they'll
                                    we'd

4. we   +   are   **we're**    we're
                               I'm

5. I   +   am   **I'm**    I'll
                          you've

6. you   +   have   **you've**    you're

---

## Words with *r*-Controlled Vowels

When the letter **r** follows a vowel, it changes the sound that the vowel letter usually stands for.

er
ir    →    new sounds
ur

Read the sentences. Write the words from the box that finish the sentences.

| fur   nurse   perfect   purr   swerved   thirsty |
|---|

1. Cathy was ___**thirsty**___ so she got a drink.

2. The kitten will ___**purr**___ when you pet her.

3. The ___**nurse**___ helped the sick boy.

4. Kim had a ___**perfect**___ score in spelling.

5. The car ___**swerved**___ on the icy road.

6. The dog's ___**fur**___ is long.

## Words with ch, tch

Sometimes two or three letters stand for the same sound. The consonants **ch** can stand for the beginning sound in **chick** and the ending sound in **March**. The consonants **tch** stand for the ending sound in **match**.

chick March

match

Write the word that names each picture.

arch    chalk    cheese    inch    porch
branch    check    ditch    patch    watch

1. patch

2. cheese

3. ditch

4. arch

5. check

6. inch

7. chalk

8. porch

9. watch

10. branch

---

## Antonyms

Some words mean the opposite.    Start _____ End

Write the opposite of each word.

go    left    little    off    won    yes

1. big    little        4. on    off

2. no    yes        5. right    left

3. lost    won        6. come    go

day    gave    in    naughty    opened    start

7. stop        10. closed

start        opened

8. good        11. night

naughty        day

9. out        12. took

in        gave

---

## Antonyms

Some words mean the opposite.    Over
    _____
    Under

Circle the opposite of each underlined word. Then write it.

liked    looked    [lost]

1. Greg found his mitten.    lost

give    [go]    grow

2. Gail will stay.    go

[opened]    out    over

3. Bill closed the door.    opened

place    [pulled]    put

4. Anna pushed the box.    pulled

---

## Comprehending Fiction

**Procedure:**

*Say to the children:* I am going to read the story "Pat's Goldfish" to you. After I have read the story, I will ask you some questions about it.

### Pat's Goldfish

Pat wanted a goldfish. Her dad went with her to the fish shop.

"We want a goldfish," said Pat to the shopkeeper.

"I can't help you," he said. "This bowl was full of goldfish, but I have sold them all."

Then Dad asked Pat if she wanted a red fish.

"No," said Pat sadly. "I just want a goldfish."

Pat and Dad went back home.

"Did you get your goldfish?" asked Pat's mom.

"No," said Pat. "The shop was all sold out of goldfish."

"Jim's fishbowl is full of fish," said Mom. "Maybe you can borrow a goldfish from him."

"I do not want to borrow a goldfish from my brother," said Pat. "I want a goldfish that is all mine."

"Don't be sad," said Mom. "Sooner or later you'll have your goldfish."

The next day, Pat and Jim went with Mom and Dad to Playland. When they were inside Playland, they sat down on a bench.

"You may go on the rides," said Mom. "Dad and I will wait for you here on this bench. Don't be too long."

Pat and Jim went on all the rides. Soon they were tired.

"It's time to go," said Jim. "Mom and Dad will be upset if we stay too long."

On the way back to the bench, they stopped to listen to a man. "Quick! Quick, while there is still time," was his yell. "Play the fish game. All you have to do is push the ball. Make it roll into one of the empty fishbowls. If you can do it, you'll win a goldfish in a bowl!"

"Did you hear that?" asked Pat. "Maybe we can win a goldfish!"

"Let me play," said Pat to Jim. "I want to win a goldfish."

"You can't play well," said Jim. "I'll push the ball."

The man gave the ball to Jim. Then he pushed the ball and let it roll. It landed on top of a bowl. It jumped up and down and then fell. It did not go into any of the empty fishbowls.

"You had your try," laughed Pat. "Let me have mine."

The man gave the ball to Pat. She gave the ball a spin and let it roll. It rolled to one of the empty fishbowls and in it fell! Pat jumped up and down. "I did it! I did it!" she said.

"You did well," said Jim. "Next time, you can try first."

The man gave Pat a goldfish in a fishbowl to take home. Pat felt proud. "This is my lucky day," she said.

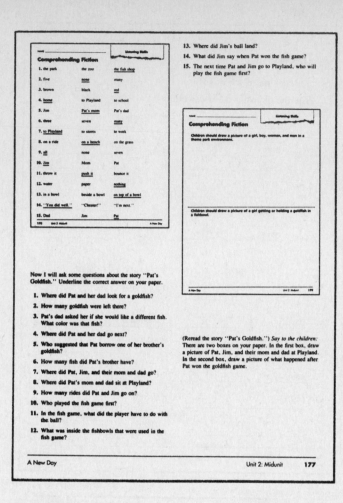

**Comprehending Fiction**

| | | |
|---|---|---|
| 1. the park | the zoo | the fish shop |
| 2. five | none | many |
| 3. brown | black | red |
| 4. home | to Playland | to school |
| 5. Jim | Pat's mom | Pat's dad |
| 6. three | seven | many |
| 7. to Playland | to stores | to work |
| 8. on a ride | on a bench | on the grass |
| 9. all | none | seven |
| 10. Jim | Mom | Pat |
| 11. throw it | push it | bounce it |
| 12. water | paper | nothing |
| 13. in a bowl | beside a bowl | on top of a bowl |
| 14. "You did well." | "Cheater!" | "I'm next." |
| 15. Dad | Jim | Pat |

13. Where did Jim's ball land?

14. What did Jim say when Pat won the fish game?

15. The next time Pat and Jim go to Playland, who will play the fish game first?

Now I will ask some questions about the story "Pat's Goldfish." Underline the correct answer on your paper.

1. Where did Pat and her dad look for a goldfish?

2. How many goldfish were left there?

3. Pat's dad asked her if she would like a different fish. What color was that fish?

4. Where did Pat and her dad go next?

5. Who suggested that Pat borrow one of her brother's goldfish?

6. How many fish did Pat's brother have?

7. Where did Pat, Jim, and their mom and dad go?

8. Where did Pat's mom and dad sit at Playland?

9. How many rides did Pat and Jim go on?

10. Who played the fish game first?

11. In the fish game, what did the player have to do with the ball?

12. What was inside the fishbowls that were used in the fish game?

(Reread the story "Pat's Goldfish.") *Say to the children:* There are two boxes on your paper. In the first box, draw a picture of Pat, Jim, and their mom and dad at Playland. In the second box, draw a picture of what happened after Pat won the goldfish game.

---

# Comprehending Fiction

| | | |
|---|---|---|
| 1. the park | the zoo | the fish shop |
| 2. five | none | many |
| 3. brown | black | red |
| 4. home | to Playland | to school |
| 5. Jim | Pat's mom | Pat's dad |
| 6. three | seven | many |
| 7. to Playland | to stores | to work |
| 8. on a ride | on a bench | on the grass |
| 9. all | none | seven |
| 10. Jim | Mom | Pat |
| 11. throw it | push it | bounce it |
| 12. water | paper | nothing |
| 13. in a bowl | beside a bowl | on top of a bowl |
| 14. "You did well." | "Cheater!" | "I'm next." |
| 15. Dad | Jim | Pat |

---

# Comprehending Fiction

---

# Elaboration: Hypothesizing

**Focus:** Using one's imagination to deal with new situations is an important thinking skill.

**Model:** This activity asks you to imagine two brand-new situations and what you would do if you were in those situations.

**Practice:** Suppose you read this: You and a friend go exploring and find a bush that grows shoes instead of berries. You would spend some time imagining that situation. Imagine what you and your friend would say and do. You might want to imagine several different possibilities.

For example, you might decide that you and your friend would pick all the shoes off the bush. You might fill up a big box with shoes and bring it home. Then you could give the shoes to people who need them.

Another person might decide to take seeds from the shoe bush and use them to plant shoe bushes all over the world.

You might write on your paper the best idea that you come up with.

**Apply:** Now work on page 181.

1. Read sentence number 1. Spend some time thinking about different things that you and your friend might do.

2. Pick your best idea and write it on the lines. If you want to write more, you can use another sheet of paper.

3. When you have finished number 1, do the same thing with sentence number 2.

**Monitor:** When children have finished, have them share and discuss their ideas. Help them focus on how they used both their knowledge of the world and their imaginations to think of ways to deal with something new.

NAME _____

## Elaboration: Hypothesizing

Your imagination can help you think about what to do when a brand new thing happens.

Pretend that you go exploring with a friend.
A. Read about the things you find.
B. Write what you and your friend would do.

1. You find a cave filled with rocks as soft as cotton.

_____
_____
_____
_____
_____
_____

2. You find a leaf that lights up when you touch it.

_____
_____
_____
_____
_____
_____
_____

A New Day                                     Unit 2: Midunit    181

---

## Problem-Solving:
### Spatial Reasoning

**Focus:** Understanding how a figure looks when it is turned or placed in a different position is an important skill.

**Model:** This activity shows you a block of a certain shape and size. You have to pick out the block that is the same shape and size from a row of blocks. The block in the row is in a different position.

**Practice:** Suppose you see this block:

Then you see this row of blocks:

You would look at the first block to see what shape it is, how tall it is, how thick it is. You can see that this block has a side that is shaped like half a circle.
Now you would look at the blocks in the row. The first block is long and thin. None of its sides look like half circles. The second block looks like a half circle lying on its side. You can see that this is the same block as the first one; it is just in a different position. You would circle this second block.

**Apply:** Now work on page 183.

1. Look at the first block for number 1. Think about how big it is, what shape it is, how tall or long it is, how thick it is.

2. Now look at the three blocks in the row for number 1. Try to picture in your mind how the first block would look if it were turned or placed in different positions. Decide which block in the row is the same as the first block but in a different position.

3. Circle the block that is the same as the first one.

**Monitor:** Discuss answers.

1. Your block is longer than it is wide. It is thin. Each side has four corners. The middle block in the row is the same size and shape, but it is standing up on its side instead of lying down.

2. Your block is square on one side. It is not very thick. It is standing up on one of its thin sides. The

first block in the row is the same size and shape, but it is lying down.

3. Your block is short and thick and round. The middle block in the row is the same size and shape, but it is lying on its side instead of standing on end.

4. Your block is small. It is longer than it is wide. It has a square side, too. It is lying on its side. The last block in the row is the same size and shape, but it is standing on end.

5. Your block is standing up. It has one side that is a triangle. The first block in the row is the same size and shape, but it is lying down rather than standing up. (The second block in the row is also a triangle, but it is bigger than your block.)

6. Your block is a cube. The last block in the row is also a cube, but it has been turned a little bit.

**Summary**

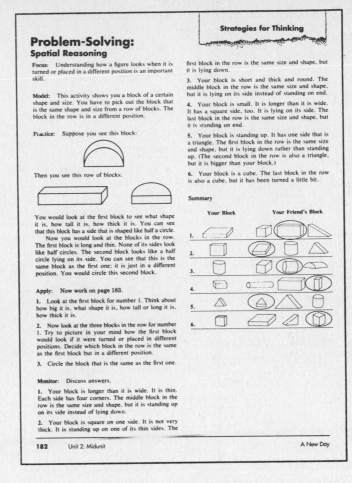

182    Unit 2: Midunit                          A New Day

---

NAME _____

## Problem-Solving:
### Spatial Reasoning

It is important to understand how objects look when they are turned different ways.

You and your friend have some blocks. You both take the same kind of block each time, but you turn them different ways.

A. Look at your block.
B. Find your friend's block. Circle it.

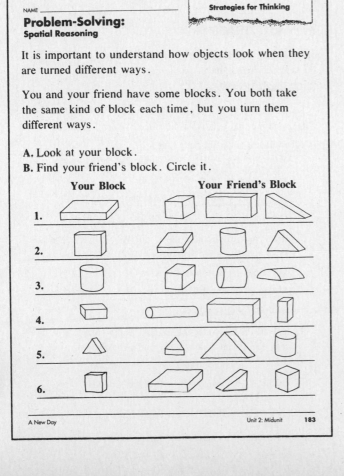

A New Day                                     Unit 2: Midunit    183

---

NAME _____

## Classification

Some words belong in the same group.
These words belong together.

Ways Things Look

bright    fat    small

Write each word under the picture it names.
Then you will have a group of words about a farm.

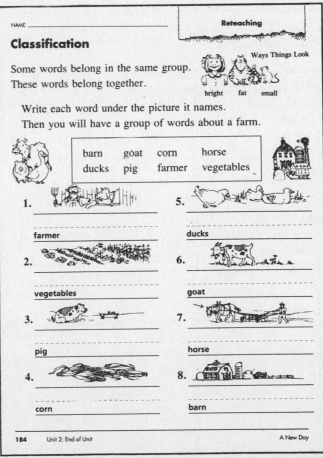

|         |         |         |            |
|---------|---------|---------|------------|
| barn    | goat    | corn    | horse      |
| ducks   | pig     | farmer  | vegetables |

1.   farmer

2.   vegetables

3.   pig

4.   corn

5.   ducks

6.   goat

7.   horse

8.   barn

184    Unit 2: End of Unit                      A New Day

## Spelling Changes

When an ending that begins with a vowel letter is added to a word that ends in **e**, the final **e** is dropped.

> place + ed = placed
> skate + ing = skating

Add **ing** or **ed** to each word. Write the new word. Remember to drop the final **e**. Answers will vary.

1. bake   baked _____

2. love   loving _____

3. smile   smiling _____

4. share   shared _____

5. move   moving _____

6. hike   hiked _____

7. dance   danced _____

---

## Spelling Changes

When an action word has one vowel letter and one final consonant letter, double the final consonant before adding -ed or -ing.

> Word + -ed/-ing = New Word

Example: stop, stop**ped**, stop**ping**

Draw a line under the right word to finish each sentence.

1. The dancers _____ dancing when the bell rang.
   <u>stopped</u>    stopping    stepped

2. The dance teacher was _____ a new dance.
   running    planned    <u>planning</u>

3. The dancers were _____ on the floor.
   stopping    <u>sitting</u>    stopped

4. They _____ when they heard the new plan.
   <u>clapped</u>    clapping    slipped

5. Lisa _____ out of the room.
   dropped    <u>slipped</u>    slipping

6. She was going to take a _____ lesson.
   <u>swimming</u>    stopping    slipping

7. She _____ her mother who was waiting for her.
   <u>hugged</u>    hugging    stopped

---

## Words with Long u

The letter **u** can stand for the vowel sound you hear in **cube** and **tube**. Look for the letter **e** at the end of a short word. It often points out that the first vowel in the word stands for a long sound.

cube    tube

Write the correct word to finish each sentence.

1. I will ride on a mule _____.    mule / muse

2. June will play a tune _____.    tube / tune

3. There are huge _____ buildings in the city.    huge / use

4. A school rule _____ is "Do not run."    rude / rule

5. We slid down the sand dune _____.    duke / dune

6. A prune _____ is good to eat.    plume / prune

---

## Main Idea/Details

A **main idea** tells about the whole story. All the sentences tell about the main idea. These sentences are **details**.

> Main Idea
> Detail   Detail

Read each story. Then draw a line under the sentence that tells what the story is mostly about.

1. People use water in many ways. We sail boats on water. We cook food in water. We swim in water.
   Cooking is done in water.
   <u>People use water in many ways.</u>
   There are many kinds of boats.

2. People cannot live under the water. People need air to live. People cannot get air from water.
   People and fish need air.
   <u>People cannot live under the water.</u>
   People can catch fish.

3. Many things are under the ground. Some animals live under the ground. Plants grow under the ground.
   You can find gold under the ground.
   Plants and animals are under the ground.
   <u>Many things are under the ground.</u>

**244**

## Words with au, aw

Sometimes two letters stand for one sound.
The letters *au* and *aw* stand for the sound
you hear in *pause* and *jaw*.

au → pause
aw → jaw

**A.** Read the words in the box. Then read the story. Write the words
from the box to finish the story.

| auto    awful    drawing    fawn    lawn    Paul    straw |
|---|

The boys found a _____**fawn**_____ that had been hit

by an _____**auto**_____ . They made a bed of

_____**straw**_____ for it on the _____**lawn**_____ .

"I am _____**drawing**_____ a picture of it,"

said _____**Paul**_____ . "I want to remember the

_____**awful**_____ thing that happened to it."

---

## Drawing Conclusions

Sometimes you may need to figure out
things that are not told in a story. This is
called drawing a **conclusion.**

Clue     Clue
↘     ↙
Conclusion

Example:

Clue 1: Becky had <u>one</u> white flower and <u>two</u> yellow ones.
Clue 2: Max had <u>two</u> purple flowers and <u>two</u> red ones.
Conclusion: Max had <u>more flowers</u> than Becky.

Read the stories. Use clues and what you already know to
circle the answers to the questions. Then write them.

1. Fran wanted to go for a swim. Her mother said she could
   go if it was a nice day. If the day was not nice, Fran could
   go to a show. It rained all day. What did Fran do?
   swim   [go to a show]

   _____**go to a show**_____

2. Farmer Woods and Farmer Brown had five cows each.
   Then Farmer Woods bought another cow. Farmer Brown
   gave two of her cows away. Who had more cows?
   [Farmer Woods]   Farmer Brown

   _____**Farmer Woods**_____

---

## Drawing Conclusions

Sometimes you need to figure out things that
are not told in a story. This is called drawing
a **conclusion.**

Clue     Clue
↘     ↙
Conclusion

Read the conclusion and the clues that led to it.
Write one more clue that goes with each conclusion.

1. Conclusion: It was time for dinner.
   Clues: Mom and Dad put the food on the table.
   They called Max.

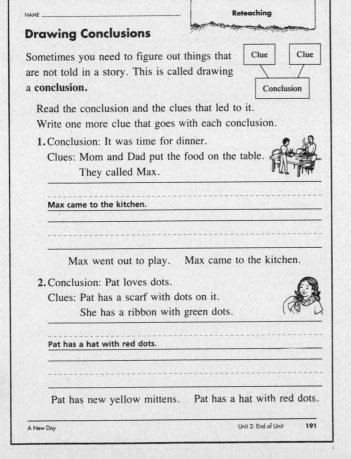

   _____**Max came to the kitchen.**_____

   Max went out to play.    Max came to the kitchen.

2. Conclusion: Pat loves dots.
   Clues: Pat has a scarf with dots on it.
   She has a ribbon with green dots.

   _____**Pat has a hat with red dots.**_____

   Pat has new yellow mittens.    Pat has a hat with red dots.

---

## Elaboration: Creative Writing

**Focus:** Creating a story from a few words selected
at random is a good exercise in imagination.

**Model:** This activity contains a word chart. You circle
a word in each row on the chart. Then you use those
words to write a sentence that starts your story. You
can write or draw the rest of the story.

**Practice:** Suppose you were given this chart:

| 1. | rain | snow |
|---|---|---|
| 2. | fell | ended |

First you would circle a word in Row 1. You might
circle **rain.** Then you would circle a word in Row 2.
You might circle **ended.**

Now you would add any other words you want
to make a sentence using the words you circled. For
example, your sentence might be At last the rain ended.
You would write that sentence on the lines under the
chart.

Then, on another sheet of paper, you would write
more sentences or draw pictures to tell the rest of
your story.

**Apply:** Now work on page 193.

1. Read the words on the chart. Do you notice that
all the words in Row 1 are words that describe? All
the words in Row 2 name animals. Think about how
the words in the other rows are the same.

2. Now choose one word from each row. Circle that
word.

3. Write a sentence using the words you circled. You
may add as many other words as you need. Remember
that the sentence you write is going to be the first
sentence of your story. You may want to try out
several different sentences on scrap paper. Then write
your best sentence on the lines.

4. On another sheet of paper, write down ideas about
what will happen next in the story and how the story
will end. You may want to draw pictures instead, or
you may combine words and pictures.

5. When your story is finished, tell it to someone.

**Monitor:** When students have finished, discuss their
results. You may want to discuss briefly the classifications for Rows 3 and 4 of the chart—action words,
and words that name people or things.

Have students share the words they chose and
the sentences they created from those words. If possible, have them tell their stories. You may want to
arrange a time and place for them to do so.

## Elaboration: Creative Writing

Your imagination can help you build a story from just a few words.

### Be a Storyteller

A. Circle one word in each row going down.
   Use the words a, an, and the, too.

| | | | |
|---|---|---|---|
| 1. | huge | tiny | brave | silly |
| 2. | ant | elephant | lion | goat |
| 3. | made | saw | found | threw |
| 4. | friend | ball | castle | hat |

B. Write a sentence that uses the words you circled.

_____

- - - - - - - - - - - - - - - - - - - - -

_____

_____

_____

_____

_____

C. Decide what will happen next. How will the story end?
D. On separate paper, write ideas for your story or draw pictures that show what happens.

---

## Problem-Solving:
### Inductive Reasoning

**Focus:** The ability to combine clues and reach a conclusion based on those clues is an important thinking skill.

**Model:** This activity gives you sets of words. The words are in boxes that are connected. You have to put all the words in the connected boxes together to figure out what the storyteller is telling about.

**Practice:** Suppose you saw this set of boxes:

children — place
learn — teacher

The word in the first box tells you that the storyteller is telling about something that has to do with children. You would look at the other boxes for more clues—place, learn, teacher.

A place for children might be a playground, but that would not fit the other two clues. A place where children learn with a teacher is school. School is the word that all the clues lead to when you put them together, so you would write **school** in the bottom box.

children — place
learn — teacher
school

**Apply:** Now work on page 195.

1. Read the five words in the first set of connected boxes.

2. Put the clues together in your mind. Let the clues lead you to the word that tells what the storyteller's story is about.

3. Write the word in the bottom box.

4. Do the others the same way.

**Monitor:** When students have finished, discuss their answers.

1. The five clues together lead to the word *frog*—a small, green animal that hops, lives near a pond, and has bumpy skin.

2. The five clues together lead to the word *carrot*—a long, thin, orange vegetable that is sometimes cut into sticks.

3. The five clues together lead to a word such as *plane, airplane,* or *jet*—a silver thing with wings that makes a loud noise and flies in the sky.

4. The five clues together lead to the word *lion*—the "king of the jungle" that is wild, strong, has a mane, and roars.

You may want to ask for examples of other word clues that the storyteller could use for each of the four items.

**Summary:**
1. frog
2. carrot
3. plane
4. lion

---

## Problem-Solving:
### Inductive Reasoning

Putting clues together to figure something out is an important thinking skill.

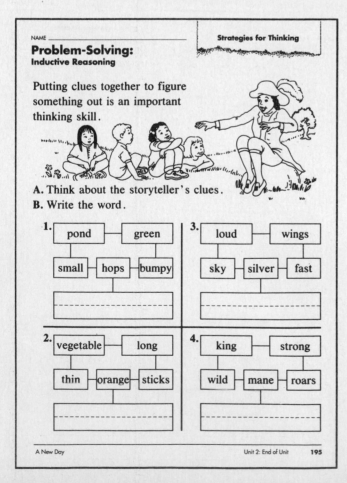

A. Think about the storyteller's clues.
B. Write the word.

1.
pond — green
small — hops — bumpy
_____

2.
vegetable — long
thin — orange — sticks
_____

3.
loud — wings
sky — silver — fast
_____

4.
king — strong
wild — mane — roars
_____

---

## Critical Thinking: Connotations

**Focus:** It is important to understand that words that mean almost the same thing can carry different feelings to the reader.

**Model:** This activity gives you a choice of two words below a blank in a sentence. You must choose the more exciting word and write it in the sentence.

**Practice:** Suppose you saw this sentence:

Rain _____ down.
came   poured

To decide which word is more exciting, you would try each word in the sentence. You would see which sentence has a more exciting feeling.

Here is the sentence with the first word: Rain came down. Here is the sentence with the second word: Rain poured down. The second sentence sounds like it is really raining hard. It sounds more active and exciting than the first sentence, so you would write **poured** in the blank.

**Apply:** Now work on page 197.

1. Read the sentence and the two words below it.

2. If you are not sure which word sounds more exciting, try reading the sentence with the first word in the blank and then with the second word.

3. Decide which word makes the sentence more exciting.

4. Write that word in the sentence.

**Monitor:** When students have finished, discuss their choices.

1. The wind blew all night long. The wind might blow hard or not so hard. That sentence is not very exciting. The wind roared all night long. The word *roared* makes the wind sound like a fierce lion. It tells you that the wind was blowing so hard that it made a roaring sound. That sentence is more exciting.

2. The ship moved to and fro. A ship might move just a tiny bit. The ship rocked to and fro. That sentence sounds like the ship is moving from one side to the other. That sentence is more exciting.

3. The word *large* is not very exciting. Many things might be large. The word *giant* is more exciting because it makes you feel that something is extremely large and unusual.

4. Something that is coming toward you might be moving slowly. Something that is tumbling toward you is rolling very, very fast. The word tumbling is more exciting.

**Summary:**
1. roared
2. rocked
3. giant
4. tumbling

## Critical Thinking: Connotations

It is important to think about the feelings
that words carry.

A storyteller is telling about a storm at
sea. Write the words that make her
story more exciting.

_____
- - - - - - - - - - - - - - - - - - - - - -

1. The wind _____ all night long.

        roared   blew

_____
- - - - - - - - - - - - - - - - - - - - - - -

2. The ship _____ to and fro.

       rocked   moved

_____
- - - - - - - - - - - - - - - -

3. Then the sailors saw a _____ wave.

      large   giant

_____
- - - - - - - - - - - - - - - -

4. The wave was _____ toward them.

     coming   tumbling

# Forms for Meeting Individual Needs

These forms are primarily for children who need assistance in organizing their thinking as they read the selections.

# Contents

# Story Map

**Beginning**

▼

**Middle**

▼

**End**

# Character Cluster

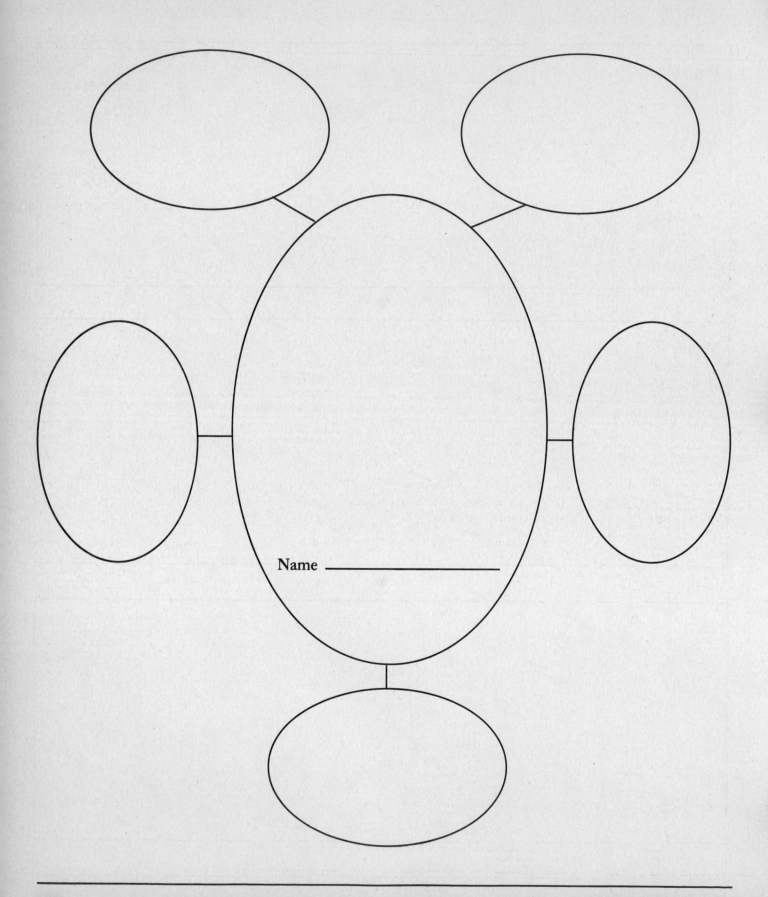

Name _____

# Problem/Solution

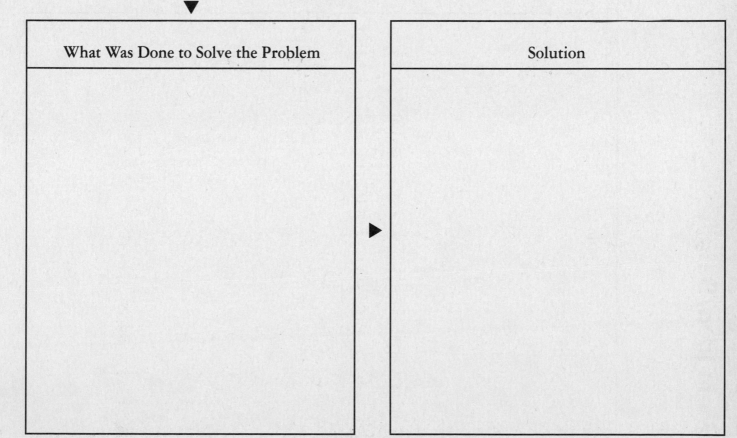

| Problem |
| --- |
| |

| What Was Done to Solve the Problem | Solution |
| --- | --- |
| | |

# Main Idea/Details

| Main Idea | Details |
| --- | --- |
| | |

# Sequence

1 ▲ 2 ▲ 3

# Comparison

| Alike | Different |
|---|---|
|  |  |

# Cause/Effect

| Cause | | Effect |
|-------|---|--------|
|  | ▶ |  |

| Cause | | Effect |
|-------|---|--------|
|  | ▶ |  |

# Predicting Outcomes

I Predict

What Happened

# Notetaking

| Key Words | Important Events or Ideas |
|---|---|
|  |  |

# Notetaking

| Who | What | Where or When |
|-----|------|---------------|
|     |      |               |

# Language Link Practice Masters

These masters provide meaningful practice in the basic building blocks of language: sentence structure, paragraph structure, parts of speech, and the mechanics of capitalization and punctuation.

Genuine understanding and long-term retention are aided by giving children this opportunity to practice grammar, usage, and mechanics skills as part of an integrated language arts curriculum.

The **Language Link Practice Masters** are referenced on the minilesson pages in the back of the Teacher Edition. The masters may be used at any time after the children have read the selection, whether or not the mini-lesson was formally conducted.

# Contents

# Complete Sentences

> • A **sentence** tells a complete idea.

► Find the sentence.

Write it.

**1. a.** Birds          **b.** Birds fly.

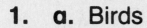 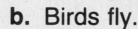

Birds fly.

**2. a.** Two birds see a tree.   **b.** Two birds

_____

_____

**3. a.** Two birds          **b.** Two birds make a nest.

_____

_____

**4. a.** Baby birds          **b.** Baby birds eat.

_____

_____

© Silver Burdett Ginn Inc.

# Asking Sentences

- An **asking sentence** asks something.
- Begin a sentence with a **capital letter**.
- End an **asking sentence** with a **question mark** [?] .

## How do birds fly?

► Write a question mark to end each asking sentence.
Draw a line to the picture the sentence asks about.

**1.** Where is Tip _____

**2.** Are you wet _____

**3.** Can it hop _____

**4.** Is this your hat _____

© Silver Burdett Ginn Inc.

# Word Order in Sentences

► Words must be in sentence order.
Find the sentence for each picture.
Underline the sentence.

1.

<u>The rain falls.</u>

rain falls. The

2.

swim. ducks Two

Two ducks swim.

3.

his Mike boots. wears

Mike wears his boots.

4.

Jenny has an umbrella.

has an Jenny umbrella.

5.

The wind blows hard.

The hard. blows wind

# Adjectives

> • An **adjective,** or **describing word,** tells more about a person, place, or thing.

**She has long hair.**

The word **long** tells more about the hair.

► Pick the describing word for each picture.
Write the describing word.

**tall        round**

1. a __tall__ tree

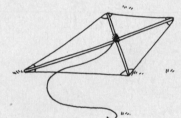

**green        short**

2. a _____ string

**long        round**

3. a _____ balloon

**soft        long**

4. a _____ kitten

# Nouns

> • A **naming word** names a person, place, or thing.

 **farmer**    **store**    **boat**

► Circle the word that names the person.
Write the word.

   child

(father)   1. ___father___

► Circle the word that names the place.
Write the word.

   farm

city   2. _____

► Circle the words that name the things.
Write the words.

   bike

horse   3. _____

car   4. _____

© Silver Burdett Ginn Inc.

# Verbs

> • A word that shows action is a **verb**.

► Write the correct action word under each picture.

**dance**     **build**     **paint**

1. ___paint___    2. _____    3. _____

► Write the correct action word in each sentence.

**laugh**     **stop**     **walk**

4. We _____ to school.

5. The children _____ at a red light.

6. They _____ at a joke.

# One or More Than One

> • Many words add **s** to mean **more than one**.

 **duck**     **ducks**

► Add <u>s</u> to mean more than one.
Write the word under the picture.

**door**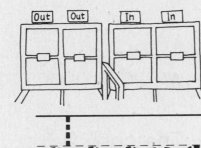

1. doors

**cart**

2. _____

**can**

3. _____

**toy**

4. _____

**jar**

5. _____

**bag**

6. _____

# Writing Telling Sentences

> - A **telling sentence** tells something .
> - Begin a sentence with a **capital letter** .
> - End a **telling sentence** with a **period** $\boxed{\cdot}$ .

▶ Find the correct sentences.
Underline them.

1. Our class has a party.

2. we have good food

3. we play games

4. The party is fun.

▶ Write the sentences correctly.

5. they have balloons

_____

- - - - - - - - - - - - - - - - - - -

_____

6. he makes a face

_____

- - - - - - - - - - - - - - - - - - -

_____

7. the party is over

_____

- - - - - - - - - - - - - - - - - - -

_____

"The Tyrannosaurus Game"

# Adding -ed To Verbs

Add **ed** to an action word to tell about the past.

**Today we walk.**     **Yesterday we walked.**

▶ Read the sentences.
Look at the action word that tells about **Now**.
Circle the action word that tells about **In the Past.**

| **Now** | **In the Past** |
|---|---|
| **1.** Today we (call) . | Yesterday we (called) . |
| **2.** Now the dogs (bark) . | Last night the dogs barked. |
| **3.** Now they (jump) . | Yesterday they jumped . |
| **4.** Today we (learn) . | Last year we learned. |
| **5.** Now we (play) outside. | Last week we played outside. |

# Telling Sentences

- A **telling sentence** tells something.
- Begin a sentence with a **capital letter**.
- End a **telling sentence** with a **period** . .

## I have a friend.

► Read the sentence.
Draw a line to the picture it tells about.

**1.** We ride our bikes.

**2.** She shows me her fish.

**3.** We read a book.

**4.** The rain comes down.

# Special Nouns

> • The names of people, pets, and places begin with **capital letters**.

**My friend <u>M</u>ike lives in <u>W</u>ashington.**

► Look at the picture.
Write the name in the sentence.

 **Amy**

1. The girl is _Amy_ .

 **Puff**

2. Her cat is _____ .

 **Florida**

3. They live in _____ .

 **Dad**

4. This man is _____ .

# Special Nouns

> • The names of people, pets, and places begin with **capital letters**.

► Circle the names that are written correctly.

**1.** Billy       billy

**2.** tina       Tina

**3.** spot       Spot

**4.** Texas       texas

► Write the names correctly in the sentences.

**5.** The girl is _____ .

**6.** The dog is _____ .

**7.** They walk on _____ .

**8.** The woman is _____ .

# Pronouns

> • **He, she,** and **it** can take the place of nouns, or naming words.

**The boy jumps.**
**He jumps.**

► Match the sentences with the pictures.

**1.** The boy sees a bird.　　　　　She has food.

**2.** The bird flies away.　　　　　It eats the food.

**3.** A girl sees the bird.　　　　　He sees a bird.

**4.** The girl has food.　　　　　It flies away.

**5.** The bird eats the food.　　　　She sees the bird.

# Pronouns

    **A. Donna** walks to school.

    **B. She** sees her friend.

Both sentences tell about Donna.

The word **she** takes the place of the word

**Donna** in Sentence B.

► Read the sentence.

Change it by writing **he**, **she**, or **it**.

**1.** Mike has a party.

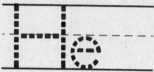 has a party.

**2.** Annie brings a present.

_____

------------------------

_____ brings a present.

**3.** Mother makes popcorn.

_____

------------------------

_____ makes popcorn.

**4.** Popcorn tastes good.

_____

------------------------

_____ tastes good.

# Writing Telling Sentences

► Write telling sentences about each picture.
Use words from the boxes.

| a    | frogs | swims |
|------|-------|-------|
| two  | fish  | hop   |

1. A fish swims.

2. _____

| some | bees   | sleep |
|------|--------|-------|
| a    | turtle | fly   |
| the  | birds  | hides |

3. _____

4. _____

5. _____

# Verbs

> • A word that shows action is a **verb**.

The man **swims**.            The men **swim**.

► Read the sentence.
Underline the action word.
Write the action word.

1. The children run.   <u>run</u> _____

2. One girl jumps.   _____

3. The cat hides.   _____

4. They wash the dog.   _____

5. The little rabbits hop.   _____

6. The teacher tells a story.   _____

# Color Words

► Think of a sunny spring day.
Draw a line from the color word to the thing it describes.

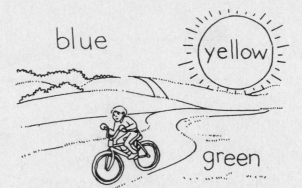

**1.** green          sun

**2.** yellow         sky

**3.** blue           grass

► Pick the best color word.
Write it in the sentence.

**yellow     red     orange     green**

_____

**4.** I want a _____ banana.

**5.** Bobby takes a _____ apple.

**6.** Bunny eats an _____ carrot.

**7.** Bug eats a _____ leaf.

# Number Words

| one | two | three | four | five |
|-----|-----|-------|------|------|
| six | seven | eight | nine | ten |

► Find the correct number word.
Write it in the sentence.

_____
------------------------------

**1.** There are _____ pencils on the table.

_____
------------------------------

**2.** We see _____ pieces of paper.

_____
------------------------------

**3.** There is _____ eraser.

_____
------------------------------

**4.** We see _____ crayons.

_____
------------------------------

**5.** There are _____ markers on the table.

# Parts of a Sentence

| Naming Part | Telling Part |
|---|---|
| The cow | eats grass. |

**The cow eats grass.**

This sentence has two parts.

The **naming part** names a person or thing.

The **telling part** tells what the person or thing does.

► Match the naming part with the telling part.

1. The ball          plays with the ball.

2. The kitten          rolls.

3. The girl          swings.

4. The boy          barks.

5. The dog          climbs high.

► Read the sentences you made above.

Write the sentence about the dog.

_____

- - - - - - - - - - - - - - - - - - - - - - -

6. _____

© Silver Burdett Ginn Inc.

# Using *Is* and *Are*

> • The words **is** and **are** tell about now.

**The cat <u>is</u> big.**

**The kittens <u>are</u> small.**

Use **<u>is</u>** to tell about **<u>one</u>**.

Use **<u>are</u>** to tell about **<u>more than one</u>**.

► Underline **<u>is</u>** or **<u>are</u>** in each sentence.
Then write the underlined word.

**1.** The ice <u>is</u> cold. _____

is

**2.** Her skates <u>are</u> new. _____

**3.** They <u>are</u> happy. _____

**4.** The game <u>is</u> fun. _____

**5.** The game <u>is</u> on the table. _____

# Writing Asking Sentences

> - An **asking sentence** asks something.
> - Begin a sentence with a **capital letter**.
> - End an **asking sentence** with a **question mark** [ ? ] .

► Underline the asking sentences.

**1.** Are you ready?

**2.** We are ready.

**3.** Today is Halloween.

**4.** Is today Halloween?

► Write the asking sentence correctly.

**5.** who are you

_____

_____

_____

**6.** which one is Tommy

_____

_____

_____

**7.** do we look funny

_____

_____

_____

# Using *Go* and *Went*

> • The word **go** tells about now.
> • The word **went** tells about the past.

► Circle the correct word for each sentence.

**1.** Last year we ( go, went ) to a lake.

**2.** Now we ( go, went ) there for a picnic.

**3.** Yesterday we ( go, went ) to the store.

**4.** Last night I ( go, went ) to the kitchen.

► Write **go** or **went** in each sentence.

**5.** Now I _____ to this school.

**6.** Last year I _____ to a different school.

**7.** Rosa _____ to this school last year.

**8.** Now Rosa and I _____ to school together.

# Adverbs

## Little Bear goes out.

The word **out** tells **where** he goes.

► Write the word that tells **where**.

_____

**1.** He runs outside. _____

_____

**2.** He jumps up. _____

_____

**3.** He walks there. _____

_____

**4.** He comes inside. _____

► Draw a picture of Little Bear.
Show where he goes.

## Complete Sentences

> • A **sentence** tells a complete idea.

► Find the sentence.
Write it.

1. **a.** Birds          **b.** Birds fly.

Birds fly.

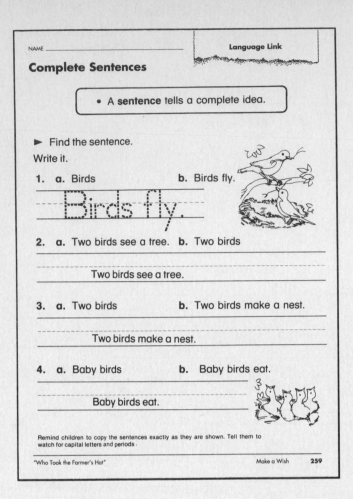

2. **a.** Two birds see a tree.   **b.** Two birds

_____

Two birds see a tree.

3. **a.** Two birds          **b.** Two birds make a nest.

_____

Two birds make a nest.

4. **a.** Baby birds          **b.** Baby birds eat.

_____

Baby birds eat.

Remind children to copy the sentences exactly as they are shown. Tell them to watch for capital letters and periods .

## Asking Sentences

> • An **asking sentence** asks something.
> • Begin a sentence with a **capital letter**.
> • End an **asking sentence** with a **question mark** [?] .

**How do birds fly?**

► Write a question mark to end each asking sentence.
Draw a line to the picture the sentence asks about.

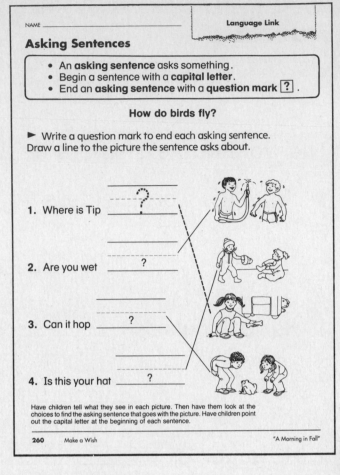

1. Where is Tip _____ ?

2. Are you wet _____ ?

3. Can it hop _____ ?

4. Is this your hat _____ ?

Have children tell what they see in each picture. Then have them look at the choices to find the asking sentence that goes with the picture. Have children point out the capital letter at the beginning of each sentence.

## Word Order in Sentences

► Words must be in sentence order.
Find the sentence for each picture.
Underline the sentence.

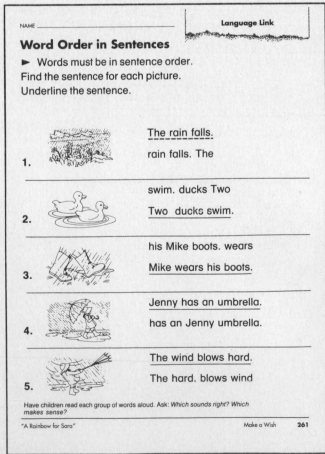

1.   The rain falls.
     rain falls. The

2.   swim. ducks Two
     Two  ducks swim.

3.   his Mike boots. wears
     Mike wears his boots.

4.   Jenny has an umbrella.
     has an Jenny umbrella.

5.   The wind blows hard.
     The hard. blows wind

Have children read each group of words aloud. Ask: *Which sounds right? Which makes sense?*

## Adjectives

> • An **adjective**, or **describing word**, tells more about a person, place, or thing.

**She has long hair.**

The word **long** tells more about the hair.

► Pick the describing word for each picture.
Write the describing word.

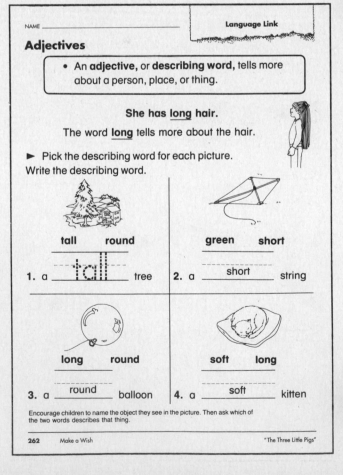

**tall     round**          **green     short**

1. a    tall    tree     2. a    short    string

**long     round**          **soft     long**

3. a    round    balloon     4. a    soft    kitten

Encourage children to name the object they see in the picture. Then ask which of the two words describes that thing.

© Silver Burdett Ginn Inc.

**282**

## Nouns

NAME _____

- A **naming word** names a person, place, or thing.

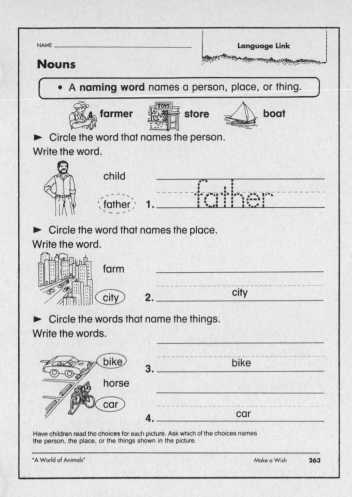

**farmer**     **store**     **boat**

► Circle the word that names the person.
Write the word.

child

(father)  1. father

► Circle the word that names the place.
Write the word.

farm

(city)  2. city

► Circle the words that name the things.
Write the words.

bike

(horse)  3. bike

(car)  4. car

Have children read the choices for each picture. Ask which of the choices names
the person, the place, or the things shown in the picture.

"A World of Animals"     Make a Wish     **263**

---

## Verbs

NAME _____

- A word that shows action is a **verb**.

► Write the correct action word under each picture.

**dance     build     paint**

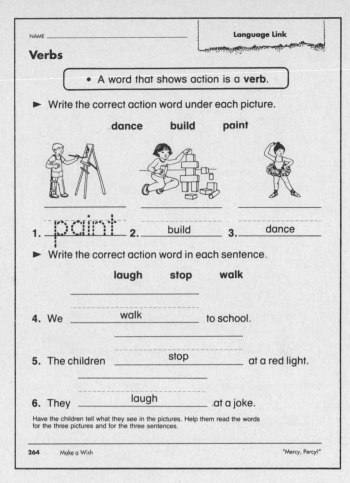

1. paint     2. build     3. dance

► Write the correct action word in each sentence.

**laugh     stop     walk**

4. We _____ walk _____ to school.

5. The children _____ stop _____ at a red light.

6. They _____ laugh _____ at a joke.

Have the children tell what they see in the pictures. Help them read the words
for the three pictures and for the three sentences.

**264**     Make a Wish     "Mercy, Percy!"

---

## One or More Than One

NAME _____

- Many words add **s** to mean **more than one**.

**duck     ducks**

► Add **s** to mean more than one.
Write the word under the picture.

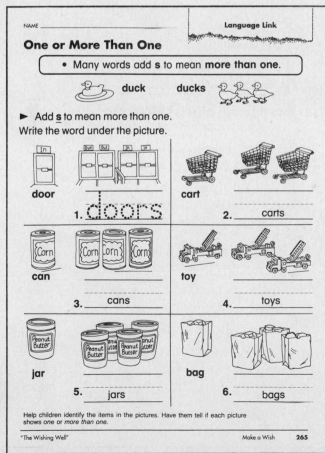

**door**

1. doors

**cart**

2. carts

**can**

3. cans

**toy**

4. toys

**jar**

5. jars

**bag**

6. bags

Help children identify the items in the pictures. Have them tell if each picture
shows one or more than one.

"The Wishing Well"     Make a Wish     **265**

---

## Writing Telling Sentences

NAME _____

- A **telling sentence** tells something.
- Begin a sentence with a **capital letter**.
- End a **telling sentence** with a **period** .

► Find the correct sentences.
Underline them.

1. Our class has a party.     2. we have good food

3. we play games     4. The party is fun.

► Write the sentences correctly.

5. they have balloons

_____ They have balloons. _____

6. he makes a face

_____ He makes a face. _____

7. the party is over

_____ The party is over. _____

Have children tell why each of sentences 1-4 is correct or incorrect. Review capital
letters and periods before children write.

**266**     Make a Wish     "The Tyrannosaurus Game"

**283**

## Adding -ed To Verbs

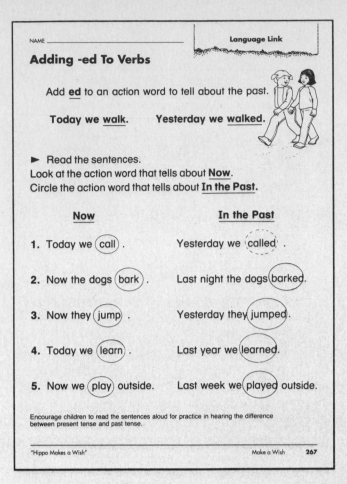

Add **ed** to an action word to tell about the past.

**Today we <u>walk</u>.**    **Yesterday we <u>walked</u>.**

► Read the sentences.
Look at the action word that tells about <u>**Now**</u>.
Circle the action word that tells about <u>**In the Past**</u>.

| <u>**Now**</u> | <u>**In the Past**</u> |
|---|---|
| **1.** Today we (call) . | Yesterday we (called) . |
| **2.** Now the dogs (bark) . | Last night the dogs (barked) . |
| **3.** Now they (jump) . | Yesterday they (jumped) . |
| **4.** Today we (learn) . | Last year we (learned) . |
| **5.** Now we (play) outside. | Last week we (played) outside. |

Encourage children to read the sentences aloud for practice in hearing the difference between present tense and past tense.

---

## Telling Sentences

- A **telling sentence** tells something.
- Begin a sentence with a **capital letter**.
- End a **telling sentence** with a **period** [ . ] .

### I have a friend.

► Read the sentence.
Draw a line to the picture it tells about.

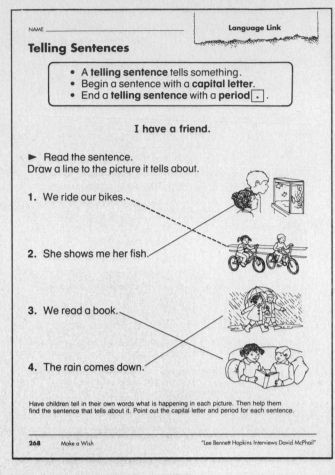

**1.** We ride our bikes.

**2.** She shows me her fish.

**3.** We read a book.

**4.** The rain comes down.

Have children tell in their own words what is happening in each picture. Then help them find the sentence that tells about it. Point out the capital letter and period for each sentence.

---

## Special Nouns

- The names of people, pets, and places begin with **capital letters**.

### My friend <u>Mike</u> lives in <u>Washington</u>.

► Look at the picture.
Write the name in the sentence.

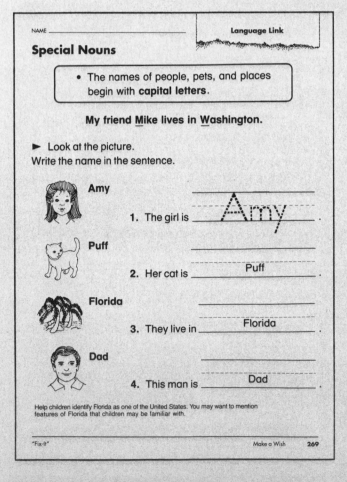

**Amy**

**1.** The girl is ___Amy___ .

**Puff**

**2.** Her cat is ___Puff___ .

**Florida**

**3.** They live in ___Florida___ .

**Dad**

**4.** This man is ___Dad___ .

Help children identify Florida as one of the United States. You may want to mention features of Florida that children may be familiar with.

---

## Special Nouns

- The names of people, pets, and places begin with **capital letters**.

► Circle the names that are written correctly.

| | | | |
|---|---|---|---|
| **1.** (Billy)  billy | | **2.** tina  (Tina) | |
| **3.** spot  (Spot) | | **4.** (Texas)  texas | |

► Write the names correctly in the sentences.

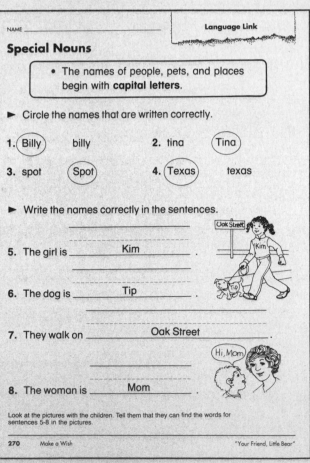

**5.** The girl is ___Kim___ .

**6.** The dog is ___Tip___ .

**7.** They walk on ___Oak Street___ .

**8.** The woman is ___Mom___ .

Look at the pictures with the children. Tell them that they can find the words for sentences 5-8 in the pictures.

## Pronouns

> • **He, she,** and **it** can take the place of nouns, or naming words.

**The boy jumps.**
**He jumps.**

► Match the sentences with the pictures.

1. The boy sees a bird.

2. The bird flies away.

3. A girl sees the bird.

4. The girl has food.

5. The bird eats the food.

She has food.

It eats the food.

He sees a bird.

It flies away.

She sees the bird.

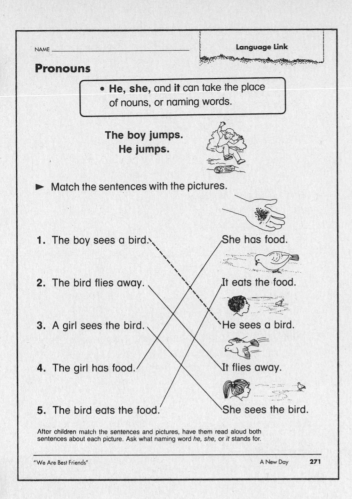

After children match the sentences and pictures, have them read aloud both sentences about each picture. Ask what naming word *he, she,* or *it* stands for.

"We Are Best Friends"  A New Day  **271**

---

## Pronouns

**A. Donna** walks to school.
**B. She** sees her friend.
Both sentences tell about Donna.
The word **she** takes the place of the word
**Donna** in Sentence B.

► Read the sentence.
Change it by writing **he, she,** or **it**.

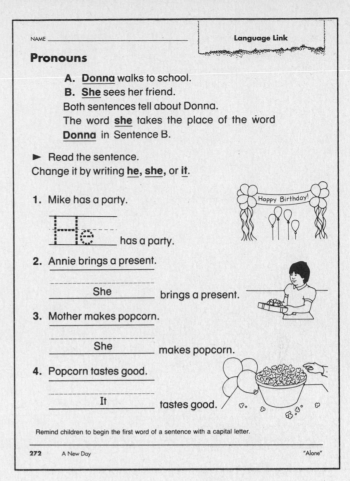

1. Mike has a party.

He _____ has a party.

2. Annie brings a present.

_____ She _____ brings a present.

3. Mother makes popcorn.

_____ She _____ makes popcorn.

4. Popcorn tastes good.

_____ It _____ tastes good.

Remind children to begin the first word of a sentence with a capital letter.

**272**  A New Day  "Alone"

---

## Writing Telling Sentences

► Write telling sentences about each picture.
Use words from the boxes.

| a | frogs | swims |
| two | fish | hop |

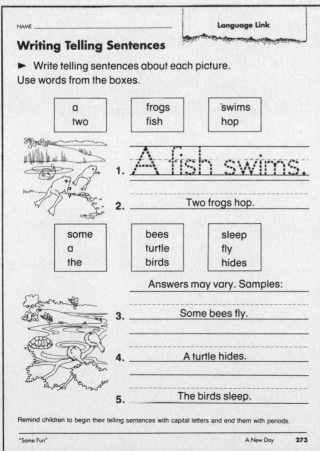

1. A fish swims.

2. Two frogs hop.

| some | bees | sleep |
| a | turtle | fly |
| the | birds | hides |

Answers may vary. Samples:

3. Some bees fly.

4. A turtle hides.

5. The birds sleep.

Remind children to begin their telling sentences with capital letters and end them with periods.

"Some Fun"  A New Day  **273**

---

## Verbs

> • A word that shows action is a **verb**.

**The man swims.**     **The men swim.**

► Read the sentence.
Underline the action word.
Write the action word.

1. The children run.     run

2. One girl jumps.     jumps

3. The cat hides.     hides

4. They wash the dog.     wash

5. The little rabbits hop.     hop

6. The teacher tells a story.     tells

Help children read the sentences and tell which word shows action.

**274**  A New Day  "Together"

---

## Color Words

► Think of a sunny spring day.
Draw a line from the color word to the thing it describes.

1. green —— sun
2. yellow —— sky
3. blue —— grass

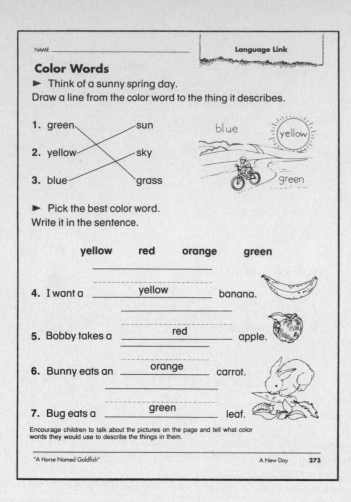

blue
yellow
green

► Pick the best color word.
Write it in the sentence.

**yellow    red    orange    green**

4. I want a ____yellow____ banana.

5. Bobby takes a ____red____ apple.

6. Bunny eats an ____orange____ carrot.

7. Bug eats a ____green____ leaf.

Encourage children to talk about the pictures on the page and tell what color
words they would use to describe the things in them.

## Number Words

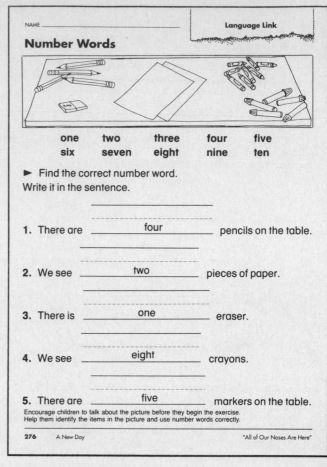

| one | two | three | four | five |
| six | seven | eight | nine | ten |

► Find the correct number word.
Write it in the sentence.

1. There are ____four____ pencils on the table.

2. We see ____two____ pieces of paper.

3. There is ____one____ eraser.

4. We see ____eight____ crayons.

5. There are ____five____ markers on the table.

Encourage children to talk about the picture before they begin the exercise.
Help them identify the items in the picture and use number words correctly.

## Parts of a Sentence

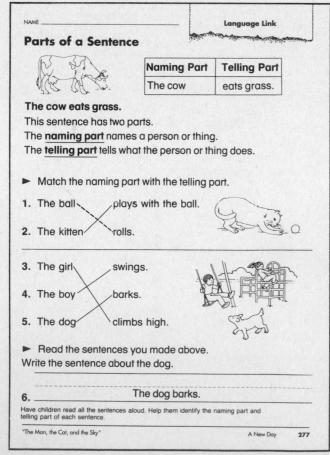

| Naming Part | Telling Part |
|---|---|
| The cow | eats grass. |

**The cow eats grass.**
This sentence has two parts.
The **naming part** names a person or thing.
The **telling part** tells what the person or thing does.

► Match the naming part with the telling part.

1. The ball —— plays with the ball.
2. The kitten —— rolls.

3. The girl —— swings.
4. The boy —— barks.
5. The dog —— climbs high.

► Read the sentences you made above.
Write the sentence about the dog.

6. ____The dog barks.____

Have children read all the sentences aloud. Help them identify the naming part and
telling part of each sentence.

## Using *Is* and *Are*

• The words **is** and **are** tell about now.

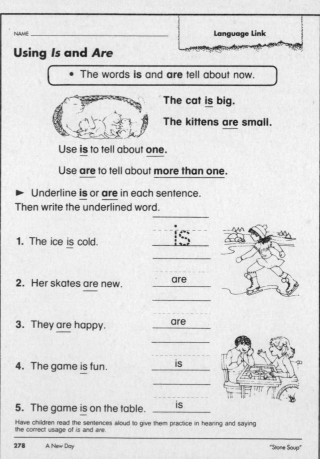

**The cat is big.**
**The kittens are small.**

Use **is** to tell about **one**.

Use **are** to tell about **more than one**.

► Underline **is** or **are** in each sentence.
Then write the underlined word.

1. The ice is cold.    ____is____

2. Her skates are new.    ____are____

3. They are happy.    ____are____

4. The game is fun.    ____is____

5. The game is on the table.    ____is____

Have children read the sentences aloud to give them practice in hearing and saying
the correct usage of *is* and *are*.

NAME _____

## Writing Asking Sentences

- An **asking** sentence asks something.
- Begin a sentence with a **capital letter**.
- End an **asking sentence** with a **question mark** ? .

► Underline the asking sentences.

1. <u>Are you ready?</u>    2. We are ready.

3. Today is Halloween.    4. <u>Is today Halloween?</u>

► Write the asking sentence correctly.

5. who are you

_____

Who are you?

6. which one is Tommy

_____

Which one is Tommy?

7. do we look funny

_____

Do we look funny?

In exercises 1-4, have children read the sentences aloud. Point out that their voices go up at the end of an asking sentence. Before children write sentences 5-7, review capital letters and question marks.

---

NAME _____

## Using *Go* and *Went*

- The word **go** tells about now.
- The word **went** tells about the past.

► Circle the correct word for each sentence.

1. Last year we ( go, (went) ) to a lake.

2. Now we ( (go,) went ) there for a picnic.

3. Yesterday we ( go, (went) ) to the store.

4. Last night I ( go, (went) ) to the kitchen.

► Write **go** or **went** in each sentence.

5. Now I _____ go _____ to this school.

6. Last year I _____ went _____ to a different school.

7. Rosa _____ went _____ to this school last year.

8. Now Rosa and I _____ go _____ to school together.

Encourage children to read sentences aloud, and to identify words that show if the action is now or in the past.

---

NAME _____

## Adverbs

**Little Bear goes out.**

The word **out** tells **where** he goes.

► Write the word that tells **where.**

1. He runs outside. _____ outside _____

2. He jumps up. _____ up _____

3. He walks there. _____ there _____

4. He comes inside. _____ inside _____

► Draw a picture of Little Bear.
Show where he goes.

# Spelling Link Practice Masters

These masters provide practice that will facilitate the process of learning to spell. Each master is based on a spelling generalization that is developmentally appropriate to the grade level.

The parts of each master are solidly grounded in and supported by current research.

• The word list has as a starting point words taken from the reading selection. Additional words are selected according to such criteria as frequency of use and level of difficulty.

• In Speller's Choice, children are given an opportunity to add words of their own to the list. Current research affirms that self-generated word lists increase children's understanding of basic spelling principles.

The **Spelling Link Practice Masters** are referenced on the minilesson pages in the back of the Teacher Edition. The masters may be used at any time after the children have read the selection, whether or not the mini-lesson was formally conducted.

# Contents

Say the words **hat** and **cake**. Listen for the short **a** sound in **hat**. Listen for the long **a** sound in **cake**.

**A.** Say each spelling word. Listen for a long or a short vowel sound.

### Spelling Words

bed   cake   hat   bike   duck   mop

**B.** Write spelling words. Name things you can sit on.

_____   _____

1. _____   2. _____

**C.** Write a spelling word for each picture.

_____   _____

3. _____   4. _____

_____   _____

5. _____   6. _____

**SPELLER'S CHOICE**   Write two new words to learn to spell.

_____   _____

_____   _____

Say the words **eat** and **sleep.** The letters **ee** and **ea** can spell the long **e** sound you hear in these words.

**A.** Say each spelling word. Listen for the long **e** sound.

### Spelling Words

dream   leaf   sleep   eat   read   tree

**B.** Write the words with long **e** spelled **ee.**

_____        _____

1. _____   2. _____

**C.** Write the words with long **e** spelled **ea.**

_____        _____

3. _____   4. _____

_____        _____

5. _____   6. _____

**SPELLER'S CHOICE**   Write two new words to learn to spell.

_____        _____

_____        _____

© Silver Burdett Ginn Inc.

Say the words **free** and **he.** Listen for the long **e** sound. The letters **ee** and **e** can spell the long **e** sound you hear in these words.

**A.** Say the spelling words. Listen for the long **e** vowel sound.

### Spelling Words

free    he    me    green    keep    see

**A.** Write spelling words that are things you can do.

_____    _____

1. _____    2. _____

**B.** Write the spelling words with long **e** spelled **e.**

_____    _____

3. _____    4. _____

**C.** Write two spelling words with long **e** spelled **ee.**

_____    _____

5. _____    6. _____

**SPELLER'S CHOICE**    Write two new words to learn to spell.

_____    _____

_____    _____

The ending **er** can compare two things.

The ending **est** can compare three things.

### Spelling Words

fast    old    strong    long    small    tall

**small**        **smaller**        **smallest**

**A.** Look at the fish. Which is the smallest? Circle it.

**B.** Find the spelling words with **er** and **est.**

   Circle them.

```
r e d f a s t e r o r
i s m a l l e s t l o
t o l o n g e r a d d
f o r s t r o n g e r
u n d e r o l d e s t
n o t t a l l e s t o
```

**SPELLER'S CHOICE**   Write two new words to learn to spell.

_____    _____

- - - - - - - - - - - - - - - - - - -    - - - - - - - - - - - - - - - - - - -

_____    _____

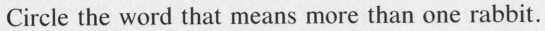

When **s** is added to a naming word, the word names more than one thing.

**A.** Read the spelling words.

Circle the word that means more than one rabbit.

**Spelling Words**

bear    dog    rabbits    cat    pig    turtles

**B.** Write spelling words. Which words mean more than one?

_____

**1.** _____

**2.** _____

**C.** Write words for the pictures. Add **s** for more than one.

_____        _____

**3.** _____    **4.** _____

**5.** _____    **6.** _____

**SPELLER'S CHOICE**    Write two new words to learn to spell.

_____        _____

© Silver Burdett Ginn Inc.

We add **ed** to an action word to tell that something happened in the past.

**A.** Say the spelling words. Circle the words that tell about the past.

### Spelling Words

cooked    play    talk    looked    stay    walk

**B.** Find the action words that tell about the past.

Write them to tell about now.

I cooked a fish, and looked for a dish.

_____          _____

**1.** _____  **2.** _____

**C.** Find the action words that tell about now.

Write them with **ed** to tell about the past.

We play in the park, but stay home after dark.

_____          _____

**3.** _____  **4.** _____

We walk in the rain, then talk on the train.

_____          _____

**5.** _____  **6.** _____

**SPELLER'S CHOICE**    Write two new words to learn to spell.

_____          _____

_____          _____

When **s** is added to a naming word, the word names more than one thing.

**A.** Say each spelling word to mean more than one.

### Spelling Words

apple    horse    tree    day    train    truck

**B.** Help to finish the story.

Add **s** to the words in (   ). Write the new words.

_____

Grandpa has many (tree) _____ on his farm.

_____

They are filled with (apple) _____ .

_____

It takes (day) _____ to pick them.

_____

Now (truck) _____ take them.

**SPELLER'S CHOICE**    Write two new words to learn to spell.

_____      _____

Two small words can be put together to make a longer word. It is called a **compound word.** It has some of the meaning of both small words.

**A.** Look at the word **rainbow.** Draw a line between the two smaller words that make up this word.

### Spelling Words

baseball  doghouse  playground  bedroom  outside  rainbow

**B.** Match the words to make compound words.

| | | |
|---|---|---|
| **1.** play | **a.** side | |
| **2.** bed | **b.** ground | |
| **3.** out | **c.** room | |
| **4.** base | **d.** bow | |
| **5.** dog | **e.** ball | |
| **6.** rain | **f.** house | |

**C.** Write the words you matched for **1** and **2.**

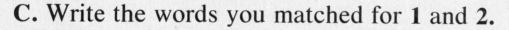

**1.** _____

_____

**2.** _____

**SPELLER'S CHOICE**   Write two new words to learn to spell.

_____     _____

_____     _____

© Silver Burdett Ginn Inc.

_____

Say the picture word **cake**. Listen for the long **a** sound.

**A.** Say each spelling word. Listen for the long **a** sound.

### Spelling Words

date    make    snake    late    say    today

**B.** Say the picture word. Write two spelling words that rhyme.

cake

_____    _____

1. _____    2. _____

gate

_____    _____

3. _____    4. _____

hay

_____    _____

5. _____    6. _____

**SPELLER'S CHOICE**   Write new words to learn to spell.

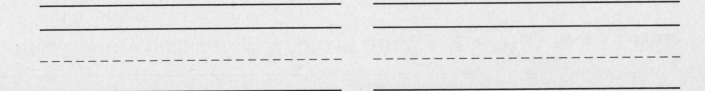

Say the words **see, find,** and **told.** Listen for three different long vowel sounds.

**A.** Say each spelling word. Circle two words that rhyme.

### Spelling Words

find    mind    trees    home    see    told

**B.** Say the picture word.

Listen for the vowel sound.

Write spelling words with the same vowel sound.

**SPELLER'S CHOICE** Write two new words to learn to spell.

_____    _____

_ _ _ _ _ _ _ _ _ _ _ _ _ _ _    _ _ _ _ _ _ _ _ _ _ _ _ _ _ _

_____    _____

Sometimes two letters spell one sound. Say the word **room.** Listen to the sound the letters **oo** spell. It is one sound.

**A.** Say each spelling word. Look for the two letters that spell one sound.

### Spelling Words

blue　four　room　feel　green　too

**B.** Choose four spelling words.

Write them in alphabetical order.

_____

1. _____

2. _____

3. _____

4. _____

**SPELLER'S CHOICE**　Write two new words to learn to spell.

_____　_____

Say the word **link**. The letters **k** and **ck** can stand for the sound at the end of **link**.

**A.** Look at the spelling words. Say each one. Find the letters that stand for the last sound in **link**. Underline them.

### Spelling Words

back    drink    pink    black    milk    thank

**B.** Which words have the last sound spelled **ck?** Write them.

1. _____    2. _____

**C.** Which words have the last sound spelled **k?**

3. _____    4. _____

5. _____    6. _____

**SPELLER'S CHOICE**    Write two new words to learn to spell.

_____    _____

Say the word **five**. Listen for the long **i** sound.

**A.** Say each spelling word. Listen for the long **i** sound.

### Spelling Words

by     fight     my     dive     five     right

**B.** Say the picture word. Write two spelling words that rhyme.

**hive**

_____     _____

1. _____     2. _____

**night**

_____     _____

3. _____     4. _____

**fly**

_____     _____

5. _____     6. _____

**SPELLER'S CHOICE**    Write two new words to learn to spell.

_____     _____

_____     _____

Say the word **king.** The letters **k** and **ck** stand for the sound at the end of **chick.**

**A.** Say each spelling word. Listen for the **k** sound.

### Spelling Words

chick    kiss    look    kick    like    think

**B.** Which words have the **k** sound spelled **k?** Write them.

1. _____    2. _____

3. _____    4. _____

5. _____

**C.** Which words have the last sound spelled **ck?** Write them.

6. _____    7. _____

**SPELLER'S CHOICE**   Write two new words to learn to spell.

_____    _____

The letters **sh** stand for the first sound in **ship** and the last sound in **dish.**

**A.** Say each spelling word. Listen for the **sh** sound.

**Spelling Words**

dish    shape    shell    fish    sheep    ship

**B.** Finish each word. Find the hidden word.

1.    f i ☐ h

2.    d i s ☐

3.  s h a p ☐

4.    s h ☐ l l

5.    s h i ☐

**C.** The letters in the boxes spell a word.
Write the word.

_____

6. _____

**SPELLER'S CHOICE**   Write two new words to learn to spell.

_____    _____

_____    _____

Say the word **first.** The letters **ir, er, ur,** and **or** stand for the vowel sound you hear.

**A.** Say each spelling word. Circle the word that rhymes with **mother.**

### Spelling Words

first    other    turtle    her    together    work

**B.** Choose four spelling words. Write them in alphabetical order.

_____

- - - - - - - - - - - - - - - - - - - - - - -

_____

- - - - - - - - - - - - - - - - - - - - - - -

_____

- - - - - - - - - - - - - - - - - - - - - - -

_____

- - - - - - - - - - - - - - - - - - - - - - -

_____

**SPELLER'S CHOICE**   Write two new words to learn to spell.

_____    _____

- - - - - - - - - - -    - - - - - - - - - - -

_____    _____

Some sounds are spelled with more than one letter. The letters **ch** and **tch** stand for the last sound in **lunch** and **catch.** The letters **th** stand for the first sound in **that.**

**A.** Say each spelling word. Find the letters **ch**, **tch**, and **th**.

### Spelling Words

catch    that    they    lunch    then    think

**B.** Write the spelling words in which you find each smaller word.

ink

cat

1. _____

2. _____

hat

hen

3. _____

4. _____

 

he 5. _____

**C.** Write the spelling word that is not hiding a smaller word.

_____

6. _____

**SPELLER'S CHOICE**   Write two new words to learn to spell.

_____    _____

_____    _____

The letters **o, oa,** and **ow** stand for the vowel sound you hear in **boat.**

**A.** Say each spelling word. Listen for the vowel sound you hear in **boat.**

### Spelling Words

boat   no   show   go   over   slow

**B.** Write the opposite for each word.

**stop**

_____

1. _____

**yes**

_____

3. _____

**under**

_____

5. _____

**fast**

_____

2. _____

**hide**

_____

4. _____

**C.** Write the word you did not use.

_____

_____

**SPELLER'S CHOICE**   Write two new words to learn to spell.

_____

_____

The letters **er** stand for the last sounds in **water** and **other**.

**A.** Say each spelling word. Underline the letters **er** in each word.

### Spelling Words

other    river    mother    never    water    father

**B.** Write a spelling word in each shape.

1. 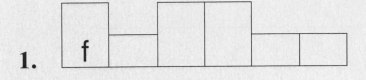 f

2. 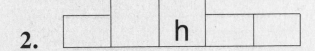 h

3. n

4. 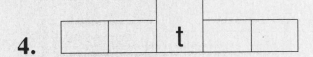 t

5. i

6. 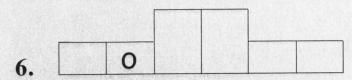 o

**SPELLER'S CHOICE** Write two new words to learn to spell.

_____    _____

- - - - - - - - - - - - -    - - - - - - - - - - - - -

_____    _____

© Silver Burdett Ginn Inc.

The letters **th** stand for the first sound in **they** and the last sound in **with**.

**A.** Say each spelling word. Listen for the **th** sound.

### Spelling Words

bath    south    they    north    teeth    third

**B.** The words in each group belong together. Add words to groups.

_____

**1.** first, second, _____

_____

**2.** mouth, lips, _____

_____    _____

**3.** east, west, _____ , _____

_____

**4.** soap, towel, _____

_____

**5.** them, their, _____

**SPELLER'S CHOICE**   Write two new words to learn to spell.

_____    _____

_____    _____

_____

Add **ed** to an action word to tell that something happened in the past.

**A.** Say each spelling word. Underline the words that tell about the past.

### Spelling Words

like    play    saved    lived    roll    walked

**B.** Which words tell about what is happening now? Make them tell about the past. Write them.

_____    _____

1. _____    2. _____

3. _____

**C.** Which words tell about what happened in the past? Make them tell about now. Write them.

_____    _____

4. _____    5. _____

6. _____

**SPELLER'S CHOICE**    Write two new words to learn to spell.

_____    _____

_____    _____

An action word with **ing** at the end shows that the action is still going on.

**A.** Say each spelling word. Underline the **ing** ending in each word.

### Spelling Words

cooking    helping    singing    drawing    jumping    smiling

**B.** Write the spelling word that tells about each picture.

1. _____

2. _____

3. _____

4. _____

5. _____

**SPELLER'S CHOICE**   Write two new words to learn to spell.

_____   _____

Say the words **here, there,** and **over.** Listen for three different vowel sounds. The letters **er** and **ere** stand for the vowel sounds you hear.

**A.** Say each spelling word. Underline the **er** and **ere** in each word.

**Spelling Words**

here     there     very

over     under     where

**B.** Choose four spelling words. Write them in alphabetical order.

_____

_____

_____

_____

**SPELLER'S CHOICE**   Write two new words to learn to spell.

_____          _____

_____          _____

Say the words **hat** and **cake**. Listen for the short **a** sound in **hat**.
Listen for the long **a** sound in **cake**.

**A.** Say each spelling word. Listen for a long or a short vowel
   sound.

### Spelling Words
bed   cake   hat   bike   duck   mop

**B.** Write spelling words. Name things you can sit on.

1. ____bed____   2. ____bike____

**C.** Write a spelling word for each picture.

3. ____hat____   4. ____cake____

5. ____duck____   6. ____mop____

**SPELLER'S CHOICE**   Write two new words to learn to spell.

_____   _____

---

Say the words **eat** and **sleep**. The letters **ee** and **ea** can spell the
long **e** sound you hear in these words.

**A.** Say each spelling word. Listen for the long **e** sound.

### Spelling Words
dream   leaf   sleep   eat   read   tree

**B.** Write the words with long e spelled **ee**.

1. ____sleep____   2. ____tree____

**C.** Write the words with long e spelled **ea**.

3. ____dream____   4. ____eat____

5. ____leaf____   6. ____read____

**SPELLER'S CHOICE**   Write two new words to learn to spell.

_____   _____

---

Say the words **free** and **he**. Listen for the long **e** sound. The
letters **ee** and **e** can spell the long **e** sound you hear in these
words.

**A.** Say the spelling words. Listen for the long **e** vowel sound.

### Spelling Words
free   he   me   green   keep   see

**A.** Write spelling words that are things you can do.

1. ____keep____   2. ____see____

**B.** Write the spelling words with long **e** spelled **e**.

3. ____he____   4. ____me____

**C.** Write two spelling words with long **e** spelled **ee**.

5. ____free____   6. ____green____

**SPELLER'S CHOICE**   Write two new words to learn to spell.

_____   _____

---

The ending **er** can compare two things.
The ending **est** can compare three things.

### Spelling Words
fast   old   strong   long   small   tall

small      smaller      smallest

**A.** Look at the fish. Which is the smallest? Circle it.

**B.** Find the spelling words with **er** and **est**.
   Circle them.

```
r e d (f a s t e r) o r
i (s m a l l e s t) l o
t o (l o n g e r) a d d
f o r (s t r o n g e r)
u n d e r (o l d e s t)
n o t (t a l l e s t) o
```

**SPELLER'S CHOICE**   Write two new words to learn to spell.

_____   _____

© Silver Burdett Ginn Inc.

**312**

When **s** is added to a naming word, the word names more than one thing.

**A.** Read the spelling words.

Circle the word that means more than one rabbit.

### Spelling Words
bear    dog    rabbits    cat    pig    turtles

**B.** Write spelling words.

Which words mean more than one?

1. __rabbits__
2. __turtles__

**C.** Write spelling words for the pictures.

Add **s** for more than one.

3. __cats__    4. __bears__

5. __dog__    6. __pig__

**SPELLER'S CHOICE**   Write two new words to learn to spell.

---

We add **ed** to an action word to tell that something happened in the past.

**A.** Say the spelling words. Circle the words that tell about the past.

### Spelling Words
cooked    play    talk    looked    stay    walk

**B.** Find the action words that tell about the past.

Write them to tell about now.

I cooked a fish, and looked for a dish.

1. __cook__    2. __look__

**C.** Find the action words that tell about now.

Write them with **ed** to tell about the past.

We play in the park, but stay home after dark.

3. __played__    4. __stayed__

We walk in the rain, then talk on the train.

5. __walked__    6. __talked__

**SPELLER'S CHOICE**   Write two new words to learn to spell.

---

When **s** is added to a naming word, the word names more than one thing.

**A.** Say each spelling word to mean more than one.

### Spelling Words
apple    horse    tree    day    train    truck

**B.** Help to finish the story.

Add **s** to the words in ( ). Write the new words.

Grandpa has many (tree) __trees__ on his farm.

They are filled with (apple) __apples__ .

It takes (day) __days__ to pick them.

Now (truck) __trucks__ take them.

**SPELLER'S CHOICE**   Write two new words to learn to spell.

---

Two small words can be put together to make a longer word. It is called a **compound word.** It has some of the meaning of both small words.

**A.** Look at the word **rainbow.** Draw a line between the two smaller words that make up this word.

### Spelling Words
baseball   doghouse   playground   bedroom   outside   rainbow

**B.** Match the words to make compound words.

1. play    **a.** side
2. bed    **b.** ground
3. out    **c.** room
4. base    **d.** bow
5. dog    **e.** ball
6. rain    **f.** house

**C.** Write the words you matched for **1** and **2.**

1. __playground__
2. __bedroom__

**SPELLER'S CHOICE**   Write two new words to learn to spell.

**Spelling Link**

Say the picture word **cake**. Listen for the long **a** sound.

**A.** Say each spelling word. Listen for the long **a** sound.

**Spelling Words**

date   make   snake   late   say   today

**B.** Say the picture word. Write two spelling words that rhyme.

cake

1. ___make___   2. ___snake___

gate

3. ___date___   4. ___late___

hay

5. ___say___   6. ___today___

**SPELLER'S CHOICE**   Write two new words to learn to spell.

_____   _____

---

**Spelling Link**

Say the words **see, find,** and **told**. Listen for three different long vowel sounds.

**A.** Say each spelling word. Circle two words that rhyme.

**Spelling Words**

find   mind   trees   home   see   told

**B.** Say the picture word.

Listen for the vowel sound.

Write spelling words with the same vowel sound.

1. f
kite 2. m i n d
n
d

3. s
bee 4. t r e e s
e

5. h
rope 6. t o l d
m
e

**SPELLER'S CHOICE**   Write two new words to learn to spell.

_____   _____

---

**Spelling Link**

Sometimes two letters spell one sound. Say the word **room**. Listen to the sound the letters **oo** spell. It is one sound.

**A.** Say each spelling word. Look for the two letters that spell one sound.

**Spelling Words**

blue   four   room   feel   green   too

**B.** Choose four spelling words.

Write them in alphabetical order.

1. _____

2. _____

3. _____

4. _____

**SPELLER'S CHOICE**   Write two new words to learn to spell.

_____

_____

---

**Spelling Link**

Say the word **link.** The letters **k** and **ck** can stand for the sound at the end of **link.**

**A.** Look at the spelling words. Say each one. Find the letters that stand for the last sound in **link.** Underline them.

**Spelling Words**

back   drink   pink   black   milk   thank

**B.** Which words have the last sound spelled **ck**? Write them.

1. ___back___   2. ___black___

**C.** Which words have the last sound spelled **k**?

3. ___drink___   4. ___milk___

5. ___pink___   6. ___thank___

**SPELLER'S CHOICE**   Write two new words to learn to spell.

_____   _____

**314**

Say the word **five.** Listen for the long **i** sound.
A. Say each spelling word. Listen for the long **i** sound.

**Spelling Words**
by   fight   my   dive   five   right

B. Say the picture word. Write two spelling words that rhyme.

hive

1. dive   2. five

night

3. fight   4. right

fly

5. by   6. my

**SPELLER'S CHOICE**   Write two new words to learn to spell.

_____   _____

---

Say the word **king.** The letters **k** and **ck** stand for the sound at the end of **chick.**
A. Say each spelling word. Listen for the **k** sound.

**Spelling Words**
chick   kiss   look   kick   like   think

B. Which words have the **k** sound spelled **k?** Write them.

1. like   2. look

3. kick   4. kiss

5. think

C. Which words have the last sound spelled **ck?** Write them.

6. chick   7. kick

**SPELLER'S CHOICE**   Write two new words to learn to spell.

_____   _____

---

The letters **sh** stand for the first sound in **ship** and the last sound in **dish.**
A. Say each spelling word. Listen for the **sh** sound.

**Spelling Words**
dish   shape   shell   fish   sheep   ship

B. Finish each word. Find the hidden word.

1. f i [S] h

2. d i s [h]

3. s h a p [e]

4. s h [e] l l

5. s h i [p]

C. The letters in the boxes spell a word.
   Write the word.

6. sheep

**SPELLER'S CHOICE**   Write two new words to learn to spell.

_____   _____

---

Say the word **first.** The letters **ir, er, ur,** and **or** stand for the vowel sound you hear.
A. Say each spelling word. Circle the word that rhymes with **mother.**

**Spelling Words**
first   other   turtle   her   together   work

B. Choose four spelling words. Write them in alphabetical order.

_____

_____

_____

_____

**SPELLER'S CHOICE**   Write two new words to learn to spell.

_____   _____

## Worksheet 1 (top left)

Some sounds are spelled with more than one letter. The letters **ch** and **tch** stand for the last sound in **lunch** and **catch**. The letters **th** stand for the first sound in **that**.

**A.** Say each spelling word. Find the letters **ch**, **tch**, and **th**. Underline them.

**Spelling Words**
catch  that  they  lunch  then  think

**B.** Write the spelling words in which you find each smaller word.

ink                              cat

1. think            2. catch

hat                              hen

3. that             4. then

                            he 5. they

**C.** Write the spelling word that is not hiding a smaller word.

6. lunch

**SPELLER'S CHOICE**  Write two new words to learn to spell.

_____        _____

## Worksheet 2 (top right)

The letters **o**, **oa**, and **ow** stand for the vowel sound you hear in **boat**.

**A.** Say each spelling word. Listen for the vowel sound you hear in **boat**.

**Spelling Words**
boat  no  show  go  over  slow

**B.** Write the opposite for each word.

stop                          fast

1. go              2. slow

yes                           hide

3. no             4. show

under

5. over

**C.** Write the word you did not use.

6. boat

**SPELLER'S CHOICE**  Write two new words to learn to spell.

_____        _____

## Worksheet 3 (bottom left)

The letters **er** stand for the last sounds in **water** and **other**.

**A.** Say each spelling word. Underline the letters **er** in each word.

**Spelling Words**
other  river  mother  never  water  father

**B.** Write a spelling word in each shape.

1. f a t h e r

2. o t h e r

3. n e v e r

4. w a t e r

5. r i v e r

6. m o t h e r

**SPELLER'S CHOICE**  Write two new words to learn to spell.

_____        _____

## Worksheet 4 (bottom right)

The letters **th** stand for the first sound in **they** and the last sound in **with**.

**A.** Say each spelling word. Listen for the **th** sound.

**Spelling Words**
bath  south  they  north  teeth  third

**B.** The words in each group belong together. Add words to groups.

1. first, second, third

2. mouth, lips, teeth

3. east, west, north , south

4. soap, towel, bath

5. them, their, they

**SPELLER'S CHOICE**  Write two new words to learn to spell.

_____        _____

Add **ed** to an action word to tell that something happened in the past.

**A.** Say each spelling word. Underline the words that tell about the past.

**Spelling Words**

like   play   <u>saved</u>   <u>lived</u>   roll   <u>walked</u>

**B.** Which words tell about what is happening now? Make them tell about the past. Write them.

1. liked        2. played

3. rolled

**C.** Which words tell about what happened in the past? Make them tell about now. Write them.

4. live        5. save

6. walk

**SPELLER'S CHOICE**   Write two new words to learn to spell.

_____   _____

---

An action word with **ing** at the end shows that the action is still going on.

**A.** Say each spelling word. Underline the **ing** ending in each word.

**Spelling Words**

cook<u>ing</u>   help<u>ing</u>   sing<u>ing</u>   draw<u>ing</u>   jump<u>ing</u>   smil<u>ing</u>

**B.** Write the spelling word that tells about each picture.

1. jumping

2. helping

3. smiling

4. singing

5. cooking

**SPELLER'S CHOICE**   Write two new words to learn to spell.

_____   _____

---

Say the words **here, there,** and **over.** Listen for three different vowel sounds. The letters **er** and **ere** stand for the vowel sounds you hear.

**A.** Say each spelling word. Underline the **er** and **ere** in each word.

**Spelling Words**

h<u>ere</u>   th<u>ere</u>   v<u>er</u>y
ov<u>er</u>   und<u>er</u>   wh<u>ere</u>

**B.** Choose four spelling words. Write them in alphabetical order.

_____
_____
_____
_____

**SPELLER'S CHOICE**   Write two new words to learn to spell.

_____   _____

© Silver Burdett Ginn Inc.

# *W*riting Masters

The Writing Masters support the Writing to Learn activities in the lesson. Complementing each activity are a brief explanation/definition statement and a "check box," which assist children in checking their own work.

# Contents

## Writing to Learn

**A.** What would the farmer's hat look like to you? Draw what you think it would look like.

**B.** Look at your picture. Label the things you see. The words in the box may help you.

| back | bottom | front | hat | top |
|------|--------|-------|-----|-----|

✓ Did you label things in your picture?

© Silver Burdett Ginn Inc.

# Writing to Learn

**A.** Whose eyes are closed this morning in fall?
Draw a picture. Show someone or something who
might be sleeping.

---

 Did you draw someone or something that is
sleeping?

© Silver Burdett Ginn Inc.

# Writing to Learn

**B.** Write what you see in your picture. The words in the box may help you.

| | | |
|---|---|---|
| a boy | a girl | a goat |
| a house | a mouse | a puppy |

I see _____

✓ Did you tell what was in your picture?

# Writing to Learn

Sara uses string in many ways.
How do you use string?
Make a list. Tell how you use string.
The words in the box may help you.

| to tie | to wrap | something |
|--------|---------|-----------|
| to hang | to play with | for a |

 Did you tell how you use string?

*"A Rainbow for Sara"*

# Writing to Learn

**A.** Pretend that you are going to make a new house. What would you use to build it? Draw a picture of your new house.

☑ Did you show what your house is made of?

# Writing to Learn

**B.** Write what would happen if the wolf came to your house. Use ideas in the box or think of your own.

I would make friends with the wolf.
I would run away.
I would call for help.
I would keep the wolf outside.

_____

- - - - - - - - - - - - - - - - - - - - - - - -

_____

- - - - - - - - - - - - - - - - - - - - - - - -

_____

- - - - - - - - - - - - - - - - - - - - - - - -

_____

- - - - - - - - - - - - - - - - - - - - - - - -

_____

✔ Did you tell about the wolf coming to your house?

## Writing to Learn

Think of the most interesting animal that you have ever seen. Draw a picture of the animal in a home you think it might have. Label the parts of your picture. The words in the box may help you.

| bushes | den | floor | hive | roof | tunnel |
| cave | entrance | grass | nest | trees | walls |

✔ Did you label the parts of your picture?

# Writing to Learn

**A.** Draw a picture of Percy. All around him write words that tell what he is like. Use these words and tell about Percy.

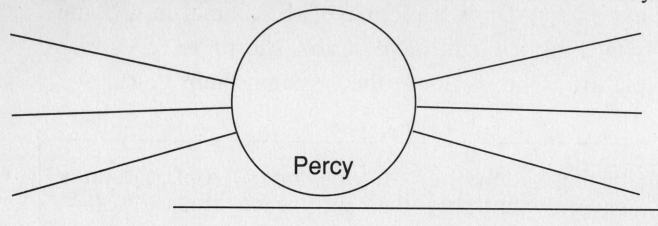

Percy is _____

_____

_____

_____

_____

_____

_____

 Did you use the words around Percy to tell about him?

# Writing to Learn

**B.** Draw a picture of yourself. Write words that describe you all around it. Use the words to write about yourself.

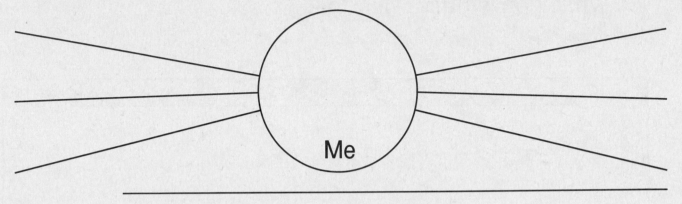

Me

I am _____

_____

_____

_____

_____

_____

_____

_____

_____

>  Did you use the words around your picture to tell about yourself?

# Writing to Learn

**A.** Pretend that you found a wishing well. Draw a picture of what you would wish for.

© Silver Burdett Ginn Inc.

✓ Did you make a wish?

# Writing to Learn

**B.** Finish each sentence.
The words in the box may help you.

| | | |
|---|---|---|
| jump | play | run |
| penny | puppy | wish |

_____

- - - - - - - - - - - - - - - - - -

**1.** I wish I had a _____ ,

_____

- - - - - - - - - - - - - - - - - -

so I could make a _____ .

_____

- - - - - - - - - - - - - - - - - -

**2.** I wish I were a _____ ,

_____

- - - - - - - - - - - - - - - - - -

so I could _____ ,

_____

- - - - - - - - - - - - - - - - - -

and I could _____ .

 Does each sentence make sense?

# Writing to Learn

**A.** What animal would you like to see in a story?
Draw a picture of it.

> ✓ Did you draw a picture of an animal you
> would like to see in a story?

# Writing to Learn

**B.** Tell about your picture. Write three things that your animal can do. The words in the box may help you.

| | | | |
|---|---|---|---|
| breathe | eat | run | swim |
| drink | play | sleep | walk |

My Animal

_____

- - - - - - - - - - - - - - - - - - - - - - - - - - - - - -

My animal can _____

_____

- - - - - - - - - - - - - - - - - - - - - - - - - - - - - -

_____

_____

- - - - - - - - - - - - - - - - - - - - - - - - - - - - - -

_____

_____

- - - - - - - - - - - - - - - - - - - - - - - - - - - - - -

_____

✓ Did you write three things your animal can do?

# Writing to Learn

**A.** Hippo wanted to make a wish. You can make a wish, too. Draw a wish.

**B.** What did you wish? Write a sentence about your wish.

_____

- - - - - - - - - - - - - - - - - - - - - - - - - - - - -

My wish is _____

_____

- - - - - - - - - - - - - - - - - - - - - - - - - - - - -

_____

- - - - - - - - - - - - - - - - - - - - - - - - - - - - -

_____

 Does your sentence have an ending mark?

# Writing to Learn

David McPhail likes books, tall trees, the warm sun, and the blue sky. What do you like? Draw a picture of some of the things you like. Then label the things in your picture.

✓ Did you label the things in your picture?

## Writing to Learn

**A.** Make a book cluster for yourself. Draw yourself in a little circle. Then put in the names of your favorite books.

✔ Does your picture tell about your favorite books?

"Fix-It"

## Writing to Learn

**B.** Think of your favorite thing to do. Finish each
sentence. The words in the box may help you.

| | | |
|---|---|---|
| draw | read | sing |
| play | run | skate |

1. I like to _____.

2. I go to the park to _____.

3. My friends and I _____.

4. When I am at home I _____.

5. In the summer I _____.

✓ Did you write a thing you like to do?

© Silver Burdett Ginn Inc.

## Writing to Learn

You are Emily. You write a letter back to Little Bear.
What would you say? Write it. Use one or two of the
sentences in the box or make up your own.

| | |
|---|---|
| I miss you, too. | I will see you next summer. |
| I like you. | Do you like your pen? |

Dear Little Bear,

_____

- - - - - - - - - - - - - - - - - - - - - -

_____

- - - - - - - - - - - - - - - - - - - - - -

_____

- - - - - - - - - - - - - - - - - - - - - -

_____

Your friend,

_____

- - - - - - - - - - - - - - - - - - - - - -

_____

✓ Did you sign Emily's name to the letter?

© Silver Burdett Ginn Inc.

"Your Friend, Little Bear"

## Writing to Learn

Pretend Alex is your friend. Write a letter to Alex.
Use the sentences in the box or make up your own.

| | |
|---|---|
| I like you. | It is nice to share. |
| We have fun together. | Please write to me. |

Dear Alex,

_____

- - - - - - - - - - - - - - - - - - - - - - - - - - - - - - -

_____

_____

- - - - - - - - - - - - - - - - - - - - - - - - - - - - - - -

_____

- - - - - - - - - - - - - - - - - - - - - - - - - - - - - - -

_____

Your friend,

_____

- - - - - - - - - - - - - - - - - - - - - - - - - - - - - - -

_____

 Did you write a capital letter for the word **I**?

## Writing to Learn

Frog left a note on his door for Toad. If you wrote a note for Toad what would you say? Write it. Use some of the sentences in the box or think of your own.

| |
|---|
| I like your story.     I would like to meet you. |
| I like to play.     I would like to be your friend. |

Dear Toad,

_____

- - - - - - - - - - - - - - - - - - - - - - - -

_____

- - - - - - - - - - - - - - - - - - - - - - - -

_____

- - - - - - - - - - - - - - - - - - - - - - - -

_____

Your friend,

_____

- - - - - - - - - - - - - - -

_____

| |
|---|
| ✓ Did you sign your name to the note? |

# Writing to Learn

**A.** Goldfish and Dog like to talk to each other. What will Goldfish ask Dog to do tomorrow? Write it in the speech balloon.

**B.** If you were Dog, how would you answer Goldfish? Write Dog's answer in his speech balloon.

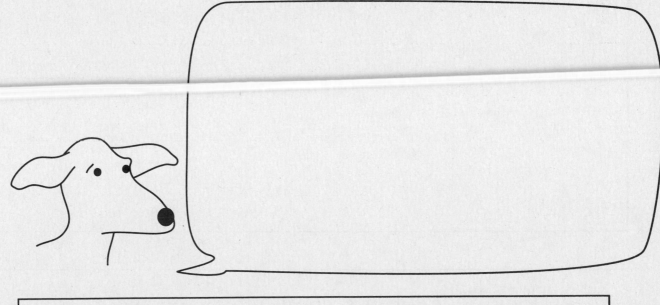

✓ Did you put a ? after Goldfish's question?

# Writing to Learn

**A.** Friends share. What would you like to share with Carol if she were your friend? Draw a picture of you and Carol.

✔ Does your picture show what you would share with Carol?

## Writing to Learn

**B.** Now think about your picture. Write about it. Tell what you and Carol are doing.

Use ideas in the box or make up your own.

| | |
|---|---|
| Carol is my friend. | a toy |
| We are sharing something nice. | food |

_____

- - - - - - - - - - - - - - - - - - - - - - - - - -

_____

_____

- - - - - - - - - - - - - - - - - - - - - - - - - -

_____

_____

- - - - - - - - - - - - - - - - - - - - - - - - - -

_____

_____

- - - - - - - - - - - - - - - - - - - - - - - - - -

_____

 Did you tell what is happening in your picture?

## Writing to Learn

Write about the farm where Terry lives. Use sentences
from the box or make up your own.

> I would see sheep, hens, and cows.
> I would plant.
> I would ride a horse.

_____

- - - - - - - - - - - - - - - - - - - - - - - -

_____

- - - - - - - - - - - - - - - - - - - - - - - -

_____

- - - - - - - - - - - - - - - - - - - - - - - -

_____

- - - - - - - - - - - - - - - - - - - - - - - -

_____

- - - - - - - - - - - - - - - - - - - - - - - -

_____

✔ Did you write what you see and do on the farm?

# Writing to Learn

One way to teach Mr. Brown to count is with a counting book. Make a counting book. Draw things for each number and word.

| | | | |
|---|---|---|---|
| 1 one | | 2 two | |
| 3 three | | 4 four | |
| 5 five | | 6 six | |

 Did you draw enough things for each number?

# Writing to Learn

 seven

 eight

 nine

 ten

 Did you draw enough things for each number?

NAME _____

# Writing to Learn

**A.** When you look into the sky, what do you see? Look
at this picture of the sky. What animals do you see?
Put an **X** on each animal.

**B.** Draw some of your own "cloud" animals.

✓ Did you find all of the animals? Did you draw
some of your own?

# Writing to Learn

**C.** Make a list of the animals you saw in the sky. These animal names may help you.

| | | |
|---|---|---|
| cat | mouse | rabbit |
| elephant | pig | sheep |

_____

_ _ _ _ _ _ _ _ _ _ _ _ _ _ _ _ _ _ _ _ _ _

_____

_ _ _ _ _ _ _ _ _ _ _ _ _ _ _ _ _ _ _ _ _ _

_____

_ _ _ _ _ _ _ _ _ _ _ _ _ _ _ _ _ _ _ _ _ _

_____

_ _ _ _ _ _ _ _ _ _ _ _ _ _ _ _ _ _ _ _ _ _

_____

_ _ _ _ _ _ _ _ _ _ _ _ _ _ _ _ _ _ _ _ _ _

_____

✔ Did you write the names of all the animals you saw?

"The Man, the Cat, and the Sky"

# Writing to Learn

**A.** Many people liked the stone soup the travelers made. Draw a soup pot. Draw what you would use to make soup.

My Pot

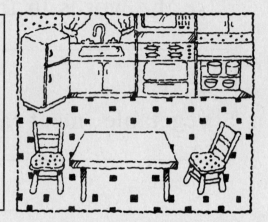

What I Would Use for Making Soup

✓ Did you draw **all** the things you need for your soup?

# Writing to Learn

**B.** A recipe is a set of directions for doing something.
Each step should be in order.
Write your own recipe for making soup.

Use the words in the box or think of your own.

| | |
|---|---|
| a pot | water in the pot |
| vegetable, meat, and salt | one hour |

_____

Get _____

_____

Put _____

_____

Add _____

_____

Cook _____

 Could someone use your recipe to make soup?

© Silver Burdett Ginn Inc.

# Writing to Learn

**A.** Pretend you are the storyteller. Choose one beginning, one middle, and one ending. Put together a story and write it.

---

### Beginnings:

A little duck called Quackers liked to say her name.

A puppy named Spot lived in a nice house.

---

### Middles:

One day Quackers became lost, but she kept saying her name.

This puppy got into a lot of trouble because it didn't do what it was told.

---

### Endings:

Spot went to obedience school and then everyone loved her.

Mrs. Duck found her baby because she followed a trail of quackers.

# Writing to Learn

**B.** Write your story here.

_____

- - - - - - - - - - - - - - - - - - - - - - - - -

_____

- - - - - - - - - - - - - - - - - - - - - - - - -

_____

- - - - - - - - - - - - - - - - - - - - - - - - -

_____

- - - - - - - - - - - - - - - - - - - - - - - - -

_____

- - - - - - - - - - - - - - - - - - - - - - - - -

_____

- - - - - - - - - - - - - - - - - - - - - - - - -

_____

- - - - - - - - - - - - - - - - - - - - - - - - -

_____

- - - - - - - - - - - - - - - - - - - - - - - - -

_____

✓ Does your story have a beginning, a middle, and an ending? Do the parts go together?

# Writing to Learn

On the stamp outline, draw your favorite person. Tell who is on your stamp. The words in the box may help you. Then write a sentence about your stamp.

| | | | | |
|---|---|---|---|---|
| aunt | father | grandfather | mother | teacher |
| brother | friend | grandmother | sister | uncle |

USA
40 C

Who Is on My Stamp

_____

- - - - - - - - - - - - -

_____

- - - - - - - - - - - - -

_____

_____

- - - - - - - - - - - - -

My stamp _____

_____

- - - - - - - - - - - - -

_____

✔ Does your sentence have an ending mark?

# Writing to Learn

In a story ending, the problem of the characters is solved. Write your ending for "The Three Wishes." The ideas in the box may help you. Draw a picture for your ending, too.

Fritz and Anna wish to live happily ever after.
Fritz and Anna wish to use their last wish wisely.
Fritz and Anna wish to have three more wishes.

✓ Does your story ending solve a problem?

# Answer Key

"Who Took the Farmer's Hat?" (page 319)
Children should draw the farmer's hat and label it.

"A Morning in Fall" (pages 320-321)
Children should draw a picture of someone or something that might be sleeping and write about it.

"A Rainbow for Sara (page 322)
Children should write a list telling how they can use string.

"The Three Little Pigs" (pages 323-324)
Children should draw a picture of a new house they would build and then write what would happen if a wolf came to their house.

"A World of Animals" (page 325)
Children should draw the home they think an interesting animal has and label its parts.

"Mercy, Percy!" (pages 326-327)
Children should complete a character cluster and write a character description.

"The Wishing Well" (pages 328-329)
Children should draw a picture of something they would wish for and then complete the "I wish . . ." sentences.

"The Tyrannosaurus Game" (pages 330-331)
Children should draw an animal they would like to see in a story and then write three things the animal can do.

"Hippo Makes a Wish" (page 332)
Children should draw a wish and write a sentence about it.

"Lee Bennett Hopkins Interviews David McPhail" (page 333)
Children should draw pictures of things they like and then label them.

"Fix-It" (pages 334-335)
Children should make a book cluster of their favorite books and then complete the sentences about things they like to do.

"Your Friend, Little Bear" (page 336)
Children should pretend they are Emily and write a letter to Little Bear.

"We Are Best Friends" (page 337)
Children should pretend Alex is a friend and write a letter to him.

"Alone" (page 338)
Children should write a note to Toad.

"Some Fun" (page 339)
Children should complete a speech balloon for Goldfish and Dog.

"Together" (pages 340-341)
Children should draw a picture of "sharing" and then write about the picture.

"A Horse Named Goldfish" (page 342)
Children should write about visiting a farm.

"All of Our Noses Are Here" (page 343-344)
Children should create a counting book.

"The Man, the Cat, and the Sky" (pages 345-346)
Children should locate animals in a cloudscape, draw some of their own "cloud" animals, and then make a list of the animals they saw.

"Stone Soup" (pages 347-348)
Children should draw a soup pot, what they would use for making soup and then write a recipe for making soup.

"Alanike and the Storyteller" (pages 349-350)
Children should select a story beginning, middle, and ending (or think of their own) and put together a story and write it.

"Lee Bennett Hopkins Interviews Jerry Pinkney" (page 351)
Children should draw their favorite person on a stamp and then write a sentence about the stamp.

"The Three Wishes" (page 352)
Children should draw a picture and write their ending for "The Three Wishes."

# *H*ome Connection Letters

These letters are designed as a means of communication between teacher, child, and the home. In *Here Comes the Band!*, *All Through the Town*, *Out Came the Sun*, and *Morning Bells*, the letters should be sent home at the beginning and end of each book. In *Make a Wish* and *A New Day*, they should be reproduced and sent home with children as each unit and book is completed. Both literary and skills features are highlighted in the letters. They open with a brief review of the theme and a list of theme-related books recommended to encourage independent reading. The letters then provide a short, defined list of skills. This is followed by two or three activities based on skills that can provide a mutual learning experience for the family members and the child.

# Contents

Dear Family of: _____

The stories in your child's reading book focus on animals. To help reinforce and extend the concept of animals, you may wish to share the following books with your child:

***Each Peach Pear Plum*** by Janet and Allan Ahlberg. Viking, 1986. The reader tries to find the nursery rhyme or story characters who are partially hidden in the illustrations.

***A Dog's Body*** by Joanna Cole. Morrow, © 1986. This book features brief, substantive text, clear informative photographs, and an open, welcoming layout.

***Catch That Cat!*** by Fernando Krahn. E.P. Dutton, © 1978. A wordless picture book in which a black cat is hotly pursued by a little boy through a variety of entertaining urban settings.

Through these stories your child will be learning about writing animal stories. Your child will be reviewing the sounds made by the letters *s, d, c, m, b,* and *p,* and will be learning the phonograms *at, an, ay,* and *ig.* You may enjoy doing the following activities with your child.

**1. Make a collage** Choose one of the letters your child will be reviewing. Get a piece of drawing paper and have your child write the letter both as an uppercase and a lowercase letter. Then help your child search through magazines for pictures of things that begin with the sound of the letter you've chosen. Cut the pictures out and have your child glue them wherever he or she chooses on the paper.

**2. Make a flip book** Cut an 8½" × 11" sheet of contruction paper into horizontal thirds. Fold each piece into thirds. Cut two of them on the folds. On the uncut piece, write the word "cat," one letter in each section. Write a letter on each small piece so that when placed in front of the phonogram *(at)* a new word is formed. Stack the separate letters over the *c* in "cat" and staple them in place. When the flip book is complete, your child can "flip" the initial letter to make and read different words.

I hope you and your child have fun sharing these books and activities.

Sincerely,

El tema principal de los cuentos en el libro de lecturas de su hijo(a) es acerca de los animales. Para apoyar y ampliar el concepto de los animales, comparta los libros siguientes con su hijo(a):

***Each Peach Pear Plum*** por Janet y Allan Ahlberg. Viking, 1986. El lector trata de encontrar la rima infantil o los personajes del cuento que están medio escondidos en las ilustraciones.

***A Dog's Body*** por Joanna Cole. Morrow, © 1986. Este libro cuenta con un diseño atractivo. El texto es corto y positivo, y las fotografías son claras e informativas.

***Catch That Cat!*** por Fernando Krahn. E.P. Dutton, © 1978. Un libro ilustrado sin texto en el cual un gato negro es perseguido por un niño a través de varias aventuras urbanas muy entretenidas.

A través de estas lecturas, su hijo(a) aprenderá cómo escribir cuentos con animales como personajes. Su hijo(a) repasará los sonidos de las letras *s, d, c, m, b* y *p* y aprenderá también de los fonogramas *at, an, ay* y *ig*. Le invito a realizar estas actividades con su hijo(a):

**1. Haga un "collage"** Escoja una de las letras que su hijo(a) tiene que repasar. Busque un pedazo de papel de dibujar y haga que su hijo(a) escriba la letra tanto en mayúscula como en minúscula. Después ayúdele a buscar fotografías o dibujos de cosas cuyos nombres empiezan con la letra que escogió Ud. Recorte las fotos y haga que su hijo(a) las pegue dondequiera en el papel.

**2. Haga un "librito animado"** Recorte un pedazo de cartulina de 8½″ por 11″ en tres partes iguales, a lo ancho. Doble cada pedazo en tres y recortedos de estos pedazos siguiendo la dobladura. En la cartulina no cortada, escriba la palabra "cat", (gato) escribiendo solo una letra en cada sección. Escriba una letra en cada pedazo chiquito así que cuando la pone delante del fonograma *(at)* se forma una nueva palabra. Apile las letras separadas sobre la *c* de "cat" y agrápelas. Cuando el "librito animado" está terminado, su hijo(a) puede levantar la hoja con la primera letra para crear y leer palabras diferentes.

Espero que usted y su hijo(a) disfruten juntos de estos libros y actividades.

Cordialmente,

Dear Family of: _____

Congratulations! Your child has just completed *Here Comes the Band*. To continue to encourage your child to read, you might wish to share these books:

***Emma's Pet*** by David McPhail. E.P. Dutton, © 1985. A brief storybook about Emma the bear searching for the perfect pet.

***The Three Billy Goats Gruff*** by Margaret Lippert. Macmillan Publishing, © 1988. A story about three goats trying to cross a bridge to get to a pasture of sweet green grass.

Through these stories your child has learned about writing animal stories. Your child has also learned about the letters *s, d, c, m, b,* and *p* and the phonograms *at, an, ay,* and *ig.*

You may enjoy doing the following activities with your child:

**1. Final *n*** Invent small stories with your child using words that end with the letter *n*. The list below will help you get started.

| run | can | men | bun | tin |
|-----|-----|-----|-----|-----|
| bin | hen | van | pen | pin |

An example might be: Ten men can run to have fun in the sun.

You may also wish to draw simple illustrations to accompany the stories.

**2. Final *m* and *g*** Look in magazines for pictures of words that end in *m* and *g*. For example:

| Pam | tag | dog | pig | log |
|-----|-----|-----|-----|-----|
| team | ham | jam | gum | Tim |

Ask your child to tell you what sound a motorcycle makes when it starts up. The answer will probably be something like "Vroom, vroom." As you hold up a picture illustrating a word that ends with final *m*, pronounce the word and have your child imitate you. Tell your child that the word ends with the same sound as "vroom." Emphasize bringing the lips together to make the *m* sound. Ask your child what the farmer found in the nest in the henhouse (egg). Pronounce with your child the words that have the final *g* sound as in egg.

I hope you and your child have fun sharing these books and activities.

Sincerely,

© Silver Burdett Ginn Inc.

¡Felicidades! Su hijo(a) acaba de completar *Here Comes the Band* en el programa de lectura. Para estimular y continuar el hábito de la lectura de su hijo(a), comparta con él o ella estos libros:

*Emma's Pet* por David McPhail. E.P. Dutton, © 1985. Este es en cuento corto sobre la osa, Emma, que va en busca de la mascota perfecta.

*The Three Billy Goats Gruff* por Margaret Lippert. Macmillan Publishing, © 1988. Esta es la historia de tres cabras que tratan de cruzar un puente para llegar a la orilla de pastos verdes.

A través de estos cuentos su niño(a) ha aprendido cómo se escriben historias de animales. Su niño(a) también ha aprendido las letras *s, d, c, m, b, p* y los sonidos *at, an, ay,* y *ig.* Le invito a realizar las siguientes actividades con su hijo(a):

**1. La *n* final** Ayude a su hijo(a) a inventar historietas cortas con palabras inglesas que terminan en *n*. A continuación hay una lista que le puede servir de ayuda:

run    can    men    bun    tin
bin    hen    van    pen    pin

Un ejemplo podría ser: *Ten men can run to have fun in the sun.* También pueden hacer dibujos para acompañar las historietas.

**2. La *m* y *g* final** En revistas, busque palabras inglesas que terminan en *m* y en *g*. Por ejemplo:

Pam    tag    dog    pig    log
team    ham    jam    gum    Tim

Pida que su hijo(a) le diga qué sonido hace una motocicleta cuando arranca. Una respuesta posible es el sonido "Vroom, vroom" como respuesta. Mientras usted le muestra una foto que ilustre una palabra que termina en *m,* pronuncie la palabra y haga que su hijo(a) la repita. Diga a su hijo(a) que la palabra termina en el mismo sonido que "vroom". Ponga énfasis en el hecho que se tiene que apretar los labios para hacer el sonido de la *m.* Pregunte a su hijo(a) qué encontró el agricultor en el gallinero (La palabra en inglés es "egg"). Conjuntamente con su hijo(a), pronuncie las palabras que terminan en una *g* final como la palabra "egg".

Espero que usted y su hijo(a) disfruten juntos de estos libros y actividades.

Cordialmente,

Dear Family of: _____

The stories in your child's reading book focus on wheels and transportation. To help reinforce and extend the concept of transportation, you might wish to share the following books with your child:

*Truck* by Donald Crews. Greenwillow, © 1980. The world and special language of the open highway is revealed to children through this simple, yet highly informative book.

*The Bear's Bicycle* by Emile McLeod. Little, Brown, © 1975. A boy describes his afternoon bicycle ride with his bear and, in a humorous manner, demonstrates bicycle safety.

Through these stories your child will be learning about reality and fantasy, sequence of events, and how to use picture details to help understand a story. Your child will also be learning about the vowels *a* and *e* and the consonants *f, w, l, b, t, g, r, n,* and *k.*

You may enjoy doing the following activities with your child.

**1. Sequence** On four separate pieces of paper draw four pictures of things you do each morning, such as getting out of bed, washing your face, eating breakfast, and leaving the house. Tell your child that Olivia Order likes to do things in the correct order. Have your child arrange the pictures in the order in which Olivia would do them. Then tell your child that Bobby Backward likes to do everything backward. In the morning, he leaves his house then eats his breakfast, then washes his face, and then gets out of bed. Have your child arrange the pictures in the order in which Bobby Backward would do them. Then tell your child that Dizzy Tizzy does things in a very mixed-up way. Have your child arrange the pictures in the order in which Dizzy Tizzy would do them. You can draw pictures of other series of events, such as going to bed or making supper. Have your child arrange the pictures the way Bobby, Olivia, and Dizzy would.

**2. Short Vowel *a*** Help your child to identify the sound of short vowel *a* by pointing out and pronouncing the names of familiar things or persons. For example:

Dad  bat  pan  cat  jam  tap
nap  cap  fan  hat  Pat  wag

Look at pictures of the objects with your child and help him or her to listen to the different sounds in sets of words like *cat/hit* and *ten/man.*

Sincerely,

Estimada Familia de: _____

El tema principal de los cuentos en el libro de lecturas de su hijo(a) es acerca de ruedas y los métodos de transporte. Para apoyar y ampliar los conceptos, comparta los libros siguientes con su hijo(a):

*Truck* por Donald Crews. Greenwillow, © 1980. Este libro revela a los niños el mundo y el lenguaje especial de la carretera de una manera muy sencilla pero informativa.

*The Bear's Bicycle* por Emile McLeod. Little, Brown, © 1975. En este cuento un niño describe su paseo en bicicleta con su oso por la tarde y, de manera muy entretenida, demuestra las reglas de seguridad para las bicicletas.

A través de estas lecturas, su hijo(a) aprenderá la diferencia entre la realidad y la fantasía, la secuencia de eventos en un relato y cómo usar los detalles en las ilustraciones de un cuento para entenderlo mejor. Su hijo(a) aprenderá las vocales *a* y *e* y los consonantes *f, w, l, h, t, q, r, n* y *k*.

**1. Secuencia** En cuatro hojas de papel individuales haga cuatro dibujos de lo que hace usted cada mañana, como por ejemplo, levantarse de la cama, lavarse la cara, comer y salir de la casa. Diga a su hijo(a) que a Olivia Order le gusta hacer las cosas en el orden apropiado. Pida a su hijo(a) que ponga los dibujos en el orden en el cual le gustaría hacerlas a Olivia. Pues, diga a su hijo(a) que a Bobby Backwards le gusta hacer las cosas de atrás para adelante. O sea, por la mañana él sale de casa primero, entonces come, después se lava la cara y, por último, se levanta de la cama. Pida a su hijo(a) de poner los dibujos en el orden en cual las haría Bobby Backward. Luego, diga a su hijo(a) que Dizzy Tizzy hace las cosas de manera muy confundida. Pida a su hijo(a) que ponga los dibujos en el orden en el cual las haría Dizzy Tizzy. Puede dibujar otra serie de eventos, como, por ejemplo, ir a la cama o preparar la cena. Pida a su hijo(a) que arregle los dibujos en el orden en que las harían sea Bobby, sea Oliva, sea Dizzy.

**2. El sonido corto de la vocal *a*** Ayude a su hijo(a) a identificar el sonido corto de la vocal *a*, indicándole y pronunciando los nombres de cosas o personas conocidas. Por ejemplo:

> Dad  bat  pan  cat  jam  tap
> nap  cap  fan  hat  Pat  wag

Mire los dibujos de los objetos conjuntamente con su hijo(a) y ayúdele a escuchar los sonidos diferentes en conjuntos de palabras como *cat/hit* y *ten/man*.

Espero que usted y su hijo(a) disfruten juntos de estos libros y actividades.

Cordialmente,

Dear Family of: _____

Congratulations! Your child has just completed *All Through the Town*. To continue to encourage your child to read, you might wish to share these books:

*Color Dance* by Ann Jonas. Greenwillow, © 1989. Four dancers show how colors combine to create different colors.

*Can I Keep Him?* by Steven Kellogg. Dial, © 1971. Lonely Arnold wants a pet. He makes some fairly outlandish requests and his mother objects to each one he suggests.

Through these stories your child has learned about reality and fantasy, sequence of events, and how to use picture details to help understand a story. Your child has also learned about the vowels *a* and *e* and the consonants *f, w, l, h, t, g, r, n,* and *k.*

You may enjoy doing the following activities with your child:

**1. Long Vowel *a*** Help your child to identify the sound of long vowel *a* by pointing out and pronouncing the names of familiar things or people. For example:

| Kate | plane | rake | vase | face |
|------|-------|------|------|------|
| cane | plate | vane | lace | Jane |
| lake | Blake | race | Nate | cake |

Using the actual objects or pictures, associate them with the sound of long vowel *a* by combining them with action words like *bake, take, rake, make, shake, wade, save,* and so on. Encourage your child to make up sentence stories.

**Example:** Nate and Jane race by the lake.

**2. Short Vowel *e*** Ask your child to find pictures of the following words or other words that have the same sound (short vowel *e*): *pet, pen, men, jet, hen, leg, bed,* and *net.*

Use other words with the same vowel sound to make up sentence stories about the pictures your child has found. For example:

| red | ten | set | let |
|-----|-----|-----|-----|
| get | beg | wet | fed |

**Examples:** The red hen left the pen. Ten men met at the net.

Encourage your child to make up his or her own stories.

I hope you and your child have fun sharing these books and activities.

Sincerely,

Estimada Familia de: _____

¡Felicidades! Su hijo(a) acaba de completar el libro *All Through the Town* en el programa de lectura. Para estimular y continuar el hábito de la lectura de su hijo(a), comparta con él o ella estos libros:

*Color Dance* por Ann Jonas. Greenwillow, © 1989. En este libro cuatro bailarines nos hacen ver cómo los colores se combinan para crear otros colores diferentes.

*Can I Keep Him?* por Steven Kellogg. Dial, © 1971. Arnold se siente tan sólo que quiere una mascota. En este cuento, él hace algunas sugerencias absurdas y su mamá las rechaza cada una.

A través de estas lecturas su hijo(a) ha aprendido la diferencia entre la realidad y la fantasía, la secuencia de eventos y cómo usar los detalles que se encuentran en los dibujos para entender mejor un cuento. Su hijo(a) ha aprendido también las vocales *a* y *e* y los consonantes *f, w, l, h, t, g, r, n,* y *k.* Le invito a realizar las siguientes actividades con su hijo(a):

**1. La *a* larga** Ayude a su hijo(a) a identificar el sonido largo de la *a* indicando y pronunciando los nombres de cosas o personas conocidas. Por ejemplo:

| Kate | plane | rake | vase | face |
|------|-------|------|------|------|
| cane | plate | vane | lace | Jane |
| lake | Blake | race | Nate | cake |

Usando los objetos mismos, o fotos de ellos, asócielos con el sonido largo de la vocal *a* combinándolas con palabras activas como *bake, take, rake, make, shake, wade, save,* etcétera. Anime a su hijo(a) a inventar cuentos de una oración con algunas de las palabras de arriba, como por ejemplo:

Nate and Jane race by the lake.

**2. La *e* corta** Pida que su hijo(a) encuentre las fotos de las palabras siguientes o de otras palabras que tienen el mismo sonido (la *e* corta): *pet, pen, men, jet, hen, leg, bed* y *net.*

Use otras palabras con el mismo sonido para crear cuentos sobre las fotos que encontró su hijo(a). Por ejemplo:

| red | ten | set | let |
|-----|-----|-----|-----|
| get | beg | wet | fed |

**Ejemplos:** The red hen left the pen. Ten men met at the net.

Anime a su hijo(a) a crear sus propias historietas.

Espero que usted y su hijo(a) disfruten juntos de estos libros y actividades.

Cordialmente,

Dear Family of: _____

The stories in your child's reading book focus on weather. To help reinforce these concepts, you might wish to share these books with your child:

*Rain and Hail* by Franklyn M. Branley. Thomas Y. Crowell Company, © 1963. One of the excellent "Let's Read and Find Out" series. This book communicates scientific facts without interfering with a child's sense of wonder.

*Umbrella* by Mitsu Yashima. Viking, © 1958. Momo is delighted when it finally rains and she can use the umbrella and boots she received on her birthday.

Through these stories your child will be learning about main idea, cause and effect relationships, and sequence.

Your child will also be learning about the vowels *i* and *o,* and the blends *sn, fr, gr, fl, st, br, sc,* and *sm.*

You may enjoy doing the following activities with your child:

**1. Cause/Effect** Many activities that you do with your child offer an opportunity to discuss cause and effect relationships. For example, you and your child can prepare a vegetable snack and at the same time perform a scientific experiment.

Cut off about an inch from the top of two carrots. Be sure to leave a piece of the stem. Place one carrot top in a shallow dish filled with pebbles and water. Place the other top in a dish without water. Each day watch to see what happens to the carrots. Your child should realize that water causes a carrot's leaves to grow.

**2. Short Vowel *i*** Tell your child that you are going to give him or her clues to certain words that he or she is to guess. Print the words on small cards as your child guesses them. For example:

1. This is a kind of glove you wear when you play baseball.  (mitt)
2. This is the number after five and before seven.  (six)
3. This is usually reddish-orange and people build houses with it.  (brick)
4. This is what the baby wears when he or she is eating.  (bib)
5. This is the cover on a box or a pan.  (lid)

You may wish to extend this activity by finding or drawing pictures of the words as your child guesses them.

I hope you and your child have fun sharing these books and activities.

Sincerely,

Estimada Familia de: _____

El tema principal de los cuentos en el libro de lecturas de su hijo(a) es acerca del tiempo. Para apoyar y ampliar el concepto, comparta los libros siguientes con su hijo(a):

***Rain and Hail*** por Franklyn M. Branley. Thomas Y. Crowell Company, © 1963. Este libro forma parte de la excelente serie de libros forma titulada "Leemos y descubrimos". Este libro comunica hechos científicos sin interferir con la curiosidad natural del niño.

***Umbrella*** por Mitsu Yashima. Viking, © 1958. Momo está encantada cuando por fin llueve y ella puede usar su paraguas y las botas que recibió por su cumpleaños.

A través de etas lecturas, su hijo(a) aprenderá acerca de la idea principal de un relato, la relación entre causa y efecto y la secuencia de eventos. Su hijo(a) aprenderá también acerca de las vocales *i* y *o* y las combinaciones de *sn, fr, gr, fl, st, br, sc* y *sm*. Le invito a realizar las siguientes actividades con su hijo(a):

**1. Causa y efecto** Muchas de las actividades que hace con su hijo(a) ofrecen la oportunidad para conversar solve la relación entre una causa y los efectos de ella. Por ejemplo, usted y su hijo(a) podrían preparar una merienda de verduras y hacer un experimento científico al mismo tiempo.

Corte como una pulgada de la parte superior de dos zanahorias. Asegúrese de dejar un pedazo del tallo. Ponga uno en un plato no muy hondo lleno de piedrecitas y de agua. Ponga el otro en un plato sin agua. Mírelos cada día para ver lo que pasa a la zanahoria. Su hijo(a) debería darse cuenta que el agua causa brotar las hojas de la zanahoria.

**2. El sonido corto de la vocal *i*** Diga a su hijo(a) que le va a dar algunas claves para palabras en inglés que él o ella tiene que adivinar. Escriba las palabras, en letra de molde y en inglés, en unas cartas pequeñas mientras su hijo(a) las adivina. Por ejemplo:

1. Este es un tipo de guante que se usa cuando se juega a béisbol.   (mitt)
2. Este es el número que viene después de siete y antes de cinco.   (six)
3. Por lo general, esta cosa es de un color rojo-anaranjado y la gente construye casas de este material.   (brick)
4. Este es lo que se pone a un bebé mientras come.   (bib)
5. Esta es la tapa de una caja o una sartén.   (lid)

Si quiere, puede ampliar esta actividad encontrando fotos o haciendo dibujos de las palabras en inglés, mientras su hijo(a) las adivina.

Espero que usted y su hijo(a) disfruten juntos de estos libros y actividades.

Cordialmente,

Dear Family of: _____

Congratulations! Your child has just completed *Out Came the Sun.* To continue to encourage your child to read, you might wish to share these books:

*The Very Busy Spider* by Eric Carle. Putnam, © 1984. Farm animals try to divert a busy spider from spinning her web.

*Mirandy and Brother Wind* by Patricia McKissack. Knopf, © 1988. Mirandy is determined to win the junior cakewalk contest even though her partner is clumsy. Her solution is to find a way to enlist the assistance of Brother Wind.

Through the stories in this level your child has learned about main idea, cause and effect relationships, and sequence. Your child has also learned about the vowels *i* and *o* and the blends *sn, fr, gr, fl, st, br, sc,* and *sm.*

You may enjoy doing the following activities with your child:

**1. Main Idea** Have your child draw a picture of a house, a tree, and a hill. Then, on a separate piece of paper, have your child draw and color a picture of a cat. Cut out the picture of the cat. Tell your child a story about the cat: how it starts at the bottom of the tree and climbs to the top, runs to the hill, comes back to the house for a drink of milk, and so on.

Your child should move his or her picture of the cat around to show where the cat is at each point in the story. Your child might enjoy telling you a story and having you move the cat.

**2. Consonant Clusters with *r*** Invent small stories with your child using words like the following that contain clusters with *r.* Use pictures or drawings to illustrate the stories.

| grin | grab | drum | break | frog |
|------|------|------|-------|------|
| broom | drink | bride | green | grapes |

**Example:** The bride grabbed the green grapes.

**3. Long Vowel *o*** Ask your child to make up sentences using the following long vowel *o* words: *no, go, so, yo-yo.*

Write each sentence and have your child draw a picture for each one. I hope you and your child enjoy sharing these books and activities.

Sincerely,

¡Felicidades! Su hijo(a) acaba de completar el libro *Out Came the Sun* en el programa de lectura. Para estimular y continuar el hábito de la lectura de su hijo(a), comparta con él o ella estos libros:

***The Very Busy Spider*** por Eric Carle. Putnam, © 1984. En este cuento animales de finca tratan de asegurar que una araña muy diligente no teja su tela.

***Mirandy and Brother Wind*** por Patricia McKissack. Knopf, © 1988. Aunque su compañero es torpe, Mirandy quiere obstinadamente ganar el concurso en el cual los jóvenes tienen que caminar sin dejar caer el pedazo de torta que llevan. Ella soluciona su problema pidiéndole ayuda al Hermano Viento.

A través de estas lecturas su hijo(a) ha aprendido cómo identificar la idea principal, la relación entre las causas y los efectos y la secuencia de eventos. Su hijo(a) ha aprendido también las vocales *i* y *o* y las combinaciones *sn, fr, gr, fl, st, br, sc* y *sm*. Le invito a realizar las siguientes actividades con su hijo(a):

**1. La idea principal** Pida a su hijo(a) que dibuje una casa, un árbol y una colina. Después en una hoja separada dígale, que dibuje un gato. Recorte el dibujo del gato. Cuenta un cuento a su hijo(a) acerca del gato: hable de cómo empieza al pie de un árbol y se trepa hasta lo alto, corre hacia la colina, vuelve a la casa para tomar un poco de leche, etcétera.

Su hijo(a) debería mover su dibujo del gato para hacer ver dónde está el gato en cada punto del relato. A su hijo(a) a lo mejor le gustaría contar un cuento a usted y mirar mientras usted mueve el dibujo del gato.

**2. Combinaciones de consonantes y *r*** Inventa cuentos cortos con su hijo(a); use palabras como las siguientes que contienen combinaciones de otros consonantes y *r*. Use fotos o dibujos para ilustrar los cuentos.

| | | | | |
|---|---|---|---|---|
| grin | grab | drum | break | frog |
| broom | drink | bride | green | grapes |

**3. La *o* larga** Pida a su hijo(a) que diga oraciones usando las siguientes palabras que contienen el sonido largo de la *o: no, go, so, yo-yo.*

Escriba cada oración y pida a su hijo(a) que dibuje algo para cada una.

Espero que usted y su hijo(a) disfruten juntos de estos libros y actividades.

Cordialmente,

Dear Family of: _____

The selections in your child's reading book include "Twins, Twins, Twins" and "Shoes from Grandpa." To help share the joy of reading with your child, you might wish to obtain the following books:

***All in a Day*** by Mitsumasa Anno. Putnam, © 1986. Brief text and illustrations by ten internationally known artists reveal a day in the lives of children in eight different countries.

***Arthur's Prize Reader*** by Lillian Hoban. Harper & Row, © 1978. Arthur is disappointed that he did not win the Super Chimp Club Contest but he is delighted that his pupil and sister, Violet, won the reading competition.

***All Kinds of Families*** by Norma Simon. Whitman, © 1975. The diversity of family structures in our multiethnic society is warmly conveyed in this picture book.

Through these stories your child will be learning about main idea, story mapping, cumulative text, and making predictions. Your child will also be learning about the vowel *u* and the blends *gr, bl, pl, sc, sm, sn, tr,* and *fl.*

You may enjoy doing the following activities with your child:

**1. Predicting Outcomes** Help your child practice predicting outcomes by describing a situation and asking your child to tell you what he or she thinks will happen. For example, say the following: "Your father has just finished painting the porch when your cat jumps up on the porch rail with muddy feet. What do you think will happen?" You should accept any reasonable answers and ask for other possible outcomes. Your child will think it is great fun if you suggest some alternative outcomes as well.

**2. Short Vowel *u*** With your child find pictures of the words that have the short vowel *u* sound, such as *tub, cub, rug, bud, jug, bug, cup, bus, sun,* and *duck.*

Combine these words with other words that contain the same vowel sound, such as action words or the names of people, to make up sentence stories about the pictures. For example: Gus and a duck run with a cub in the sun.

Encourage your child to create his or her own stories. You may also wish to cut out, mount, and label some of the pictures you and your child have found.

I hope you and your child have fun sharing these books and activities.

Sincerely,

Las selecciones en el libro de lectura de su hijo(a) incluyen "Twins, Twins, Twins" y "Shoes from Grandpa". Para apoyar y ampliar el concepto, comparta los libros siguientes con su hijo(a):

*All in a Day* por Mitsumasa Anno. Putnam, © 1986. En este libro contextos cortos y ilustraciones hechas por diez artistas mundialmente renombrados revelan las vidas de los niños de ocho países diferentes.

*Arthur's Prize Reader* por Lillian Hoban. Harper & Row, © 1978. Arthur se siente mal cuando no gana el Concurso del Super Chimp Club, pero se alegra que su estudiante, y hermana, Violet, gana la competición de lectura.

*All Kinds of Families* por Norma Simon. Whitman, © 1975. Este libro ilustrado revela las diferentes estructuras familiares que existen en nuestra sociedad multi-étnica.

A través de estas lecturas, su hijo(a) aprenderá cómo identificar la idea principal de un relato, hacer mapas de los acontecimientos en el relato, hablar del texto cumulativamente y predecir los desenlaces. Su hijo(a) aprenderá también acerca de la vocal *u* y las combinaciones de *gr, bl, pl, sc, sm, sn, tr* y *fl*. Le invito a realizar las siguientes actividades con su hijo(a):

**1. Predecir los desenlaces** Ayude a su hijo(a) mientras practica a predecir los desenlaces describiendo una situación y preguntándole qué piensa él o ella que pasará. Por ejemplo, diga lo siguiente: "Tu padre apenas terminó de pintar el porche cuando tu gato salta en la balaústre con los pies sucios. ¿Qué piensas que pasará?" Trate de aceptar cualquier respuesta razonable y de preguntar por otros resultados posibles. Su hijo(a) pensará que esta actividad es muy divertida si usted también participa y le sugiere algunos resultados.

**2. El sonido corto de la vocal *u*** Conjuntamente con su hijo(a), busque fotos de las palabras que tiene el sonido corto de la *u,* como: *tub, cub, rug, bud, jug, bug, cup, bus, sun* y *duck.* Combine estas palabras con otras que tienen el mismo sonido, como verbos o nombres de personas, para crear cuentos acerca de las fotos. Por ejemplo: *Gus and a duck run with a cub in the sun.* Anime a su hijo(a) crear sus propios cuentos. Podría también recortar, rotular y clasificar algunas de las fotos que ustedes encontraron.

Espero que usted y su hijo(a) disfruten juntos de estos libros y actividades.

Cordialmente,

Dear Family of: _____

Congratulations! Your child has just completed *Morning Bells*. To continue to encourage your child to read, you might wish to share these books:

***Pinkerton, Behave!*** by Steven Kellogg. Dial Press, © 1979. Pinkerton is a puppy who is difficult to train. His owners are exasperated until they learn how Pinkerton understands their commands.

***Leo the Late Bloomer*** by Robert Kraus. Windmill Books, © 1971. This book tells the story of Leo, a lion cub who blooms when his parents aren't looking.

Through the stories in this level, your child has learned about main idea, story mapping, cumulative text, and making predictions. Your child has also learned about the vowel *u* and the blends *gr, bl, pl, sc, sm, sn, tr,* and *fl.*

You may enjoy doing the following activities with your child:

**1. Cumulative Text** Obtain a story such as the Dr. Seuss book, *Green Eggs and Ham*. As you come to the section that repeats, see how much of it your child can remember and encourage him or her to "read" that part of the story.

**2. Consonant Blends with *l*** Find pictures of some of the following words for your child. If possible, cut them out, mount them and label them. Ask your child to help you look for the pictures and glue them in place on cards.

| | | | | |
|---|---|---|---|---|
| blade | glove | flag | clown | clock |
| slipper | blanket | flower | flashlight | flute |
| clip | floor | glass | cloud | globe |

When your cards are ready, make up sentences orally like the examples below. Ask your child to choose a picture card that will provide the missing idea.

**Examples:** 1. May I have a _____ of water?   (glass)
2. The hands of the _____ stopped at four.   (clock)
3. Put another _____ on the bed.   (blanket)

I hope you and your child have fun sharing these books and activities.

Sincerely,

Estimada Familia de: _____

¡Felicidades! Su hijo(a) acaba de completar el libro *Morning Bells* en el programa de lectura. Para estimular y continuar el hábito de la lectura de su hijo(a), comparta con él o ella estos libros:

*Pinkerton, Behave!* por Steven Kellogg. Dial Press, © 1979. Pinkerton es un cachorro difícil de entrenar. Sus dueños están exasperados hasta que no aprenden cómo hace Pinkerton para entender sus órdenes.

*Leo the Late Bloomer* por Robert Kraus. Windmill Books, © 1971. Este es el cuento de Leo, un leoncito que se desarrolla mientras sus padres no lo notan.

A través de estas lecturas su hijo(a) ha aprendido cómo identificar la idea principal, cómo crear un mapa de los eventos en el relato, leer el texto cumulativo y predecir los desenlaces. Su hijo(a) ha aprendido también la vocal *u* y las combinaciones *gr, bl, pl, sc, sm, sn, tr* y *fl*. Le invito a realizar las siguientes actividades con su hijo(a):

**1. El texto cumulativo** Obtenga un cuento como el del Dr. Seuss entitulado *Green Eggs and Ham*. Cuando llega a la sección donde empieza la repetición, vea cuánto de ese texto se acuerda su hijo(a) y anímele a "leer" esa parte del cuento.

**2. Combinaciones de consonantes con *l*** Encuentre algunas fotos que representan las palabras que siguen para su hijo(a). Si es posible, recorte y pegue y clasifíquelas. Pídale a su hijo(a) que le ayude a buscar las fotos y a pegarlas en cartas.

| blade | glove | flag | clown | clock |
|-------|-------|------|-------|-------|
| slipper | blanket | flower | flashlight | flute |
| clip | floor | glass | cloud | globe |

Cuando estén listas las cartas, crea oraciones en voz alta, y en inglés, según los ejemplos que siguen. Pídale a su hijo(a) que escoja una foto que podría proveer la palabra que falta.

**Ejemplos:** 1. ¿Me puedes dar un _____ de agua?   (vaso)

2. Las manecillas del _____ se pararon en las cuatro.   (reloj)

3. Pun otra _____ sobre la cama.   (manta)

Espero que usted y su hijo(a) disfruten juntos de estos libros y actividades.

Cordialmente,

Dear Family of: _____

The stories in Unit 1 deal with animals in realistic and fantastic settings. The stories depict situations involving animals and humans. Here are several books about animals you may wish to share with your child.

***The Exploding Frog and Other Fables*** from Aesop retold by John McFarland and illustrated by James Marshall. Little, Brown, © 1981. Adaptations of some of Aesop's best-known tales are accompanied by cheery illustrations.

***What Is a Bird? and Where Do Birds Live?*** written by Ron Hirschi and photographed by Galen Burrell. Walker, © 1987. These magnificently photographed companion books introduce the young reader to the special beauty of birds and their homes. Vivid photographs reflect the simple line of text on each page.

***Crictor*** by Tomi Ungerer. Harper & Row, © 1958. Crictor, a lovable pet who also happens to be a boa constrictor, lives a charmed life in a French town.

Through the stories your child has been learning how to predict outcomes (how to tell what happen next in a story). Your child has also learned: alphabetical order, contractions with *will* and *would,* long and short vowels, and words with *-er, -est, -ed, -ing.*

Digraphs are two letters grouped together to make one sound. Consonant clusters are two or more consonants grouped together.

You might enjoy doing the following activities with your child:

**1. Predicting Outcomes** Look through a magazine with your child. Point out a picture of a kitten or a puppy. Ask your child questions such as, "What do you think the kitten (or puppy) is going to do?" Make up a story about the small animal's day. As you tell the story, continue asking your child, "What do you think will happen next?" Your child might enjoy telling a story from a picture and having you predict what will happen next.

**2. Reality/Fantasy** Whenever you are watching television with your child, ask him or her if events you are seeing could really happen. For example, if you are watching an advertisement for a breakfast cereal, ask your child if tigers really can talk and eat their breakfast at a table. Contrast this with animals portrayed in a zoo or another setting.

I hope you and your child have fun sharing these books and activities.

Sincerely,

Estimada Familia de: _____

Las lecturas de la Unidad 1 tratan de los animales en situaciones reales y de fantasía. En estas lecturas se representan situaciones con animales y con seres humanos. Tal vez le gustaría compartir con su hijo(a) estos libros sobre los animales:

***The Exploding Frog and Other Fables*** from Aesop adaptado por John McFarland e ilustrado por James Marshall. Little, Brown, © 1981. Adaptaciones de las conocidas fábulas de Esopo, con ilustraciones simpáticas.

***What Is a Bird? and Where Do Birds Live?*** por Ron Hirschi con fotografías de Galen Burrell. Walker, © 1987. Estos libros con excelentes fotografías presentan la belleza única de las aves y sus hogares.

***Crictor*** por Tomi Ungerer. Harper & Row, © 1958. Crictor, un animalito doméstico muy especial (¡una boa constrictor!) lleva una vida encantada en un pueblecito en Francia.

A través de las lecturas, su hijo(a) ha aprendido a predecir desenlaces (a saber qué es lo que sigue en un cuento). Su hijo(a) también ha aprendido lo siguiente: el orden alfabético, la vocal larga *o* y el sonido corto de la *s,* las contracciones con *will* y *would* y las palabras que terminan en *-er, -est, -ed, -ing.*

Un digrama es la unión de dos letras con un solo sonido. Una combinación de consonantes es la unión de dos o más consonantes.

Le invito a realizar las siguientes actividades con su hijo(a):

**1. Predicción de desenlaces** Junto con su hijo(a), busque en una revista la ilustración de un gatito o de un perrito. Hágale preguntas a su hijo(a), tales como "¿Qué crees tú que el gatito (o perrito) va a hacer?" Invente un cuento sobre un día en la vida del animalito. A medida que relate el cuento, siga preguntándole a su hijo(a), "¿Qué crees tú que va a seguir?" A su hijo(a) quizás le guste ser él o ella quien inventa el cuento y pedirle a usted que prediga lo que seguirá.

**2. Realidad/Fantasía** Cuando mire la televisión con su hijo(a), pregúntele si lo que están mirando podría suceder realmente. Por ejemplo, si están mirando un anuncio de un cereal para el desayuno, pregúntele si realmente los tigres pueden hablar y desayunar sentados a la mesa. Preséntele un contraste a su hijo(a) con los animales en un zoológico o en otro lugar.

Espero que a usted y a su hijo(a) les agraden estos libros y actividades.

Cordialmente,

Dear Family of: _____

The stories in Unit 2 are about how people use their imaginations. In one selection, a child pretends to be various objects. One selection focuses on a classroom of children making up a story. To reinforce the concept of using your imagination, you may wish to share the following books with your child:

***The Mixed-Up Chameleon*** by Eric Carle. Crowell, © 1975. This classic picture book tells the story of the mixed-up chameleon who wishes it could be more like all the other animals it sees. The bold, colorful mixed-up illustrations offer a visual delight for children.

***Me and Neesie*** by Eloise Greenfield. Harper & Row, © 1975. Janell's imaginary friend Neesie is just the friend Janell needs as she starts school and awaits a visit from Aunt Bea.

***Truck Song*** by Diane Siebert. Harper & Row, © 1984. Children can pretend to be riding on a truck as they read or listen to this rhymed text.

Through the stories your child has been learning about alphabetical order, and sequence of events. Your child has also learned: reviewing long vowels; words with *-es;* using /s/c, /j/g; and vowel digraphs *ai, ay, ea, ee.*

**1. Sequence** Play "Oh, No!" with your child. Read these sentences aloud. Ask your child to say "Oh, No!" as soon as he or she hears something out of order.

1. This is how I get dressed.      4. I put on my shoes.
2. I put on my shirt.               5. I put on my socks.
3. I put on my jeans.              6. I put on my hat.

Your child should say "Oh, No!" after "I put on my socks."

Make up other simple "Oh, No!" situations for your child. Examples might be mailing a letter, feeding the dog, or washing one's face.

**2. Cause/Effect** Identifying cause/effect relationships will help your child to better understand a story or other people's behavior. A *cause* is what makes something happen. An *effect* is what happens. Some cause/effect signal words are *so* and *because.* Use the example shown here as a model for your own cause/effect sentences. Write a few sentences on a sheet of paper and ask your child to identify the cause, the effect, and the signal word.

**Example:** It was cold outside so I put on my hat and mittens.

I hope you have fun sharing these books and activities with your child.

Sincerely,

Estimada Familia de: _____

Las lecturas de la Unidad 2 tratan sobre cómo la gente y los animales usan su imaginación. En una de las lecturas, un niño se imagina ser diferentes objetos. Una de las lecturas se trata de unos niños en la escuela que están inventando un cuento. Para recalcar el concepto de usar la imaginación, comparta estos libros con su hijo(a):

*The Mixed-Up Chameleon* por Eric Carle. Crowell, © 1975. Un libro ilustrado clásico acerca de un camaleón confuso que quiere parecerse aun más a los otros animales.

*Me and Neesie* por Eloise Greenfield. Harper & Row, © 1975. Janell y su amiga imaginaria Neesie van a la escuela y se preparan para la visita de la tía Bea.

*Truck Song* por Diane Siebert. Harper & Row, © 1984. Los niños pueden imaginarse que viajan en un camión con este libro en rima.

A través de estas lecturas, su hijo(a) ha aprendido acerca del orden alfabético y del orden en que ocurren las cosas. También ha aprendido lo siguiente: la revisión de las vocales largas; cómo usar *sc, j, g;* el digrama de vocales *ai, ay, ea, ee* y palabras que terminan en *-es.*

**1. Orden** Juegue al *"¡Oh, No!"* con su hijo(a). Lea estas oraciones en voz alta. Pídale a su hijo(a) que exclame *"¡Oh, No!"* tan pronto escuche algo fuera del orden lógico.

1. This is how I get dressed.
2. I put on my shirt.
3. I put on my jeans.
4. I put on my shoes.
5. I put on my socks.
6. I put on my hat.

Su hijo(a) debe decir *"¡Oh, No!"* después de *"I put on my socks".*

Invente otras situaciones sencillas para que su hijo(a) use *"¡Oh, No!"* Algunos ejemplos pueden ser enviar una carta por correo o lavarse la cara.

**2. Causa y efecto** El identificar la relación entre las causas y los efectos ayudará a su hijo(a) a entender mejor sea un cuento o sea el comportamiento de las personas. Una *causa* es lo que lleva a un resultado. Un *efecto* es el resultado. Algunas palabras que señalan una relación de causa y efecto son *entonces* y *porque.* Use el ejemplo modelado aquí para crear sus propias oraciones que indiquen una causa y efecto. Escriba algunas oraciones en una hoja de papel y pida a su hijo(a) identificar la causa, el efecto y la palabra que señala esta relación.

**Ejemplo:** Hacía frío afuera, entonces me puse mi gorro y mis guantes.

Espero que usted y su hijo(a) se diviertan con estos libros y actividades.

Cordialmente,

Make a Wish

Dear Family of: _____

Congratulations! Your child has just completed *Make a Wish* in the reading program. To continue to encourage your child to read, you might wish to share these books:

***Martin's Hats*** by Joan W. Blos. Morrow, © 1984. A variety of hats offers Martin an endless series of adventures before bedtime.

***The Secret Birthday Message*** by Eric Carle. Harper & Row, © 1972. For his birthday, Tim receives a message, written in code. Children accompany Tim as he follows the clues on this special treasure hunt that ends with a birthday surprise.

***Make Way for Ducklings*** by Robert McCloskey. Puffin Books, 1988. This beloved childhood classic follows Mr. and Mrs. Mallard and their ducklings in their search for a home.

In this level your child has learned about predicting outcomes and sequence of events. Your child has also learned about:

vowel digraphs *ai, ay*                    inflectional endings *-ing, -ed*
contractions with *will, would* and *not*    words with *-er, -est, -s, -es*

Your child has also learned to distinguish between reality and fantasy, to classify, and to use alphabetical order.

You might enjoy doing the following activities with your child:

**1. Drawing Conclusions** Drawing conclusions will help your child better understand and appreciate what he or she reads. With your child, choose a book or story neither of you has read. Read aloud to your child the first few pages. Ask your child: "What do you think will happen next?" Suggest that your child think about what he or she already knows about this situation or the characters in the story. This can help him or her to draw conclusions about the rest of the story.

**2. Words with *-er, -est*** Use familiar household objects to demonstrate such concepts as big, bigger, biggest, and small, smaller, smallest with your child. For example, ask your child to tell which of two objects is bigger and which of three objects is biggest.

I hope you enjoy sharing these books and activities with your child.

Sincerely,

¡Felicidades! Su hijo(a) acaba de terminar el libro *Make a Wish* en el programa de lectura. Para seguir animando a su hijo(a) a leer, comparta estos libros con él o ella:

*Martin's Hats* por Joan W. Blos. Morrow, © 1984. Una colección de sombreros le ofrece a Martin una serie interminable de aventuras antes de la hora de dormir.

*The Secret Birthday Message* por Eric Carle. Harper & Row, © 1972. Tim recibe un mensaje en cifra para su cumpleños. El lector acompaña a Tim mientras éste sigue las pistas en una búsqueda de tesoro que termina con una sorpresa.

*Make Way for Ducklings* por Robert McCloskey. Puffin Books, 1988. Este cuento clásico infantil presenta al señor y la señora Mallard y sus patitos en busca de un hogar.

En este nivel, su hijo(a) ha aprendido acerca de la predicción de los desenlaces y el orden en que ocurren las cosas. Su hijo(a) también ha aprendido acerca de: los digramas de vocales *ai, ay*; las contracciones con *will, would* y *not*; la terminación flexional *-ing, -ed*; palabras que terminan en *-er, -est, -s, -es*.

Su hijo(a) también ha aprendido a distinguir entre realidad y fantasía, a clasificar y a ordenar alfabéticamente.

Le invito a realizar las siguientes actividades con su hijo(a):

**1. Cómo sacar conclusiones** El sacar conclusiones ayudará a su hijo(a) a entender mejor y apreciar lo que él o ella lee. Conjuntamente con su hijo(a), escoja un libro o cuento que ninguno de los dos haya leído. Lea en voz alta las primeras páginas. Pregunte a su hijo(a): "¿Qué piensas que sucederá?" Sugiere que su hijo(a) piense de lo que ya sabe acerca de esta situación o de los personajes en el cuento. Esto le podrá ayudar a sacar conclusiones acerca del resto del cuento.

**2. Palabras que terminan en *-er* y *-est*** Use objetos de su casa para mostrarle a su hijo(a) conceptos como *big* (grande), *bigger* (más grande), *biggest* (el más grande), y *small* (pequeño), *smaller* (más pequeño), *smallest* (el más pequeño). Por ejemplo, pregúntele a su hijo(a) cuál de dos objetos es más grande *(bigger)* y cuál de tres objetos es el más grande *(biggest)*.

Espero que a usted y a su hijo(a) se diviertan con estos libros y activadades.

Cordialmente,

Dear Family of: _____

The stories in Unit 1 focus on friendships and examine the qualities of various relationships. To help reinforce the concept of friendship, you may wish to share the following books with your child:

*A Bargain for Frances* by Russell Hoban. Harper & Row, © 1970. Thelma the badger tricks her friend Frances into buying a tea set she doesn't want. When Frances gets back at Thelma, both friends come to the conclusion that they have to stop tricking each other if they are to remain friends.

*Days with Frog and Toad* written and illustrated by Arnold Lobel. Harper & Row, © 1979. Frog and Toad are such good friends that they spend most days together doing such things as flying a kite and telling ghost stories by the fire, cleaning house, and losing and finding buttons.

*Stringbean's Trip to the Shining Sea* by Vera B. and Jennifer Williams. Greenwillow Books, © 1988. The unusual format of this cross-country travel book is a series of post cards that two brothers send home to Kansas.

In this unit your child has learned about cause and effect relationships, characterization, and synonyms. Other skills learned in this unit include: compound words; long vowel *e*; and contractions with *am, is, are, have.*

You might enjoy doing the following activities with your child:

**1. Compound Words** Use the following list of words to play a guessing game: *barefoot, wildcat, blackbird, bulldog, football, goldfish, haircut, rowboat, railroad, wristwatch, tiptoe, mailbox, sunburn, dishpan, shoelace, snowdrift.*

Ask, "What would you call a foot that is bare?" "What would you call a cat that is wild?" Each answer that your child gives will be a compound word.

**2. Cause/Effect** Play "Because" with your child. Tell him or her you will say two sentences. Ask your child to repeat them using the word "because" in front of the first sentence or in the middle of the sentences, depending on their meaning.

You say: I went to bed. It was late.
Child says: I went to bed because it was late.
You say: I jumped in a puddle. I got all muddy.
Child says: Because I jumped in a puddle, I got all muddy.

I hope you and your child enjoy sharing these books and activities.

Sincerely,

Las lecturas de la Unidad 1 se concentran en la amistad y examinan las características de las diferentes relaciones. Para apoyar y ampliar el concepto de la amistad, comparta los libros siguientes con su hijo(a):

*A **Bargain for Frances*** por Russell Hoban. Harper & Row, © 1970. Thelma, un tejón travieso, le hace un truco a su amiga Frances. Cuando Frances se venga haciéndole otro truco a Thelma, las amigas deciden que es hora de dejarse de trucos.

***Days with Frog and Toad*** cuento e ilustraciones por Arnold Lobel. Harper & Row, © 1979. Rana y Sapo son buenos amigos, y se pasan el día volando barriletes, contando botones, haciéndose cuentos y limpiando la casa.

***Stringbean's Trip to the Shining Sea*** por Vera B. y Jennifer Williams. Greenwillow Books, © 1988. Este relato de un viaje se desenvuelve por medio de tarjetas postales que dos hermanos envían a su familia.

En esta unidad, su hijo(a) ha aprendido acerca de las relaciones de causa y efecto, la caracterización y los sinónimos. También ha aprendido acerca de: palabras compuestas; la vocal larga *e*; las contracciones con *am, is, are, have*.

Le invito a realizar las siguientes actividades con su hijo(a):

**1. Palabras compuestas** Use la lista de palabras a continuación para un juego de adivinanzas: *barefoot, wildcat, blackbird, bulldog, football, goldfish, haircut, rowboat, railroad, wristwatch, tiptoe, mailbox, sunburn, dishpan, shoelace, snowdrift.*

Pregúntele a su hijo(a), "What would you call a foot that is bare?" "What would you call a cat that is wild?" Cada respuesta de su hijo(a) debe ser una palabra compuesta.

**2. Causa y efecto** Juegue al *"Because"* (porque) con su hijo(a). Dígale que usted dirá dos oraciones. Pídale que las repita usando la palabra *"because"* antes de la primera oración o entre las dos oraciones, según el significado.

Usted dice: *I went to bed. It was late.*
Su hijo(a) dice: *I went to bed* because *it was late.*
Usted dice: *I jumped in a puddle. I got all muddy.*
Su hijo(a) dice: Because *I jumped in a puddle, I got all muddy.*

Espero que a usted y a su hijo(a) les agraden estos libros y actividades.

Cordialmente,

Dear Family of: _____

Stories and how they were passed on from one person to another are the focus of Unit 2. To help reinforce these concepts, you may wish to share the following books with your child:

*Why Mosquitoes Buzz in People's Ears* by Verna Aardema and illustrated by Leo and Diane Dillon. Dial Press, © 1978. A chain reaction (beginning with Mosquito telling a lie to Iguana and ending with Owl refusing to tell the sun to come up) helps explain why we are annoyed when mosquitoes buzz.

*The Patchwork Quilt* by Valerie Flournoy and illustrated by Jerry Pinkney. Dial Books, © 1985. Tanya's grandmother spends months working on a quilt that tells the story of their family with patches of fabric from everyone. The love that made the quilt is reflected in the luminous illustrations.

*Emma* by Wendy Kesselman and illustrated by Barbara Cooney. Harper, 1985. Lonely Emma takes up painting at age 72. She paints her childhood village and scenes she sees out her window. Her house becomes full of pictures of people and places she loves.

Through the stories your child has been learning about main idea/details (finding the most important idea in a story), drawing conclusions, and classification (grouping words by category). Your child has also learned about certain sounds in words, such as vowel digraph *oa*, and about dropping final *e* before a suffix. Vowel digraphs are two vowels grouped together to make one sound.

You might enjoy doing the following activities with your child:

**1. Main Idea/Details** Tell your child that you are going to play a game in which you pretend that your child has something new, such as a bicycle. When you name the thing, ask your child to use his or her imagination to tell you more about it. He or she can be serious (it has 16-inch wheels) or humorous (it is covered with fur).

**2. Drawing Conclusions** Look through a magazine with your child. Point out a picture, such as a boy holding a puppy. Ask questions such as, "Do you think the boy likes the puppy?" "How do you know?" "Do you think the boy will take care of the puppy?" "How do you know?" "What else do you know about the boy and the puppy?" Find other pictures in the magazine and ask your child similar questions.

I hope you and your child have fun sharing these books and activities.

Sincerely,

Las historias y cómo pasaron de una persona a otra son el tema principal de la Unidad 2. Para apoyar estos conceptos, comparta los libros siguientes con su hijo(a):

***Why Mosquitoes Buzz in People's Ears*** por Verna Aardema con ilustraciones de Leo y Diane Dillon. Dial Press, © 1978. Una reacción en cadena (que empieza cuando Mosquito le miente a Iguana y termina cuando Lechuza se niega a pedirle al sol que salga) explica por qué nos molesta el zumbido de los mosquitos.

***The Patchwork Quilt*** por Valerie Flournoy con ilustraciones de Jerry Pinkney. Dial Books, © 1985. La abuelita de Tanya dedica meses a coser una cobija hecha de piezas de tela de todo el mundo que representa la historia de la familia. Las ilustraciones reflejan la ternura que creó la cobija.

***Emma*** por Wendy Kesselman con ilustraciones de Barbara Cooney. Harper, 1985. Emma se siente sola y comienza a pintar a los 72 años. Pinta la aldea de su niñez y escenas que ve desde su ventana. Su casa se llena de cuadros de la gente y los paisajes que ella quiere.

A través de las lecturas, su hijo(a) ha aprendido lo que significa idea principal/detalles (encontrar la idea más importante de una lectura), sacar conclusiones y clasificar (agrupar palabras por categoría). Su hijo(a) también ha aprendido acerca de ciertos sonidos en las palabras, tales como el digrama de vocales *oa* y la eliminación de la *e* final antes de un sufijo. Un digrama de vocales es la unión de los vocales con un solo sonido.

Le invito a realizar las siguientes actividades con su hijo(a):

**1. Idea principal/Detalles** Dígale a su hijo(a) que van a hacer un juego en el cual usted simulará que él o ella tiene algo nuevo, como una bicicleta. Cuando usted mencione el objeto, pídale a su hijo(a) que use su imaginación para decir algo más sobre el objeto. El comentario podría ser serio (tiene ruedas de 16 pulgadas), o humorístico (está cubierto de pelo).

**2. Cómo sacar conclusiones** Con su hijo(a), mire una revista y señale alguna ilustración, como la de un niño cargando a un perrito. Hágale preguntas tales como "¿Crees que al niño le gusta el perrito?", "¿Cómo lo sabes?", "¿Crees que el niño cuidará al perrito?", "¿Cómo lo sabes?", "¿Qué más sabes sobre el niño y el perrito?" Busque otras ilustraciones en la revista y hágale a su hijo(a) preguntas similares.

Espero que usted y su hijo(a) se diviertan con estos libros y actividades.

Cordialmente,

Dear Family of: _____

Congratulations! Your child has just completed *A New Day* in the reading program. To continue to encourage your child to read you might wish to share these books:

***Feelings*** written and illustrated by Aliki. William Morrow, © 1984. Almost every emotion expressed by a child is found in this illustrated catalog of feelings and the situations that cause them.

***Little Bear*** by Else Minarik, illustrated by Maurice Sendak, Harper & Row, © 1957. In four charming stories, Little Bear asks Mother Bear for clothes to keep him warm in the snow; makes birthday soup for his friends Hen, Duck, and Cat; and pretends to fly to the moon.

***Three Days on a River in a Red Canoe*** by Vera B. Williams. Greenwillow Books, © 1981. A camping trip is made exciting and educational. Learn how to put up a tent, cook over a fire, and lower a canoe by rope!

Your child has studied cause/effect, main idea/details, and drawing conclusions. Other skills taught at this level include: compound words, vowel digraph *oa*, characterization, synonyms, and dropping *e* before a suffix.

You might enjoy doing the following activities with your child:

**1. Characterization** Choose a person that you and your child know and like. Do not tell your child who the person is. Give your child four or five words that tell what the person is like; for example, *angry, shy, kind, helpful, thoughtful.* Tell your child that these are traits and emotions of the person. See if your child can guess whom you are describing. Then have your child choose someone you both know and have you guess who it is. Continue taking turns.

Make sure your child understands that traits refer to qualities a person has rather than to physical description. You might want to precede this activity by going through examples of what is and what is not a character trait.

Traits: brave, selfish, generous    Not Traits: tall, pretty, thin

**2. Synonyms** Have your child complete sentences with synonyms. For example: hat/cap: My _____ is on the table. Your child should complete this sentence first with the word *hat* and then with the word *cap*. Other synonyms are: *house/home, race/run, stone/rock, build/make, shout/yell, enjoy/like, road/street, lock/close.*

I hope you and your child enjoy sharing these books and activities.

Sincerely,

¡Felicidades! Su hijo(a) acaba de terminar el libro *A New Day* en el programa de lectura. Para seguir animando a su hijo(a) a leer, comparta con él o ella los libros siguientes:

*Feelings* por Aliki. William Morrow, © 1984. Un catálogo ilustrado de casi todas las emociones que un niño siente y las situaciones que las ocasionan.

*Little Bear* por Else Minarik, con ilustraciones de Maurice Sendak. Harper & Row, © 1957. En estos cuatro cuentos, un osito le pide a su mamá ropa abrigada para jugar en la nieve, aprende a hacer una sopa de cumpleaños para sus amigos y hace un viaje imaginario a la luna.

Su hijo(a) ha estudiado las relaciones de causa y efecto, idea principal y detalles y cómo sacar conclusiones. También ha aprendido acerca de: las palabras compuestas, el digrama de vocales *oa*, la eliminación de la *e* antes de un sufijo, la caracterización y los sinónimos.

Le invito a realizar las siguientes actividades con su hijo(a):

**1. Caracterización** Elija una persona que usted y su hijo(a) conozcan y quien les agrade. No le diga a su hijo(a) de quién se trata. Describa a la persona con cuatro o cinco palabras; por ejemplo, *angry* (enojada), *shy* (tímida), *kind* (amable), *helpful* (servicial), *thoughtful* (considerada). Dígale a su hijo(a) que estas palabras representan los rasgos de carácter (traits) y las emociones de la persona, y que trate de adivinar quién es. Luego, haga que su hijo(a) elija a alguien que ambos(as) conozcan y trate usted de adivinar quién es. Continúen esta actividad por turnos.

Asegúrese de que su hijo(a) comprenda que los rasgos de carácter se refieren a las cualidades de una persona y no a su descripción física. Tal vez sería provechoso que antes de la actividad le dé ejemplos de palabras que definan el carácter de las personas.

Rasgos de carácter: *valentía, egoísmo, generosidad*

Rasgos que no son de carácter: *altura, belleza*

**2. Sinónimos** Haga que su hijo(a) complete oraciones con sinónimos. Por ejemplo: *hat/ cap: My _____ is on the table.* Primero debe completar la oración con la palabra *hat* y luego con la palabra *cap*. He aquí otros sinónimos: *house/home, race/run, stone/rock, build/ make, shout/yell, enjoy/like, road/street, lock/close.*

Espero que usted y su hijo(a) disfruten juntos de estos libros y activadades.

Cordialmente,

# Forms and Transparencies

These forms and transparencies are time-saving devices which help children organize information and their thinking. They provide opportunities for in-depth work with the class or with small groups. They may also be used by individuals as they read fiction or nonfiction.

# Contents

**Transparencies of the Forms**

# Cooperative Learning Plan

Goals:


Objectives:


Materials:


Accountability criteria:


Rewards:


Social skills:


Organization of groups:


---

**383**

# Story Map

Title: _____ Author: _____

Beginning:
    Who
    Where
    When

▼

Middle:
    Problem

▼

Ending:
    Solution

# Circle Story Framework

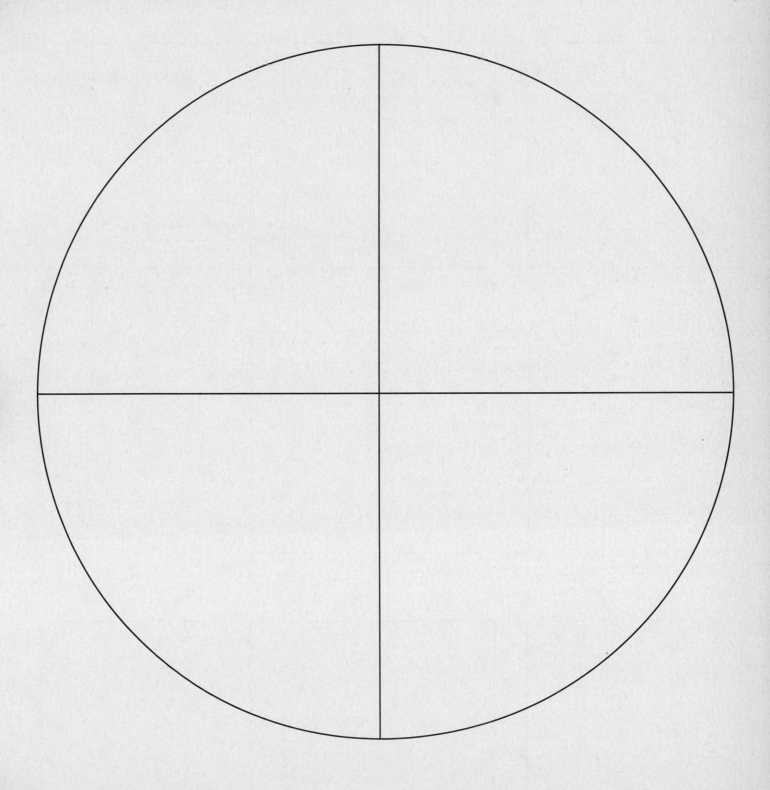

# Semantic Map

# Semantic Feature Analysis

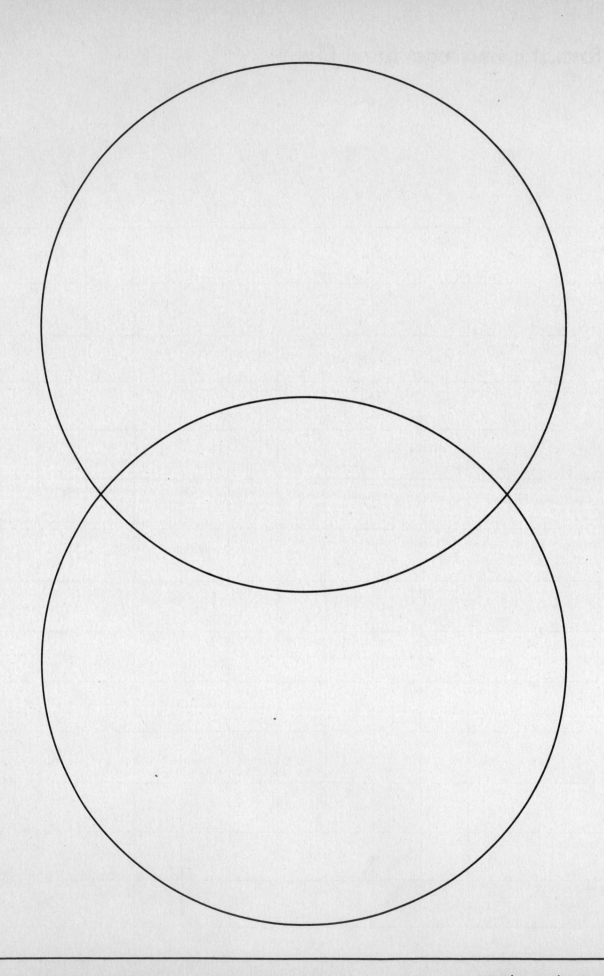

**Venn Diagram**

# Information Organizer Chart

|  |  |  |  |
|---|---|---|---|
|  |  |  |  |
|  |  |  |  |
|  |  |  |  |
|  |  |  |  |
|  |  |  |  |

# Flow Chart

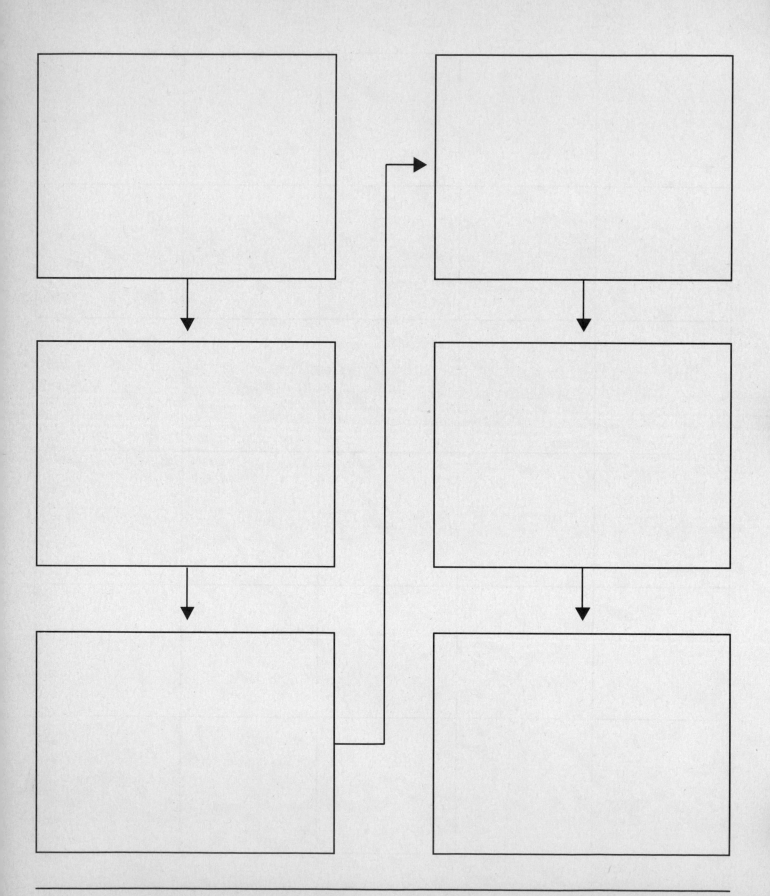

# KWL Chart

| What I know | What I want to know | What I learned |
| --- | --- | --- |
| | | |

# Cause/Effect

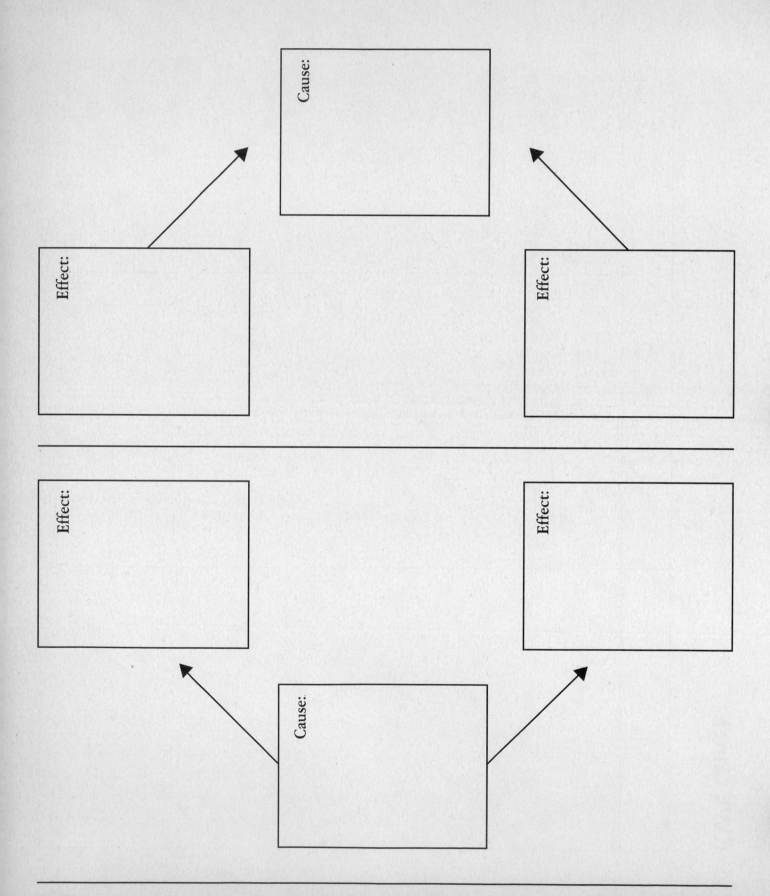

Cause:

Effect:

Effect:

Effect:

Effect:

Cause:

# Cause/Effect Chart

Cause

Effect

_____          _____

_____          _____

_____          _____

_____          _____

_____          _____

_____          _____

_____          _____

_____          _____

_____          _____

# Main Idea/Details

Main Idea

Detail

Detail

Detail

# Making Inferences

Story Clues

Experience Clues

+

Inference

# Friendly Letter

_____

_____

_____

_____

_____

_____

_____

_____

_____

_____

_____

_____

_____

_____

_____

_____

_____

_____

_____

_____

# Business Letter

_____

_____

_____

_____

_____

_____

_____

_____

_____

_____

_____

_____

_____

_____

_____

_____

_____

_____

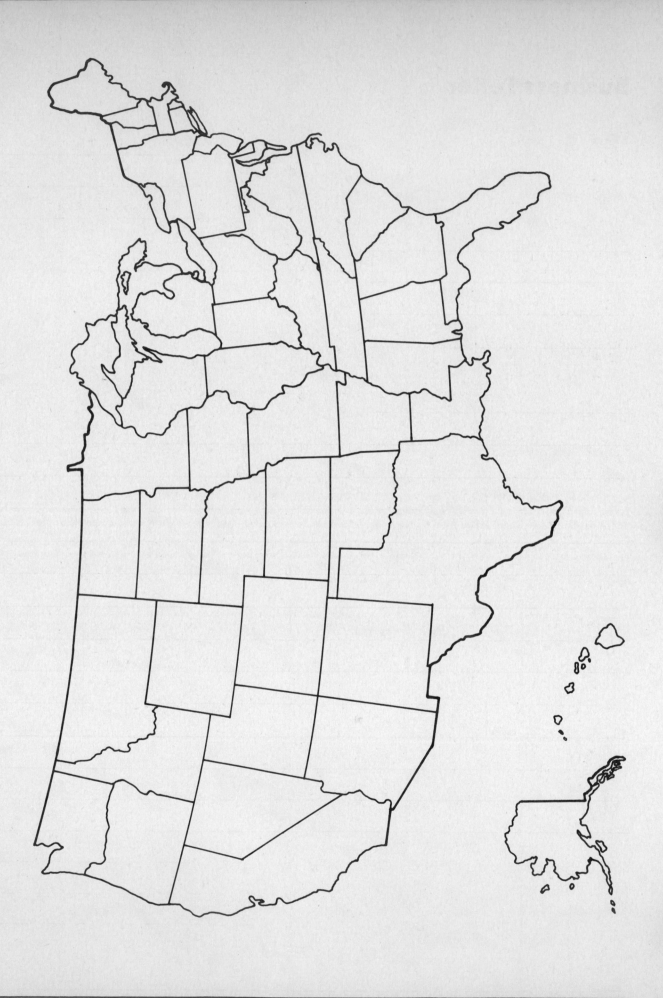

United States Map

© Silver Burdett Ginn Inc.

# World Map

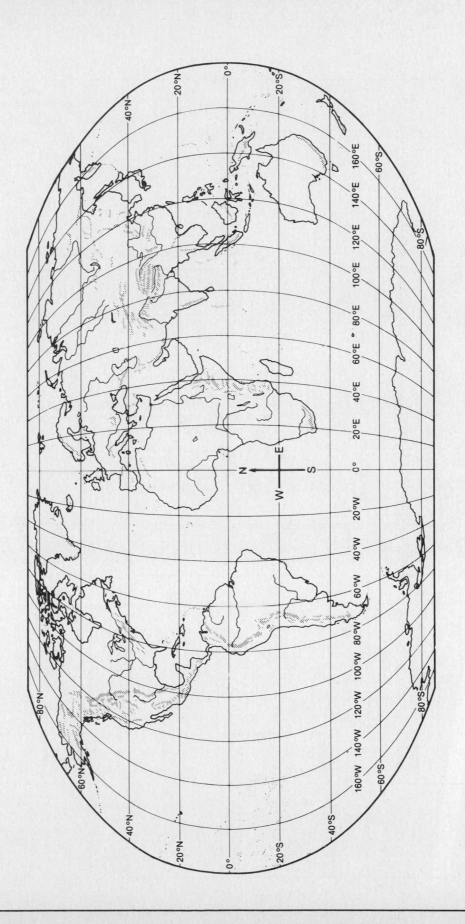

# Classification

# Classification

# Web

# Fact/Opinion

| Opinion | Supported by Fact | Nonfact | Agree | Disagree | Why? |
|---------|-------------------|---------|-------|----------|------|
|         |                   |         |       |          |      |
|         |                   |         |       |          |      |
|         |                   |         |       |          |      |
|         |                   |         |       |          |      |
|         |                   |         |       |          |      |

# Summary

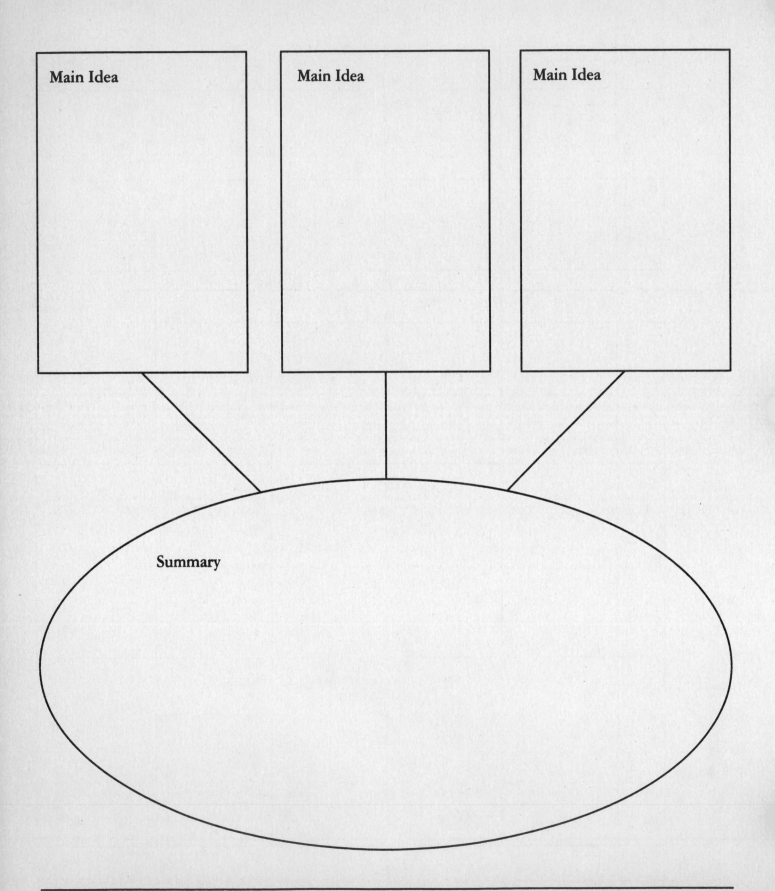

**Main Idea**

**Main Idea**

**Main Idea**

Summary

# Action Frame

| Goals |
| --- |
| |

▼

| Actions |
| --- |
| |

▼

| Results |
| --- |
| |

# Explanation/Description Frame

What it is

What it does

What it looks like